# THE
# HOUSEBUILDER'S
# YEAR
# BOOK
# 2008

A QUICK REFERENCE GUIDE TO THE
LATEST BUILDING REGULATIONS,
INDUSTRY CONTACTS AND MORE

**INCLUDES BUILDING REGULATIONS UPDATE**

an
ovolo
book

THE
**HOUSEBUILDER'S**
**YEAR**
**BOOK**
**2008**
A QUICK REFERENCE
GUIDE TO THE LATEST
BUILDING REGULATIONS&
INDUSTRY CONTACTS

**Ovolo Publishing Ltd**
**I The Granary, Brook Farm,**
**Ellington, Huntingdon,**
**Cambridgeshire**
**PE28 0AE**

The Building Regulations are Crown Copyright and used by permission Ovolo Publishing PSI Licence No: C2006011100
The material in Mark Brinkley's Year is © Mark Brinkley 2006-2007
The title Housebuilder's Yearbook and this edition © Ovolo Publishing Ltd 2007

Publisher: Mark Neeter
Design: Gill Lockhart

ISBN: 978-0-9548674-7-8

Printed in the UK

For the best selection of books about housebuilding and property visit:
www.buildingbooksdirect.com

an
**ovolo**
book

# HOUSEBUILDER'S YEAR BOOK

# CONTENTS

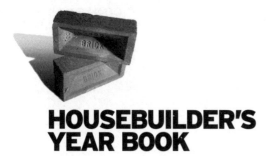

# HOUSEBUILDER'S YEAR BOOK

# INTRODUCTION

Welcome to *The Housebuilder's Yearbook*. Inside you will find the Building Regulations that have been substantially amended since January 2006. These are Parts B, F, L and P, which represent a significant change in the way homes have to be constructed.

In addition, we have included a look at the year by Mark Brinkley, author of the best-selling book *The Housebuilder's Bible,* and a selection of useful addresses and information.

This book is designed to be a one-volume reference source for both housebuilders and selfbuilders. We are keen to provide the best possible service and would like to hear if you have any ideas about addition material you'd like to see in the 2009 edition. We will send a free copy of *The Housebuilder's Yearbook 2009* to anyone whose ideas are used. E-mail us at info@ovolopublishing.co.uk

# HOUSEBUILDER'S YEAR BOOK

# MARK BRINKLEY'S YEAR

# HOW SHOULD WE MANAGE HOME WATER USE?

The more I learn about the Code for Sustainable Homes, the more uncomfortable I get. I have just been in on an interesting seminar, on the water use guidelines set out in the Code, and this week I investigated a little further, armed with an Excel spreadsheet. Water use is one of two mandatory aspects of the Code (the other being energy use). Mandatory, in this instance, means that you have to meet certain targets as regards notional water use in order for the house to gain a particular Code Level. It's no good building a zero carbon house if it fails to meet the water use standards as well.

The target water usage levels that the Code demands go like this:

• Levels 1 and 2: theoretical 120 litres/person/day

• Levels 3 and 4: theoretical 105 litres/person/day

• Levels 5 and 6: theoretical 80 litres/person/day

Now I guess many people have read the Code and noticed these figures and probably thought very little more about them. I certainly hadn't until I sat in on this seminar. Until then, they were just numbers jumping at me off the page: they didn't relate to anything or any actions. But my eyes have been opened and what I am now seeing is a little disturbing. The point is that it doesn't matter how much water you actually use, the Code judges everything by Mr and Mrs Average, Joe and Joanna public, and according to water company statistics, they use about 130lts per day each. They break it down thus:

• They each flush the loo 4.8 times a day (c 20lts)

• They wash their hands or brush their teeth for 40 seconds a day (10lts)

• They use about 25lts at the kitchen sink each day

• Their washing machines account for 16lts per day each (49lts per cycle, and J&J each use it once every three days)

• Their dishwasher uses another 4lts per day each

• And then there's showering and bathing. It gets complex here because Jo likes showers and Joanna likes baths, but overall it evens out and tends to account for 50lts per day each

I make that 125lts a day each. Give or take 5lts, that's it. This might have been better with a pie chart, but it wouldn't have been so much fun.

The standards set out in the Code would seem to indicate implicitly that this amount of water usage (i.e. 130lts per person per day) is unsustainable – i.e. wicked and to be strongly discouraged. The challenge set out in the Code is not to change the washing or bathing habits of Joe and Joanna, but rather to engineer in solutions which enable them to live exactly as they do now whilst consuming much less piped water.

Welcome to the world of water-efficient appliances. Low flush toilets help matters, and that without any apparent pain. If you can specify aerated taps on the kitchen sink and a water-efficient washing machine you can rapidly reduce that notional figure of 130lts per person per day down to just over 100lts per day.

So far so good. Just as with energy efficiency measures, the first steps are easy and cost effective. So you can get to Code Level 4 without too much hassle. It's that 80 litres a day at Level 5 and 6 which is the problem. You see there just aren't any water efficient products that can get Joe and Joanna's usage down to such a low notional figure. That's where my spreadsheet came in: I was tinkering with all the very low water usage appliances out there and I still couldn't get below 102lts per person per day. This includes:

• dual flush toilets that work on 4.5lts full and 3lts half flush

• showers that use just 7lts per minute

• aerated kitchen taps using 2.5lts per minute

• washing machines using 35lts per cycle rather than 49lts

So how do you go that extra mile, or in this case 22lts, and get the notional consumption down to Code Level 5 and 6 requirements? The answer the Code is steering us towards is, of course, recycling, either via rainwater harvesting or grey water systems. But even by taking this big leap, you are not guaranteed a result. This is because Joe and Joanna, even with the most water efficient appliances installed in their home, are still using more than 80lts a day before so much as a loo is flushed.

Grey water systems, which reuse bath, shower and basin water for toilet flushing purposes, aren't going to get you under the 80lts per person per day figure on their own. Rainwater harvesting systems can be set up to run washing machines as well as flush toilets and so in theory could get your notional usage figure down below 80lts per person per day, but only if they operate at near 100% efficiency which is unlikely over the course of a year – in prolonged periods without rain, the storage tanks empty and the systems switch over to tap water.☐

The conclusion has to be that this 80lts per person per day figure is really at the limits of what is technically possible at the moment. It may well be that you have to fit both a grey water and a rainwater recycling system to meet the target. Grey water systems seem to cost anywhere between £1500 and £2000, rainwater rather more. That's not a problem if you are building exemplar homes for demonstration purposes but remember we are aiming this at every new home built after 2016. That is a phenomenal challenge and a phenomenal expense to be borne.

There are some further strange anomalies in how the guidance has been put together. If you specify a bidet, you take an instant 5lt per person per day penalty; if you specify a water softener, you take a 12.5lt per person per day penalty. It's hard to see how anyone will be able to fit these into a new home and still make Code Level 6. On the other hand, if you specify a swimming pool or an outdoor whirlpool bath, there is no penalty at all!

Rather than tinkering about with how we distribute water around the home, wouldn't it be a lot easier and a lot less hassle just to charge the correct price for tap water in the first place? All new homes in England have metered supplies now in any event, so we already have a perfectly responsive mechanism in place for restricting water usage. As has been pointed out elsewhere, there are many parts of the country where water shortage is not and is never likely to be an issue. Shouldn't the water restriction measures in the Code reflect this?

Underlying this is a debate very similar to the one raging over renewable energy. The government seems to be keen to promote onsite renewable energy (also via the Code) despite all the evidence being that it is much cheaper and more efficient to green the National Grid. With water, there is no national water grid but coincidentally, there is an article in Building by David Lush arguing that there should be. The main argument used against building a national water distribution system is cost and Lush quotes an Environment Agency consultation paper suggesting that it would cost between £9billion and £15billion. That may sound like a lot, but £2,500 spent on water reduction measures in every house after 2016 would cost £625million a year and would end up surpassing the cost of building a national water grid after 20 years.

Neither option is exactly cheap. It may be that we should do both: I am not against recycling grey water or rainwater, but I do worry about the Code's insistence that we must keep putting more and more stuff into our homes in order to make them sustainable. Stuff not only costs, but it breaks down, it needs servicing. It's all very well enthusiasts fitting stuff, but 250,000 homes a year? Has anyone seriously thought through the implications?

# MULTIFOILS AND PRIVATE BUILDING CONTROL

It's now nearly a year since the two most important building control bodies in the UK moved to stop the use of multifoils, at least as a substitute for conventional insulation materials. Under pressure from government, the LABC (Local Authority Building Control) and the NHBC (National Housebuilders Council) simultaneously stated that in future they would only accept insulation that met the standards laid out in BR443, which translates as using the U value figures derived from the guarded hot box test.

Multifoil insulation performs very poorly in guarded hot box testing. The manufacturers claim that it's the guarded hot box test which is at fault. Their case rests on them performing well in comparison tests against conventional insulation, usually 200mm or 250mm of mineral wool. Such tests have been carried out several times by the multifoil manufacturers, to the satisfaction of some independent accreditation providers, but they have yet to win a European Technical Approval for their testing methods and they remain highly controversial.

I don't want to dig too deeply down into the multifoil debate here – it has been covered extensively elsewhere – but what is worth mentioning at this point in time is that there are still a number of private building control bodies out there who are more than happy to accept multifoil roof insulation. I was talking to a director of MLM and he remains an enthusiastic supporter of multifoils and is more than happy to sign off building works that use multifoil insulation. And I came away with the impression that MLM are far from unique in this respect, and that private building control saw this as a positive way of differentiating their services from the strictures of both local authority building control and the NHBC.

# CAN I STILL DO DIY ELECTRICS?

*I am in the very early thought process stage for building my own home. I have every intention of carrying out as much of the work myself as I possibly can, and this ranges from ground works to electrical installation, plumbing etc, etc. However, the recent changes in legislation now mean that I have to employ someone else to do what I could do myself the day before the changes came into force. To comply with this new legislation, my thinking is that I need to be approved under the "Competent Persons Scheme", and therefore, I need to know exactly what qualifications I need to gain, and what my next move is once I have the qualifications. Is it purely a case of gaining BS7671 and the like? It seems very odd that as a "layman" I can visit my DIY store or similar merchants and purchase all of the equipment I require to install systems, but I can't actually do anything with regard to fitting them. Can you please clarify what the situation is.*

Ian Thorley

*Mark writes:* It wasn't until 2005 that electrical work came under the auspices of building control in England & Wales. Part P, as it is known, doesn't actually state that only competent persons are allowed to carry out electrical work: rather it suggests you have two choices.

Firstly, you can elect to have a suitably Part P qualified electrician undertake the work for you and sign it off as having been carried out in accordance with BS7671. Alternatively, you can apply to have the electrical work inspected – and hopefully passed – by your local authority building inspector, or an agent acting for them. This, in theory, allows DIYers to undertake their own electrical work, in the time-honoured fashion, but adds in a measure of quality control that wasn't previously there.

If this work was being carried out as part of a larger project – i.e. building a house – then there shouldn't be any additional charge for inspecting the electrics, though this may be at the discretion of the building inspector. However, not every local authority is happy to undertake electrical inspections. Some of them have hired qualified electricians to undertake this new workload, others haven't bothered and are instead insisting that all electrical work is undertaken by suitably qualified electricians. I suggest you make some enquiries to your local authority building inspectors and find out where they stand. If they insist on you using a qualified electrician, and you still wish to undertake the work yourself, you then have a further two choices.

• One is to find a Part P electrician who will mentor you through the job, do some inspection and sign off the job as their own. They do exist. One who works regularly with selfbuilders across the land is Ben Addison.

The other is to undertake the training yourself. There are various places you can do this training. One such is Trade Skills 4U.co.uk, who offer a range of courses suitable for your needs at a cost of around £1,500. This must include a City & Guilds 2381 qualification to show you understand the essentials of BS7671, and a further qualification for Part P Domestic Installers. Having successfully completed the courses, you would also need membership of a certifying body such as The Electrical Contractors Association in order to be able to sign off your own work. It would probably cost you around £2,000 for the qualifications and a year's membership. However, at the end of this process, you would also have a very sellable skill. If you really enjoy electrical work, maybe this is what you have been waiting for!

# HOW HOUSING DEMAND IS ASSESSED

The housebuilding lobby insists that demand for new homes is outstripping supply, and that this has been the case for many years, decades even. But whilst it is fairly straightforward to measure housing supply, how is demand assessed?

One place to look is Kate Barker's review into the state of UK housebuilding. Her brief was to look at supply side issues but she does acknowledge that the relationship with demand is complex. She makes the crucial point that simply increasing the supply of new homes may in itself affect demand: Higher rates of housebuilding could also lead to higher household formation rates (Barker Report 1.43). But she doesn't really explore these issues in any depth.

A more fruitful area to dig in is the work of the Cambridge Centre for Housing and Planning Research. They have produced various pieces of research on housing need and housing demand. One piece in particular, More Households to be Housed: Where is the increase coming from? by Alan Holmans and Christine Whitehead, is very pertinent and seems to set out the methodology for how these figures are calculated. Which is:

• work out how many more old people there are going to be

• work out how many more broken families there will be

• work out what net migration levels will be.

The answer habitually comes out at something like 215,000 extra households per annum. So this figure is taken as the basis of housing demand. And if we build less than this each year (we do), this is responsible for the shortage of housing and, it follows, the increase in house prices.

But dig down into Holman's and Whitehead's report and you can begin to uncover a number of assumptions and guesses that call into question the accuracy of their work.

• whilst it is easy to measure the marriage rate and the divorce rate, because each event is recorded, there are no accurate figures for co-habiting couples, nor for what happens to couples (both married and co-habiting) once they separate. How many couple up again? No one knows, they just guess.

• migration rates: everyone knows that the amount off net migration in the past few years has been enormous, but no one knows just how enormous. Not until the 2011 census will there be any hard figures to go on, and even then, it is widely anticipated that illegal migrants will mostly not appear on the census.

• longevity: we are as a population living longer and the models build in an assumption that life expectancy rates will continue to increase at the rates they have done over the past century. But will they? Again, no one has a clue.

But even if their assumptions are correct, there is still a fundamental flaw in the way their demand figure is arrived at. It's all just too mechanistic: the model makes no allowance for the fact that demand is itself affected by supply. The size of the average household has been falling consistently ever since records began, but does this represent a profound social change or is it simply a reflection of the fact that there are far more houses around now and, given the choice, many people would prefer to live on their own or in small units. Back in Victorian times, it was not unusual to have families of seven, eight or nine living in two-up, two-downs. For them, this was normal; for us it would be seen as appalling overcrowding.

What this demonstrates is that our standard of living has increased and we now expect to share bedrooms with no more than one other person. And without setting a notional accommodation standard for the country as a whole, how is it possible to determine whether our housing demand is real or just aspirational? If our aspirations are to live in smaller and smaller household units, then we cannot hope to meet demand until such time as everybody has a house of their own. Or maybe two. Why not?

So demand as it is now defined will remain unquenchable. If we were to be building, say, 300,000 new homes a year, rather than the 180,000 that we manage at present, we would simply be the moving the goalposts and would find that the demand for new homes had inexplicably risen to 350,000 a year. And probably work out all manner of household formation statistics as if to prove it. The tail appears to be wagging the dog.

So behind this lies a debate which has yet to be started. The subject is this: Is it the responsibility of government to provide a home for everybody who wants one? And does this include everyone who pitches up on our shores in future? Or do we now have to accept that there must be limits to household growth, and learn to adapt to what we already have?

# WHEN WILL COMPACT FLUORESCENTS CUT THE MUSTARD?

I spotted an interesting article in June 2007's Lighting magazine on Compact Fluorescent (CFL) lamps. In summary:

• Invented in 1981 by Philips. The original SL18 weighed over half a kilogram, but its 18W consumption delivered 900 lumens, on a par with a 75W incandescent, and lamp life was an unheard of 5,000 hours.

• The average EU home now contains 24 lamps, but fewer than 30% of these homes own any CFLs.

• The EU seems to be in the process of banning incandescents GLS bulbs, but it's not yet clear when this will come into effect.

• Minaturisation: size used to be a major problem with CFLs but the development of electronic ballasts has addressed the size issue, although there are still many light fittings which won't accept CFLs because they are too big.

• Shape: As size has been getting smaller, so we are seeing more and more conventionally lightbulb-shaped CFL bulbs coming onto the market. Megaman and Firefly Lighting (both Chinese) have got ranges of lamps very similar in shape to conventional bulbs but the prize goes to Japan's Toshiba whose Neoball Z Real is identical in shape, size, profile and output to an ordinary 60W bulb.

• Dimming: This has been another problem for CFLs as the pulsed output of conventional dimmers can damage the electronic ballasts. You can buy specialised CFL dimmers but that is far from ideal. However technology seems to be riding towards a solution. Megaman have been producing DORS technology (DORS stands for Dim OR Switch). First switch gives you 100% output; then flick on and off a second time and the output falls to 66%, then 33% then 5%. It's not quite dimming as we have grown to know it but it's a fair approximation. But in June 2007, Korean firm Feelux launched a smoothly dimmable CFL lamp into the UK, which works with conventional dimmer switches. Look out for their DimPac range.

• Speed: one of the most frequent complaints about CFLs is that they don't reach full power for half a minute or more. Not very good for bathrooms or stairwells. However Sylvania's MiniLynx Fast-Start is designed to address these issues: it comes on in just 0.2 seconds and reaches 80% output in ten seconds. Lamp life is not compromised. Expect more fast start lamps from other manufacturers soon.

• Colour quality: many (most?) consumers complain that CFLs emit a cold light that makes colours appear flat and dull. Whilst colour temperature is now similar to GLS lamps (2700K), the other quality of artificial light, colour render, is still proving problematic, especially on the all-important R9 Red Rendition, which incandescent bulbs excel at and CFLs don't. But it's quite possible that this will improve over the coming years.

• Disposal: small amounts of mercury reside in every CFL lamp. No one has ever really bothered about this before but if they are to become much more common, then some procedures are going to have to be put in place for safe disposal of CFL lamps. One to ponder.

# SHOULD WE RATION HOME OWNERSHIP?

I have recently been sounding off about house prices. Or the affordability issue, as the great and the good like to refer to it. My contention is that we can no longer build our way out of this problem because

a) any new homes will just fill up with migrants from all over the world because everyone wants to come and live and work in the South-East and

b) the climate change issue is more important and, until this is solved, it is foolish to embark on large building programmes, however climate-friendly. We should, instead, be concentrating on upgrading what we have already built.

What I have avoided to date is discussing what else could be done about the affordability issue. This is because I haven't given it a moment's thought, although somewhere in the back of my mind I am aware that it's easy for a baby-boomer like me, owning unmortgaged property, to be complacent about it all. On the other hand, our three sons are, or soon will be, at the sharp end of the problem and it would be nice to think that they can house themselves without having to wait for both their parents to drop dead, and then for them to fight over what's left after the government has had its fill.

There was a fine article about these very issues in the Evening Standard by Andrew Gilligan entitled Yes, we can solve our housing shortage. In it, Gilligan suggests that, instead of trying to increase the supply of new homes, it is time now to start dampening the demand. Gilligan started by pointing out that two thirds of new homes built last year in London were sold to investors, a somewhat staggering statistic. He elaborated, and I think I agree with him, that housing has become an investment asset class, decoupled from the normal rules of supply and demand, and that the London market in particular is being driven ever higher by speculation. Those that have property have become wealthy beyond their wildest dreams and now have the wherewithal to purchase second, third and fourth homes, whereas those without property have become locked out, unless they earn top dollar.

Gilligan makes two specific suggestions:

1) that we should insist that the buyers of at least some of our new properties should actually live in them and

2) we should clamp down on tax breaks that buy-to-let landlords now enjoy. It sounds like a plausible enough platform. But actually I don't think he has gone far enough. I am struggling to think of buy-to-let tax breaks. I don't think there are any, unlike the family home, which enjoys the status of a mini-tax haven, thanks to the miracle of Principal Private Residence Relief. And as for insisting that people actually live in the homes they buy, well this is already happening to some extent with the many affordable and shared ownership housing schemes around.

On the other hand, even if the detail is a little wonky, I think Gilligan is onto something. If you made the tax and incentive signals strong enough, I am sure you could dampen down property speculation. It's not as though demand management has completely gone out of fashion: indeed it's having a mini revival politically with the introduction of the London Congestion Charge, proposals afoot for nationwide road pricing and tentative discussions about carbon rationing. Why not add housing to the list? It's a nearly finite commodity, and it's being allocated according to wealth, not need. Ideal material for vouchers or a rationing system of some description.

But how might it work? Imagine every year each adult would be granted a notional housing footprint, say around 50 sq m each, about the size of a one or two bedroomed flat. If you didn't own property, you could then sell your housing entitlement: if you wanted to own more than this, you would have to buy it from those who were selling. A market would be established, rather like the carbon trading exchanges, where allowances could be bought and sold. The more distorted the balance between the haves and the have-nots became, the higher the value of the entitlements would be.

Such a scheme would aim to greatly reduce the attractiveness of owning property purely as an investment. In effect, it becomes a distributive tax, just as how people envisage carbon rationing as working.

Sure, it would be complex to set up and probably involve about two zillion civil servants to police. It might have all kinds of unanticipated side-effects. Incentive schemes often do. I know, I know. But it's a start. And it has to have a better chance of succeeding than the total non-policy that the government is currently putting forward.

# OFT INVESTIGATION INTO HOUSEBUILDING

News that the Office of Fair Trading is launching an investigation into the housebuilding industry had me exclaiming "OK, but why now?"

Nothing has really changed that much in the past ten or even twenty years; certainly not the nature of the cozy cartel that exists between the housebuilders, the planners and the amenity groups such as the Council of Preservation for Rural England (CPRE). Both the low rates of new housebuilding and the poor standards of that housebuilding are symptomatic of a general market failure, but then this is no ordinary market.

The OFT obviously wants someone to blame for this state of affairs. Housebuilders point to intransigent planners, planners point at huge landbanks being held back to artificially inflate prices. According to the BBC website, the OFT have appointed an eight-strong team to take representations, but I expect them to get pushed from pillar to post and back, and to end up more or less back where they started.

To my mind, the problem really starts with 1947 Town & Country Planning Act, which effectively nationalised land use. Instead of land being freely brought forward for building by whoever fancied their chances, the new planning authorities started ring-fencing areas suitable for development. As these areas were often large, the small players were effectively cut out from the market. Over the years, this policy of concentration and densification has grown more and more pronounced and the whole development process has been professionalised. The current consolidation going on in the housebuilding industry is merely the latest phase of a process that dates back to 1947.

What the OFT should be looking at is how development took place in the 1920s and 30s, when there were very few controls and no massive national building concerns. There was genuine competition back then and also a high rate of housebuilding. Also they should look closely at what has been happening in Ireland. And France. And Germany. And Scandinavia. And North America. And Australia. They will quickly find out that what goes on in the UK is unique.

Other countries build more houses and they generally have far fewer quality issues. Land is often set aside by rural communities for small developers and selfbuilders to create homes and thereby organically grow communities. New development isn't restricted to all but a few mega-sites, as it is in the UK. Mega-sites may be regarded as sustainable, but they do nothing to enhance competition. The land supply in the UK is now so restricted that the whole process is managed by a small number of very large businesses, who carve up the cake between themselves. The fact that there is little competition is because there is often only one new housing site for miles around. But rather than blaming everybody or indeed anybody for letting this state of affairs come about, the OFT should come to realise pretty quickly that it's a creation of our restrictive planning policies. If you really want to reform the housebuilding industry, that is where to start. I don't think it'll even be on the agenda.

# WHO OWNS WHAT

Earlier this year, Hanson was taken out by Heidelberg Cement in an £8billion deal that all but brought to a close the British ownership of its building materials sector. Whilst the City scribes used the takeover as an excuse to rerun the colourful history of Hanson Trust, they largely ignored the fact that a whole sector of our industry has disappeared from our stock market in less than ten years.

Simultaneously, the much smaller Baggeridge Brick was taken over by the Austrian brick giant Weinerberger in an acquisition worth just £87million and towards the end of the year Akzo Nobel moved for ICI, makers of Dulux paint. The rout was all but complete.

What's left? It looks to me that there are now only two medium sized companies quoted in London that are active in this area. They are:

• Ennstone, the aggregates and readymix business, worth £180million

• Marshalls, the paving and landscaping people, worth £500million

Here follows a list of what went where.

• RMC: readymix concrete and cement. Now owned by Cemex of Mexico. Also own Russell roof tiles and Rugby Cement and Thermabate

• Blue Circle: Britain's original cement company, an original constituent of the FT30 in 1953, taken over by Lafarge (large French conglomerate) in 2001

• ARC: part of Hanson, which includes Hanson Brick (the old London Brick Company, makers of the LBC) and Thermalite and the old Marshall's Floors business. Now Hanson is about to be taken over, see above.

• Castle Cement: now part of Heidelberg Cement, quoted in Germany

• Bradstone: a brand owned by Aggregate Industries, a UK asphalt and concrete conglomerate which was itself taken over by Holcim of Switzerland in March 2005 for £1.8bn

• Tarmac: now the Industrial Minerals Division of Anglo American plc, which includes Tarmac Topfloor and Durox

• Ibstock Brick: taken over by CRH, large Irish conglomerate, in 1999

• Celcon: Owned by H+H International A/S, a Danish company.

• Baggeridge Brick: about to be taken over by Weinerberger of Austria

• Redland: taken over by Lafarge

• BPB: once British Gypsum, bought by St.Gobain in 2005. As well as plasters and plasterboard, it owns Artex and Rawlplug

• Marley: now owned by Etex Group of Belgium

• Boulton & Paul Joinery: originally bought by Rugby cement, sold to privately owned US joinery business Jeld Wen in 1999

• John Carr: another independent joinery producer, also owned by first Rugby and merged with Boulton & Paul, now subsumed into Jeld Wen

• Magnet Joinery: once quoted, now owned by the Swedish kitchen company, Nobia

• Premdor Crosby: owned by Masonite of Canada, quoted in Toronto

• Anglian Windows: based in Norwich, went public in 1992, MBO in 2001

• Velux: private Danish company

• Osma: always owned by Dutch group Wavin. Wavin is short for WAter and VINyl! Used to be part owned by Shell but is now jointly owned by Overijssel Water Board (who started it in the 1950s) and CVC Capital Partners, private equity.

• Terrain: sold by Caradon to Geberit. Swiss plumbing supplies company, in 1999

• Hepworth: bought out by Vaillant, sold on to Wavin

• Baxi Potterton: now part of a plc owned by private equity, includes Heatrae Sadia, makers of Megaflo

• Aqualisa: part of Baxi group

• Myson Radiators: owned by Rettig, a privately owned Finnish company

• Pilkington: leading glass manufacturers, bought by Nippon Glass in 2006

• Ideal Stelrad: based in Hull, once part of Caradon, sold to HSBC private equity in 2002

• MK Electric: part of Caradon group, which seems to have disappeared

• Celotex: private UK company, MBO from larger American business using the same name

• Kingspan: acquisitive Irish public company, makes insulation but also owns timber frame and SIPS suppliers, (cf Potton Homes, Century Homes, Pace, Tekhaus SIPs)

• Jablite: brand name of Vencil Resil, taken over by Synbra Group BV from Holland

• Rockwool: Danish public company

• Sadolin and Sikkens: part of European conglomerate Akzo Nobel which includes what was left of Courtaulds and Crown Berger paints

• Dulux: still part of ICI, as are Cuprinol and Hammerite. ICI, once a bellweather of British industrial strength, is currently being taken over by Akzo Nobel, making for one very big paint company

• Jewson: UK's largest builder's merchant, owned by St Gobain

• Travis Perkins: Britain's No 2 builder's merchant, independent, bought Wickes in 2005

# WELCOME TO THE WORLD OF IMPACT ASSESSORS

I have been reading the government's White Paper on Planning, published at the beginning of the week. Much of the interest in this document has focused, rightly, on the government's intention to sub out difficult infrastructural works (i.e. new nukes, new runways) to an independent commission. Environmentalists have been jumping up and down saying this is going to make big planning decisions unaccountable, but I am not sure it will make that much difference because the government always gets its way in any event. What they are hoping to do is to make the process a little quicker.

I am more interested in the other end of the spectrum, how the government intends to streamline the processing of domestic planning applications. It looks like it needs some attention because the number of applications has mushroomed in recent years, due in no small part to the penal rates of stamp duty being charged for moving house, which causes everyone to start extending instead.

However the White Paper sandwich has an awful lot of bread and very little meat and, once you've dusted off the pages and pages of good intentions, what you are left with in terms of concrete proposals is not much more than guesswork.

Chapter 9 is where it gets written up and it all hinges on the future of Permitted Development Rights. This is a system that has existed since planning controls on domestic development were first introduced in 1948 and it allows certain minor works to be carried out without the need for planning permission. Each house comes with its own PD Rights but once these have been used up, any additional development requires planning permission.

The intention expressed in the White Paper is to replace the PD Rights system as it now exists with Impact Assessments. No or low impact development – and by impact we are talking principally about the effect on the neighbours – will be permitted, whilst high impact developments will require planning permission.

Reads well on the page but the problem that immediately sticks out about this proposal is that impact is subjective. Who is going to decide the difference between low and high impact? Hmm, it's a difficult one.

But if you think about it for a couple of minutes and look at Labour's past record on housing matters (think Home Information Packs here, not to mention its various competent person schemes aimed at streamlining the building regs), you can sort of figure out where this is all heading. Answer: Impact Assessors.

So I can see the future going something like this. If you want to make changes to your home you will have to first contact an Impact Assessor. They will determine whether you need to apply for planning permission. They will also levy from you an Impact Fee for environmental improvements to your neighbourhood – on the basis that a new bedroom is another school place or a hospital bed. And then you will be required to carry out additional eco-improvements to your home. By paying these fees and committing yourself to undertake the extra works, you will buy yourself a permit to develop. If you go ahead illegally, you risk fines (having been snitched up by nosey neighbours), not to mention difficulties selling your home when the time comes.

From the government's point of view, this will streamline the planning process and vastly reduce the number of applications clogging up the system. Instead of having to hire expensive graduates to staff planning departments, school leavers will be able to train as Impact Assessors on a three-day intensive, get their competency badge and off they go, just like we are seeing with Domestic Energy Assessors at the moment. The assessments will be done by feeding measurements and checkbox answers into a laptop, which ordinary mortals won't have a hope of understanding. And will therefore be unchallengable. It all sounds horribly 1984 but the strange thing is it sort of makes sense and I am not sure it's actually any worse than what happens already. In fact, it makes rather more sense than the current proposal to have Energy Performance Certificates every time a house is sold, as an impact assessment would be made prior to building work, which is the best time to make changes to the house. It could be a transformational tool for upgrading the existing housing stock, but it's more likely to be construed as yet another stealth tax – which it is – and will therefore be hugely unpopular. Maybe the government will be able to use its new independent planning commission to force this new measure through!

# CDM 2007

On April 6, 2007 a new version of the CDM (Construction Design & Management) regs came into effect. So what should we make of them?

I was not a great fan of the old CDM health and safety regs, which came into effect in 1994 and had precisely no effect whatsoever on building site accident levels. Lots of paperwork, lots of money to be paid out and no positive outcomes. How very UK today.

News that the CDM regs were to be overhauled just filled me with excitement. I have turned down the offers of attending free or near-free CPD seminars to help me 'get up to speed', partly because I can still recall the terror of having to sit through a CDM awareness event back in 1994. I'd opt for a day in Guantanamo Bay every time. I decided I would do my catching up this time via newsprint.

Trouble is, every time I try and read a This is what CDM 2007 really means article, I find myself nodding off somewhere in the second paragraph. Building magazine today has no less than three explanatory articles and despite trying to read all three I was really not much wiser about just what was changing, as from April 6th.

Following an industry-wide consultation, writes Peter Caplehorn there is a chance for the new regulations to make a real difference. Only a chance? I am confused already. The irrelevant paperwork has been binned and there is a focus on improving health and safety standards by keeping the regulations proportionate to the task and by focusing on outcomes rather than process. What on earth is he talking about?

All projects will now be subject to CDM except domestic works. Correct me if I am wrong but this is no different to how the old CDM worked. Any projects involving more than 500 person days work or lasting longer than 30 days need to be notified to the Health & Safety Executive using the F10 notification form. Well, there I have learned something. The form you need is called an F10. Remember that, because it's probably the only really useful thing you will learn from this article.

A construction phase health and safety plan must be drawn up. Hang on, I thought we had dispensed with irrelevant paperwork? Seemingly not. A big bugbear of the old CDM was that you had to produce a risk assessment plus a health and safety file, and that this work was time consuming and no one ever looked at them. But we still seem to have a H&S file. Funny, there's no mention of that pesky risk assessment. Maybe that's the result everyone was hoping for?

One thing that has happened is that the key roles have been given a dust-down and in some instances some new names. The client is still the client, but this time they have to take their responsibilities more seriously. Previously they could sub-out their responsibilities to an agent, but from now on there can be no subbing-out. The client is the client. Except where of course there is more than one client, then they have a duty to co-operate with one another. All good stuff this, isn't it?

The planning supervisor is now the CDM co-ordinator. Got that. The CDM co-ordinator must either generate or ensure the generation of the health and safety file. But there is, I think, just a suggestion that if the project is low risk, then you needn't bother with risk assessments and all that hullabaloo. At least that's the drift I get. But in my semi-comatose state, I may have it all wrong. Now can I summarise it all in a sentence?

The form you need to send off to HSE is F10 and the role you need to appoint is the CDM co-ordinator. I think that should just about take care of it.

# ON ASBESTOS REMOVAL

Asbestos was widely used in the UK building industry through most of the last century. It was only during the 1980s that it started to become blacklisted and it was still being used, mixed with cement, through till 1999.

It was used in all kinds of places: Artex was 2% asbestos until 1984, asbestos-cement roofing sheets, inside airing cupboards and around stoves and boilers, pipe lagging, ironing boards, night storage radiators, fire doors, artificial slates, wall boards. One of the most dangerous formats was a board made by Cape called Astbestolux, later replaced by an asbestos-free version called Supalux.

There is a lot of asbestos about and if you get involved with demolition or renovation of an old building, you need to know how to handle the risk. There are some fairly exacting requirements in place for commercial enterprises, including builders and demolition contractors. Every commercial building is now meant to have an Asbestos Register detailing if and where asbestos is located. But the situation with private householders is still largely unregulated, which means that if you have asbestos in your house you can more or less dispose of it as you wish. Except you can't just take it to any old tip, but to one designated to take hazardous waste.

Whether this is a sensible idea is open to doubt. There is a big debate in asbestos circles about the exact nature of the risk involved. Everybody agrees that the really dangerous forms are brown and blue asbestos but white asbestos, which is the commonest one you are likely to come across, is less of a risk, especially when bound with cement. You have to breathe the dust to be at any danger at all, so an inert sheet of asbestos cement is not a significant risk, anymore than say an unopened packet of cigarettes.

There is a lot of confusion and fuzziness here. Caused in no little part by the activities of John Bridle and his Asbestos Watchdog business, which makes a living rubbishing mainstream asbestos claims. Bridle is of the opinion that there is an Asbestos Scare Industry out there which is all set to rob us all blind by first finding asbestos where it isn't and then charging us exorbitant amounts of money to remove it.

Maybe Bridle is right, maybe he isn't, but he has powerful friends in the media and gets a lot of exposure, mainly in the Sunday Telegraph. The asbestos contractor I was speaking to wished, ruefully, that he made as much money as Bridle suggested he did. Just to stay in business as a licensed contractor, he has to pay £30,000 in insurance premiums every year for a business that turns over just under half a million. He said he thought it was quite possible that Bridle is right about white asbestos not being dangerous but he still had to remove it as if it was because he wouldn't be allowed to practice otherwise. And there is also the distinct possibility that Bridle is wrong: lots of eminent scientists think white asbestos could well be harmful. If so, why take an unnecessary risk?

But the question which concerns me here is what exactly do you do when you are dismantling an old building and you want to know if any asbestos is present. I think it's probably not a bad idea to have an asbestos survey at the outset. These cost anywhere between £100 and £500, depending on the size and complexity of the survey. The surveyor will most likely take a few samples which cost a further £10 or so each to analyse. My bill for vetting the 60s house we have just purchased was £111 inc VAT and including five samples. A good surveyor will then advise you of both the risks and the most appropriate way of handling them. As a commercial contractor, you are bound by law to dispose of asbestos in an appropriate manner but there is much less regulation placed on private householders. My local council, South Cambs, offers sealable sacks to householders to place their own asbestos remains in and there is one tip in the county you can take it all to, for which there is no additional charge. I guess they have to consider the alternative: fly tipping. You can search for asbestos surveyors and contractors by county on the website of the Asbestos Removal Contractors Association.

# PELLET BOILERS: THE OKEFEN EXAMINED

To Welshpool, to take a look at Europe's most advanced pellet boiler. I am guest of Andy Buroughs and his company Organic Energy. Andy Buroughs has been in the renewables business for 20 years, mostly in solar panels, and has recently got interested in pellet boilers after visiting Austria and tracking down Okefen. He has become the UK agent for Okefen and also for another Austrian company, solar panel maker Gasokol.

Now the Okefen pellet boiler is a very impressive piece of kit. I instinctively feel that a pellet boiler is a sort of upmarket wood stove but I am surprised to see just how upmarket a wood stove can get. This is, as Andy points out, the Mercedes of wood-fuelled boilers. It doesn't actually burn the wood pellets, it gasifies them and then burns the resulting gas at something like 93% efficiency. As there is as much heat value in a wood pellet as there is in heating oil, by weight, you can see that it is a very efficient method of extracting heat from wood. And, of course, the pellets aren't shovelled in by hand: they are fed in automatically by an auger or a vacuum tube (you choose). And the grate doesn't need riddling out every morning – the residue can be cleaned up once every few weeks.

Indeed, on a forthcoming model, things should have moved on to such a point that the proud owner of an

Okefen pellet boiler can get by with an annual visit from someone who a) delivers a year's worth of pellets into the hopper b) empties the ash can for the year and c) carries out the annual service. Wow, that really is hi-tech. Renewables without tears.

However there is a big ask here. The cost of the kit comes to around £12,000. From this you can deduct a £1,500 grant from the Low Carbon Build, but even so, that is a ball-achingly large amount of money for what is, after all is said and done, a boiler. This price would include the pellet hopper arrangement but doesn't go anywhere downstream from the boiler itself. No hot water tank, no radiators or underfloor heating system. The Okefen is competing with such kit as oil boilers – cost maybe £2,500 including storage tank– and ground source heat pumps – perhaps £8,000 up to £10,000. OK, you get to burn a green fuel, unlike the alternatives, but even if pellet supply turns out to be as cheap and as plentiful as promised, it is never going to stack up financially.

One of the very first things Andy said to me was that the Okefen "was very much an aspirational product." I didn't quite understand what he was on about until I got home and processed all the cost information. Now I see what he means. It's a hell of a big ask.

But I have no doubt that there will be a number of well-heeled selfbuilders who will see the Okefen and fall in love and just have to have it. It's a bit like that. It may even become the Aga for the Zero Carbon generation. Although I wouldn't try cooking on it. But then, I wouldn't recommend cooking on an Aga either.

# ON ICFS

There is an ingenious way of building walls using polystyrene and concrete. You use the polystyrene as formwork to build up the walls into the shape you want, then you pour concrete into the formwork and, voila, you have a structural wall with insulation already built in. These systems, and there are several, are known generically as Insulated Concrete Formwork (ICFs). They are not new and they haven't really made the splash that their proponents had hoped for, but there are signs that the market for ICF systems is at last coming alive. In the UK and Ireland, there are now about a dozen active promoters whereas five years ago it was basically just one. And there are indications that the crucial developer market is at last coming on board and seeing the potential of building homes with ICFs.

What are the plus points?
• It's a quick building method – comparable with timber frame
• It's semi-skilled
• It's simple: the number of elements needed to make up an external wall are greatly reduced
• It can be cheaper – if you restrict your choice of external wall cladding to pre-coloured renders
• You get fantastic insulation levels
• Other benefits include good airtightness and soundproofing

And the negatives?
• The headline price, usually around £30 per m² for the polystyrene formwork, plus £10 per m² for the readymix to fill it, puts a lot of people off. You can construct a blockwork wall, labour included, for around £20 per m², so why would you want to start with a wall system that costs twice as much?

I know one or two people who have got as far as this and no further. But if you compare finished wall costs, it looks very different. A fully finished brick and block wall with insulated cavity costs between £80 and £100 per m². An ICF really shouldn't be any more than this and if finished with an external render should be less than £80 per m² overall.

• Pouring the concrete is critical and can be a little bit scary. Building with ICFs may be "semi-skilled," but it's definitely not unskilled. There is a knack, which you have to learn. The walls wobble about and you have to be confident that you have your bracing just right.

• Bursts. It's not difficult to overstress the formwork when pouring concrete. This can cause the formwork to split open and for the readymix to spill over onto the ground. It looks worse than it actually is and it's part of the skill to know how to handle the odd burst without panicking. But it doesn't look good and it contributes in no small part to a negative perception of ICFs.

• Concrete. Although all the ICF promoters sell their systems as a green method of building, they can't get away from the fact that concrete is not perceived as a green building material. Far from it. It is regularly subject to scathing attack from environmentalists and is blacklisted from many deep-green projects, along with all cement-based products. Personally, I think this is a ridiculous state of affairs, especially as these projects almost always promote the questionable use of lime as a replacement for cement. But nevertheless, these perceptions count. Concrete is just not sexy, in the way timber, glass or handmade bricks are sexy.

• Neither, for that matter, is polystyrene!

• Not so much thermal mass as thermal mish-mash. I have written recently on the blog about the perceived joys of thermal mass as a method of storing passive solar heat and evening-out temperature fluctuations. I remain somewhat sceptical of the wilder claims made by thermal mass advocates but the problem for ICF walls is that the concrete is insulated by the polystyrene casing both inside and out, so it's not readily available to admit heat radiation. Thermal mass fans find this incredibly frustrating, so much so that I know of at least one project where the architect instructed the builders to peel off the entire inside layer of polystyrene after the concrete had set and to then stick it onto the outside. Inelegant or what?

*Summary*

I have written at far greater length about the negatives than I have about the positives. If word counters measured opinions, you would surmise I am therefore broadly negative. But that's not so. It really doesn't bother me that ICFs are made of concrete, or that the thermal mass is compromised by the insulation, or that headline price looks high, or that they are not quite as easy to build with as you might initially think.

In July and August 2007, I visited two ICF sites, one a selfbuild and the other a 25 unit development, where the respective builders were both chuffed to bits with their decision to use ICFs. The selfbuilder was particularly instructive as he was a carpenter by trade and you would have thought he would naturally have gravitated towards a timber house. But no, he wanted full control of the project and he wanted to undertake virtually every trade himself. As he put it, "I'd rather just do it myself than spend time explaining to someone else what I wanted them to do, only for them to do it wrong." In fact, the skills of a carpenter are far more appropriate for ICF builds than the skills of a blocklayer, which they are designed to replace.

It remains to be seen just where ICFs go from here. As the regulations demand more and more insulation, it becomes increasingly challenging to work this into the standard cavity wall routine and builders become more open to novel format like ICFs and SIPs. At the moment, you can still build with a 100mm cavity and pass muster with Part L but the next version may require a 150mm cavity and that is stretching it some. At that point, we may suddenly see a really big switchover to ICFs, especially by those builders who instinctively don't like timber based wall systems. Ireland has already seen a significant take-up of ICFs, but there it seems to be more about meeting the seemingly insatiable demand for new homes by whatever means available. In the UK, the new homes market is very different.

# WHAT IS A ONE-AND-A-HALF STOREY HOUSE?

I was posed this question by a guy from Essex at the *Homebuilding & Renovating* show in London. I said I had an idea that it was something like a bungalow with a loft conversion, although on reflection it seems strange to count a loft conversion as half a storey.

So in turn I asked him why he wanted to know. Turns out, of course, that he was in dispute with the planners over just what he could and couldn't build in his garden. He'd won planning permission, at appeal, for a one-and-a-half storey house and had subsequently drawn up plans for a house where the eaves lines intersects with the bottom of the upper floor windows, in effect turning them into dormers. It's a common enough design, a sort of English country cottage look. But was it one-and-a-half storeys or two?

Guess what the planners thought? They are insisting that he redraw his plans with the eaves line about 1500mm lower so that it was immediately above the top of the ground floor windows. That, to them, was a one-and-a-half storey house. He felt it made for an inferior design and he showed me a sketch of both options. I tended to agree with him. The low eaves version was in fact exactly the same floor area but headroom was lost on the upper floor and he reckoned he would lose a bedroom in the planner's preferred arrangement. Also the planners' preferred version was much more roof-dominant, which he felt just didn't look as good. Basically he wanted a country cottage look whilst the planners were insisting on…a bungalow with a loft conversion.

Of course, nowhere in any planning guidance is there a definition of what is meant by a one-and-a-half storey house. No, that would be far too helpful. So the very vagueness of the term allows lots of room for planners to make up arbitrary rulings. The planning inspector who had granted permission for this house on appeal hadn't seen fit to mention any specific ridge height, which would have introduced a little clarity to the situation. In fact, there was a difference in ridge heights – 8m for our man's preferred version as against 7.1 for the planners. However, the position of the house hardly merited any height restriction and none of the neighbours had expressed any concern about the design of the house.

So just what should he do? He had yet to put in a detailed application for either version of the house. Should he go for the easy life and get permission for the version the planners had given the nod to? Or fight for the version he wanted? The planners would recommend refusal on that but that would give the final say to the committee who, he thought, might just see sense. His best bet was probably to apply for his preferred version and be prepared to take it to appeal if it was turned down, whilst subsequently making a second application for the uncontroversial design so that he would be sure of at least being able to build something before the whole planning application went dead after three years.

But what a palaver? Why should anyone have to jump through such an extraordinary set of hoops in the first place. In ten years' time, whatever gets built there will have become accepted as part and parcel of the neighbourhood and no one will bat an eyelid if the house is 8m high or 7.1m high, or where the eaves level is. So why the compulsion to meddle in the minutiae of house design like this? Why not just let him get on and build what he thinks of as a one-and-a-half storey house?

# DOES THERMAL MASS REALLY SAVE ENERGY?

There is quite a significant body of opinion that holds that high thermal mass is one of the keys to low energy consumption. A house with high mass can absorb passive solar gain in winter and takes less energy to keep cool in summer. That is the theory. I think it's questionable at best. Let's examine the issues.

Firstly, what is meant by thermal mass? The mass bit refers to the heaviness or density of an object or a material. High mass building materials are concrete, brick, stone and tiles. In the low mass corner, we have not so much materials like timber and plasterboard, which are still relatively heavy, but the hollow, lightweight building systems such as timber or steel frame. Already, you can see that what we are lining up here is a re-run of the old timber frame versus brick and block argument.

The thermal bit refers to the capacity of a material to absorb heat. Broadly speaking, the heavier and denser an object or a material, the more heat is absorbs. A cubic metre of concrete can store around 80kWh of heat energy: in contrast, a cubic metre of air holds almost nothing. A whole house full of air, kept 20°C above external temperature, holds as little as 5kWh of heat energy. The structural fabric enclosing it holds anywhere between 50kWh – if it's lightweight – up to 500kWh if it's really heavyweight. Heavyweight doesn't just mean masonry. Although all forms of masonry construction are heavier than framed techniques, concrete and dense blocks are much heavier than aerated concrete blocks, as made by Celcon and Thermalite.

Now, according to the theory of passive solar design, if you can capture lots of free solar energy (via large glazed walls or conservatories), you can store this heat inside the walls and floors of your heavyweight structure. Then during the night, instead of having to put the heating system on full whack, you can enjoy a free ride from the heat stored inside the structure.

But here is Problem No 1. You need lots of glazing to draw lots of heat during the day: at night time, this glazing will be leaking much of this stored heat back outside. In fact, even really good double glazed units leak six times more heat at night than walls or roofs. You can design this problem out by using insulated shutters, which cover the glazing during the night but, for many reasons, insulated shutters have never caught on and seem unlikely to do so. The fashion for large glazed areas doesn't go with shutters or even heavy draped curtains. An awful lot of your passive solar gains will be given back through the glazing at night.

Problem No 2. In climates like the UK, you can't get more than a proportion of your winter space heating from solar radiation. It's often estimated to be in between 20% and 35% of the total space heating load. It's difficult to increase this proportion because if you insulate the house massively, you reduce the overall heat load but, in so doing, you also reduce the useful contribution from solar gain. Why? Because a massively insulated house shortens the period for which you require space heating to the just the very coldest months of the year, precisely the time when passive solar has the least energy on offer.

Problem No 3 concerns winter holidays. If you were to go on holiday for a while and turn the heating off, then all the heat stored in your high mass building will leak away. This is something I have learned from bitter experience, having twice returned to a freezing cold house in the depths of winter to find that it takes 48 hours of continuous heating for it to become comfortable. And that's in a house that has been built using heavy masonry materials only on the ground floor.

The phenomenon at work here is referred to as *coolth*. That is what happens when the surrounding surfaces are relatively cool and you yourself radiate a lot of your own body heat out towards them. This makes you feel colder than the air temperature suggests. As the surfaces warm up, you radiate less, which in turn makes you feel warmer.

In winter, coolth is bad news and takes a lot of energy to eliminate. But in summer, it's a very different story. The physics at work in summer is no different to what happens in winter – you feel cooler than the air temperature because you are radiating large amounts of heat towards a cool surface. Because of this, the high massers contend that you need a lot less air conditioning in a high mass house. Not that we use a lot of air conditioning in the UK yet, but global warming is expected to change all that very soon. In the USA, the summer cooling demand is almost as large as that for winter heating so an ability to cope with this energy load is likely to become a significant part of our future fuel bills.

However, there is a snag here as well. Call it Problem No 4. During a prolonged hot spell, the structure eventually achieves equilibrium with the surrounding air temperature. Consequently, your body stops radiating heat away and the coolth effect vanishes. A massive structure will still tend to even out the difference between day and night time temperatures, this is true, but this means that whilst you will feel marginally cooler in the day time, you will feel just a little bit hotter during the night. Now whilst this is not a problem in offices and schools, it is with housing, an awful lot of which is empty during the day. Now, the high massers argue that air conditioning is less likely to be turned on in a heavy house because of the coolth effect, but methinks they are exaggerating the effect of the phenomenon. There is no coolth to be had in the middle of the night during a heatwave.

So, as regards low energy building strategies, I believe thermal mass is a classic case of the curate's egg – i.e. it's good in parts. It's probably seen at its best in places which are occupied mostly during the daylight hours – schools, offices, workshops. It can be a useful technique to employ with buildings in constant use such as hospitals and rest homes and, indeed, some housing. But to get any benefit, these homes must be occupied throughout the year and throughout the day. Or, as we have learned to say, 24/7/365. If the occupation is going to be intermittent then there is every chance that high mass can end up being an energy drain.

The Building Regulations 2000

# FIRE SAFETY
## APPROVED DOCUMENT
Volume 1 - Dwellinghouses

**B1 MEANS OF WARNING AND ESCAPE**

**B2 INTERNAL FIRE SPREAD (LININGS)**

**B3 INTERNAL FIRE SPREAD (STRUCTURE)**

**B4 EXTERNAL FIRE SPREAD**

**B5 ACCESS AND FACILITIES FOR THE FIRE SERVICE**

Came into effect April 2007

## VOLUME 1

## MAIN CHANGES IN THE 2006 EDITION

This edition of Approved Document B, Fire safety, replaces the 2000 edition. The main changes are:

### General

a. **Approved Document B:** The Approved Document has been split into two volumes. Volume 1 deals with dwellinghouses, Volume 2 deals with buildings other than dwellinghouses.

Wherever possible the guidance in Volume 1 has been tailored and simplified to be more directly relevant to dwellinghouses.

### Introduction

b. **Certification Schemes:** Suitable schemes may be accepted by Building Control Bodies as evidence of compliance.

c. **Residential Sprinklers:** The use of sprinkler systems in accordance with BS 9251:2005 is recognised.

d. **Adult Placements:** Reference is made to the code of practice for fire safety in adult placements.

### B1

e. **Fire Alarms:** The guidance on smoke alarms has been amended such that alarms should be installed in accordance with BS 5839- 6:2004.

Simple guidance has been retained, in the form of a commentary on this standard, so that most users of the Approved Document will not necessarily need to obtain a copy of the standard.

All smoke alarms should have a standby power supply.

Where a dwellinghouse is extended smoke alarms should be provided in the circulation spaces.

f. **Means of escape:** The guidance on means of escape has been restructured to make it easier to use.

i. Additional guidance has been provided in relation to work on existing houses.

ii. Locks and child resistant safety stays may be provided on escape windows.

iii. The alternative approach for loft conversions to two storey houses has been removed.

iv. New guidance has been provided on the provision of galleries and inner inner rooms.

v. An option of providing sprinkler protection instead of alternative escape routes has been included for dwellinghouses with a floor more than 7.5m above ground level.

vi. Guidance on the application of B1 to replacement windows has been included.

vii. Guidance on the use of air circulation systems in houses with protected stairways is given.

### B3

g. **Integral Garages:** The provision of a sloping floor has been included as an alternative to the 100mm step between dwellinghouses and integral garages.

h. **Compartmentation:** Guidance on the junction between compartment walls and roofs has been clarified and expanded.

i. Cavity Barriers: Window and door frames are only suitable for use as cavity barriers if they are constructed of steel or timber of an appropriate thickness.

### B4

j. **Roof Coverings:** The guidance on roof coverings incorporates the new European system of classification set out in BS EN 13501-5:2005.

### B5

k. **Vehicle Access:** There should be access for a pump appliance to within 45m of all points within a dwellinghouse.

### Appendix B

l. **Self-Closing Devices:** Other than doors between a dwellinghouse and an integral garage, fire doors need not be provided with self closing devices.

# Contents

**APPENDIX D: PURPOSE GROUPS**

**APPENDIX E: DEFINITIONS**

**APPENDIX F: STANDARDS AND OTHER PUBLICATIONS REFERRED TO**

## DIAGRAMS

# Use of guidance

## THE APPROVED DOCUMENTS

This document is one of a series that has been approved and issued by the Secretary of State for the purpose of providing practical guidance with respect to the requirements of Schedule 1 to and Regulation 7 of the Building Regulations 2000 (Sl 2000/2531) for England and Wales.

**At the back of this document is a list of all the documents that have been approved and issued by the Secretary of State for this purpose.**

The Approved Documents are intended to provide guidance for some of the more common building situations. However, there may well be alternative ways of achieving compliance with the requirements.

**Thus there is no obligation to adopt any particular solution contained in an Approved Document if you prefer to meet the relevant requirement in some other way.**

### Other requirements

The guidance contained in an Approved Document relates only to the particular requirements of the Regulations which that document addresses. The building work will also have to comply with the Requirements of any other relevant paragraphs in Schedule 1 to the Regulations.

There are Approved Documents which give guidance on each of the other requirements in Schedule 1 and on Regulation 7.

## LIMITATION ON REQUIREMENTS

In accordance with Regulation 8, the requirements in Parts A to D, F to K, N and P (except for paragraphs H2 and J6) of Schedule 1 to the Building Regulations do not require anything to be done except for the purpose of securing reasonable standards of health and safety for persons in or about buildings (and any others who may be affected by buildings or matters connected with buildings). This is one of the categories of purpose for which Building Regulations may be made.

Paragraphs H2 and J6 are excluded from Regulation 8 because they deal directly with prevention of the contamination of water. Parts E and M (which deal, respectively, with resistance to the passage of sound, and access to and use of buildings) are excluded from Regulation 8 because they address the welfare and convenience of building users. Part L is excluded from Regulation 8 because it addresses the conservation of fuel and power. All these matters are amongst the purposes, other than health and safety, that may be addressed by Building Regulations.

## MATERIALS AND WORKMANSHIP

Any building work which is subject to the requirements imposed by Schedule 1 of the Building Regulations should, in accordance with Regulation 7, be carried out with proper materials and in a workmanlike manner.

You may show that you have complied with Regulation 7 in a number of ways. These include the appropriate use of a product bearing CE marking in accordance with the Construction Products Directive (89/106/EEC)[1]. the Low Voltage Directive (73/23/EEC and amendment 93/68/EEC)[2] and the EMC Directive (89/336/ EEC)[3], as amended by the CE Marking Directive (93/68/EEC)[4], or a product complying with an appropriate technical specification (as defined in those Directives), a British Standard, or an alternative national technical specification of a Member State of the European Union or Turkey[5], or of another State signatory to the Agreement on the European Economic Area (EEA) that provides an equivalent level of safety and protection, or a product covered by a national or European certificate issued by a European Technical Approval Issuing body, and the conditions of use are in accordance with the terms of the certificate.

You will find further guidance in the Approved Document supporting Regulation 7 on materials and workmanship.

### Independent certification schemes

There are many UK product certification schemes. Such schemes certify compliance with the requirements of a recognised document which is appropriate to the purpose for which the material is to be used. Materials which are not so certified may still conform to a relevant standard.

Many certification bodies which approve such schemes are accredited by United Kingdom Accreditation Service (UKAS).

Since the fire performance of a product, component or structure is dependent upon satisfactory site installation and maintenance, independent schemes of certification and accreditation of installers and maintenance firms of such will provide confidence in the appropriate standard of workmanship being provided.

Building Control Bodies may accept the certification of products, components, materials or structures under such schemes as evidence of compliance with the relevant standard. Similarly, Building Control Bodies may accept the certification of the installation or maintenance of products, components, materials or structures under such schemes as evidence of compliance with the relevant standard. Nonetheless, a Building Control Body will wish to establish, in advance of the work, that any such scheme is adequate for the purposes of the Building Regulations.

### Technical specifications

Building Regulations are made for specific purposes, such as health and safety, energy conservation and the welfare and convenience of people. Standards and technical approvals are relevant guidance to the extent that they relate to these considerations. However, they may also address other aspects of performance such as serviceability, or aspects which, although they relate to health and safety, are not covered by the Regulations.

When an Approved Document makes reference to a named standard, the relevant version of the standard is the one listed at the end of the publication. However, if this version of the standard has been revised or updated by the issuing standards body, the new version may be used as a source of guidance provided it continues to address the relevant requirements of the Regulations.

The appropriate use of a product which complies with a European Technical Approval as defined in the Construction Products Directive will meet the relevant requirements.

The Department intends to issue periodic amendments to its Approved Documents to reflect emerging harmonised European Standards. Where a national standard is to be replaced by a European harmonised standard, there will be a co-existence period during which either standard may be referred to. At the end of the co-existence period the national standard will be withdrawn.

## INTERACTION WITH OTHER LEGISLATION

### Houses in multiple occupation

This guidance may also be applicable to the design and construction of dwellings which are considered to be 'houses in multiple occupation' (HMOs), as defined in the Housing Act 2004, providing there are no more than six residents in any self-contained dwelling. The licensing of HMOs is typically overseen by the Local Authority who may require additional precautions over and above this guidance. Technical guidance on the assessment of hazards from fire and preventive measures for HMOs is contained in the Housing Health and Safety Rating System Operating Guidance issued in February 2006 (ISBN: 978 185112 846 4).

### The Workplace (Health, Safety and Welfare) Regulations 1992

The Workplace (Health, Safety and Welfare) Regulations 1992 contain some requirements which affect building design. The main requirements are now covered by the Building Regulations but for further information see: Workplace healthy safety and welfare, The Workplace (Health, Safety and Welfare) Regulations 1992, Approved Code of Practice and Guidance; The Health and Safety Commission, L24; published by HMSO 1992; ISBN: 0 11886 333 9.

The Workplace (Health, Safety and Welfare) Regulations 1992 apply to the common parts of flats and similar buildings if people such as cleaners, wardens and caretakers are employed to work in these common parts. Where the requirements of the Building Regulations that are covered by this Part do not apply to dwellings, the provisions may still be required in the situations described above in order to satisfy the Workplace Regulations.

1    As implemerrted by the Construction Products Regulations 1991 (Sl 1991 No 1620)

2    As implemented by the Electrical Equipment (Safety) Regulations 1994 (Sl 1994 No 3260)

3    As implemented by the Electromagnetic Compatibility Regulations 1992 (Sl 1992 No 2372)

4    As implemented by the Construction Products (Amendment) Regulations 1994 (Sl 1994 No 3051) and the Electromagnetic Compatibility (Amendment) Regulations 1904 (Sl 1994 No 3080)

5    Decision No. 1/96 of the EC-Turkey Association Coundl of 22 December 1996

## The Construction (Design and Management) Regulations 2006

The purpose of this Approved Document is to provide guidance on the fire safety requirements for the completed building. It does not address the risk of fire during the construction work which is covered by the Construction (Design and Management) Regulations 2006 and the Regulatory Reform (Fire Safety) Order. HSE has issued the following guidance on fire safety in construction:

Construction Information Sheet No 51 Construction fire safety, and HSG 168 Fire safety in construction work (ISBN: 071761 332 1).

When the construction work is being carried out on a building which, apart from the construction site part of the building, is occupied, the Fire and Rescue Authority is responsible for the enforcement of the 2006 Regulations in respect of fire. Where the building is unoccupied, the Health and Safety Executive is responsible for enforcement on the construction site.

## The Construction Products Directive

The Construction Products Directive (CPD) is one of the 'New Approach' Directives, which seek to remove technical barriers to trade within the European Economic Area (EEA) as part of the move to complete the Single Market. The EEA comprises the European Community and those states in the European Free Trade Association (other than Switzerland).

The intention of the CPD is to replace existing national standards and technical approvals with a single set of European-wide technical specifications for construction products (i.e. harmonised European standards or European Technical Approvals). Any manufacturer whose products have CE marking showing that they are specified according to European technical specifications cannot have these products refused entry to EEA markets on technical grounds. In the UK, the CPD was implemented by the Construction Products Regulations, which came into force on 27 December 1991 and were amended on 1 January 1995 by the Construction Products (Amendment) Regulations 1994.

This document refers to, and utilises within its guidance, a large number of British Standards, in relation to Codes of Practice and fire test methods (typically the BS 476 series of documents). In order to facilitate harmonisation and the use of the new technical specifications and their supporting European test standards, guidance is also given on the classification of products in accordance with those standards.

Guidance is given for the appropriate use and/or specification of a product to which one or more of the following apply:

1.    a product bearing CE marking in accordance with the Construction Products Directive (89/106/EEC) as amended by the CE marking Directive (93/68/EEC);

2.    a product tested and classified in accordance with the European Standards (BS EN) referred to in the Commission Decision 2000/147/EC[1] and/or Commission Decision 2000/367/EC[2];

3.    a product complying with an appropriate technical specification (as defined in the CPD Directive 89/106/EC as amended by 93/68/EEC).

The implementation of the CPD will necessitate a time period during which national (British) Standards and European technical specifications will co-exist. This is the so-called period of co-existence. The objective of this period of co-existence is to provide for a gradual adaptation to the requirements of the CPD. It will enable producers, importers and distributors of construction products to sell stocks of products manufactured in line with the national rules previously in force and have new tests carried out. The duration of the period of co-existence in relation to the European fire tests has not yet been clearly defined.

As new information becomes available and further harmonised European standards relevant to this document are published, further guidance will be made available.

## Designation of standards

The designation of 'xxxx' is used for the year referred to for standards that are not yet published. The latest version of any standard may be used provided that it continues to address the relevant requirements of the Regulations.

## Commission guidance papers and decisions

The following guidance papers and Commission Decisions are directly relevant to fire matters under the Construction Products Directive:

### Guidance paper G
The European classification system for the reaction to fire performance of construction products.

### Guidance paper J
Transitional arrangements under the Construction Products Directive.

Commission Decision of 8 February 2000 (2000/147/EC) implementing Council Directive 89/106/EEC as regards the classification of the reaction to fire performance of construction products.

Commission Decision of 3 May 2000 (2000/367/ EC) implementing Council Directive 89/106/EEC as regards the classification of the resistance to fire performance of construction products, construction works and parts thereof.

Commission Decision of 26 September 2000 (2000/605/EC) amending Decision 96/603/EC establishing the list of products belonging to Classes A 'No contribution to fire' provided for in Decision 94/611/EC implementing Article 20 of Council Directive 89/106/EEC on construction products.

Corrigenda – Corrigendum to Commission Decision 2000/147/EC of 8 February 2000 implementing Council Directive 89/106/EEC as regards the classification of the reaction to fire performance of construction products.

The publication and revision of Commission guidance papers and decisions are ongoing and the latest information in this respect can be found by accessing the European Commission's website via the link on the Communities and Local Government website at: www.communities.gov.uk/buildingregs.

### Environmental Protection
Requirements under Part B of the Building Regulations and the guidance in this Approved Document are made for the purpose of ensuring the health and safety of people in and around buildings.

The Environment Agency publishes guidance on the design and construction of buildings for the purpose of protecting the environment. This includes Pollution Prevention Guidelines (PPG18) on Managing Fire Water and Major Spillages, which seeks to minimise the effects of water run-off from firefighting. It is aimed at medium to large (and small, high-risk) commercial and industrial sites and sets out requirements for the construction of containment areas for contaminated water and such other measures.

It should be noted that compliance with the Building Regulations does not depend upon compliance with other such guidance.

1   Implementing Council Directive 8Q/106/EEC as regards the classification of the reaction to fire (2000/147/EC) performance of construction products.

2   Implementing Coundl Directive 89/106/EEC as regards the classification of the resistance to fire (2000/367/EC) performance of construction products, construction works and parts thereof.

# General introduction: Fire safety

## Scope

**0.1**  Approved Document B (Fire safety) has been published in two volumes. Volume 1 deals solely with dwellinghouses (see Appendix E and Building Regulation 2(1)), while Volume 2 deals with all other types of building covered by the Building Regulations.

Where very large (over 18m in height) or unusual dwellinghouses are proposed some of the guidance in Volume 2 may be needed to supplement that given by Volume 1.

## Arrangement of sections

**0.2**  The functional requirements B1 to B5 of Schedule 1 of the Building Regulations are dealt with separately in one or more Sections. The requirement is reproduced at the start of the relevant Sections, followed by an introduction to the subject.

**0.3**  The provisions set out in this document deal with different aspects of fire safety, with the following aims:

**B1:** To ensure satisfactory provision of means of giving an alarm of fire and a satisfactory standard of means of escape for persons in the event of fire in a building.

**B2:** To ensure fire spread over the internal linings of buildings is inhibited.

**B3:** To ensure the stability of buildings in the event of fire; to ensure that there is a sufficient degree of fire separation within buildings and between adjoining buildings; to provide automatic fire suppression where necessary; and to inhibit the unseen spread of fire and smoke in concealed spaces in buildings.

**B4:** To ensure external walls and roofs have adequate resistance to the spread of fire over the external envelope, and that spread of fire from one building to another is restricted.

**B5:** To ensure satisfactory access for fire appliances to buildings and the provision of facilities in buildings to assist firefighters in the saving of life of people in and around buildings.

**0.4**  Whilst guidance appropriate to each of these aspects is set out separately in this document, many of the provisions are closely interlinked. For example, there is a close link between the provisions for means of escape (B1) and those for the control of fire growth (B2), fire containment and/or suppression (B3) and facilities for the fire and rescue service (B5). Similarly there are links between B3 and the provisions for controlling external fire spread (B4), and between B3 and B5. Interaction between these different requirements should be recognised where variations in the standard of provision are being considered. A higher standard under one of the requirements may be of benefit in respect of one or more of the other requirements. The guidance in the document as a whole should be considered as a package aimed at achieving an acceptable standard of fire safety.

### Appendices: provisions common to more than one of Part B's requirements

**0.5**  Guidance on matters that refer to more than one of the Sections is in a series of Appendices, covering the following subjects:

Appendix A – fire performance of materials, products and structures

Appendix B – provisions regarding fire doors

Appendix C – methods of measurement

Appendix D – a classification of purpose groups

Appendix E – definitions

Appendix F – Standards and other publications referred to.

### Fire performance of materials, products and structures

**0.6**  Much of the guidance throughout this document is given in terms of performance in relation to standard fire test methods. Details are drawn together in Appendix A to which reference is made where appropriate. In the case of fire protection systems, reference is made to standards for system design and installation. Standards referred to are listed in Appendix F.

### Fire doors

**0.7**  Guidance in respect of fire doors is set out in Appendix B.

### Methods of measurement

**0.8**  Some form of measurement is an integral part of much of the guidance in this document and methods are set out in Appendix C.

### Purpose groups

**0.9**  Much of the guidance in this document is related to the use of the building. The use classifications are termed purpose groups, and they are described in Appendix D. This document deals only with buildings in Purpose Groups 1 b and 1c.

### Definitions

**0.10**  The definitions are given in Appendix E.

## Building maintenance and the provision of information

**0.11**  For the provisions of this Approved Document to be effective it is essential that the measures incorporated into the design of a dwellinghouse are adequately maintained. Building Regulations do not impose any requirements on the management of a building. However, the eventual owners and occupiers should be provided with sufficient information to operate, maintain and use the building in reasonable safety.

For individual dwellinghouses, basic advice on the proper use and maintenance of systems provided in the building, such as emergency egress windows, fire doors, smoke alarms, sprinklers etc., can help to ensure that these systems are maintained and kept available for use. Householders should also be made aware that unauthorised material alterations (see paragraph 0.20) may leave them liable to prosecution.

In providing fire protection of any kind in dwellinghouses, it should be recognised that measures which significantly interfere with the day-to-day convenience of the occupants may be less reliable in the long term.

## Property protection

**0.12**  There are often many stakeholders, including insurers, who have a valid interest in the fire protection measures which are incorporated into a building's design. To ensure that the most effective fire protection measures are applied which are appropriate to the specific property, early consultation with the main stakeholders is essential. Failure to consult with stakeholders at an early stage could result in additional measures being required after completion, the use of the building being restricted, or insurance premiums and/or deductibles being increased.

Building Regulations are intended to ensure that a reasonable standard of life safety is provided in case of fire. The protection of property, including the building itself, often requires additional measures and insurers will, in general, seek their own higher standards before accepting the insurance risk.

Guidance for asset protection in the Civil and Defence Estates is given in the Crown Fire Standards published by the Property Advisers to the Civil Estate (PACE).

## Independent schemes of certification and accreditation

**0.13**  Much of the guidance throughout this document is given in terms of performance in relation to standard fire test methods. Details are drawn together in Appendix A to which reference is made where appropriate. In the case of fire protection systems, reference is made to standards for system design and installation. Standards referred to are listed in Appendix F.

**0.14**  Since the performance of a system, product, component or structure is dependent upon satisfactory site installation, testing and maintenance, independent schemes of certification and accreditation of installers and maintenance firms of such will provide confidence in the appropriate standard of workmanship being provided.

Confidence that the required level of performance can be achieved will be demonstrated by the use of a system, material, product or structure which is provided under the arrangements of a product conformity certification scheme and an accreditation of installers scheme.

Third party accredited product conformity certification schemes not only provide a means of identifying materials and designs of systems, products or structures which have demonstrated that they have the requisite performance in fire, but additionally provide confidence that the systems, materials, products or structures actually supplied are provided to the same specification or design as that tested/assessed.

Third party accreditation of installers of systems, materials, products or structures provides a means of ensuring that installations have been conducted by knowledgeable contractors to appropriate standards, thereby increasing the reliability of the anticipated performance in fire.

Many certification bodies which approve such schemes are accredited by UKAS.

**0.15** Building Control Bodies may accept the certification of products, components, materials or structures under such schemes as evidence of compliance with the relevant standard. Similarly, Building Control Bodies may accept the certification of the installation or maintenance of products, components, materials or structures under such schemes as evidence of compliance with the relevant standard. Nonetheless, a Building Control Body will wish to establish, in advance of the work, that any such scheme is adequate for the purposes of the Building Regulations.

## Residential sprinklers

**0.16** Sprinkler systems installed in dwellinghouses can reduce the risk to life and significantly reduce the degree of damage caused by fire. Sprinkler protection can also sometimes be used as a compensatory feature where the provisions of this Approved Document are varied in some way.

**0.17** Where a sprinkler system is recommended within this document it should be designed and installed in accordance with BS 9251:2005 Sprinkler systems for residential and domestic occupancies – Code of practice and DD 252:2002 Components for residential sprinkler systems – Specification and test methods for residential sprinklers.

Where sprinklers are provided, it is normal practice to provide sprinkler protection throughout the building. However, where the sprinklers are being installed as a compensatory feature to address a specific risk or hazard it may be acceptable to protect only part of a building.

Further guidance can also be found in Sprinklers for Safety: Use and Benefits of Incorporating Sprinklers in Buildings and Structures, BAFSA (2006) ISBN: 0 95526 280 1.

**0.18** There are many alternative or innovative fire suppression systems available. Where these are used it is necessary to ensure that such systems have been designed and tested for use in domestic buildings and are fit for their intended purpose.

## Inclusive design

**0.19** The fire safety aspects of the Building Regulations are made for securing reasonable standards of health and safety of persons in and about buildings. This is intended to include all people including people with disabilities. The provisions set out in this Approved Document are considered to be a reasonable standard for most buildings. However, there may be some people whose specific needs are not addressed. In some situations additional measures may be needed to accommodate these needs. This should be done on a case by case basis.

## Material alteration

**0.20** Under Regulation 3, the term "material alteration" is defined by reference to a list of "relevant requirements" of Schedule 1 to the Building Regulations. That list includes the requirements of Parts B1, B3, B4 and B5. This means that an alteration which, at any stage of the work, results in a building being less satisfactory than it was before in relation to compliance with the requirements of Parts B1, B3, B4 or B5 is a material alteration, and is therefore controlled by Regulation 4 as it is classed as "building work". Regulation 4(1) requires that any building work carried out in relation to a material alteration complies with the applicable requirements of Schedule 1 to the Regulations, while Regulation 4(2) requires that once that building work has been completed, the building as a whole must comply with the relevant requirements of Schedule 1 or, where it did not comply before, must be no more unsatisfactory than it was before the work was carried out.

## Alternative approaches

**0.21** The fire safety requirements of the Building Regulations should be satisfied by following the relevant guidance given in this Approved Document. However, Approved Documents are intended to provide guidance for some of the more common building situations and there may well be alternative ways of achieving compliance with the requirements.

If other codes or guides are adopted, the relevant recommendations concerning fire safety in the particular publication should be followed, rather than a mixture of the publication and provisions in the relevant sections of this Approved Document. However, there may be circumstances where it is necessary to use one publication to supplement another.

Guidance documents intended specifically for assessing fire safety in existing buildings will often include provisions which are less onerous than those set out in this Approved Document or other standards applicable to new buildings. As such, these documents are unlikely to be appropriate for use where building work, controlled by the Regulations, is proposed.

### Registered group homes

**0.22** Depending on the nature of the occupants and their management needs, it may be acceptable to treat an unsupervised group home with up to six residents as an ordinary dwelling house.

However, because such places have to be registered, the registration authority should be consulted to establish whether there are any additional fire safety measures that the authority will require.

Where an existing house of one or two storeys is to be put to use as an unsupervised group home for not more than 6 mental health service users, it should be regarded as a Purpose Group 1 (c) building if the means of escape are provided in accordance with HTM 88: Guide to fire precautions in NHS housing in the community for menially handicapped (or mentally ill) people. Where the building is new, it may be more appropriate to regard it as being in Purpose Group 2(b).

### Adult placements

**0.23** Where a dwellinghouse is used for the purposes of an Adult Placement Scheme and fulfils the criteria of the Adult Placement Schemes (England) Regulations (Sl 2004 No 2070) and where no building work is proposed, the guidance in the joint code of practice published by the National Association of Adult Placement Services (www.naaps.co.uk) should be sufficient to satisfy Part B of the Building Regulations if a material change of use has taken place.

### Sheltered housing

**0.24** Where a sheltered housing scheme consists of individual houses then each unit may be designed in accordance with this volume of Approved Document B. Any communal facilities that are provided within the scheme should be designed in accordance with Approved Document B Volume 2 (Buildings other than dwellinghouses).

### Fire safety engineering

**0.25** Fire safety engineering can provide an alternative approach to fire safety. It may be the only practical way to achieve a satisfactory standard of fire safety in some large and complex buildings. Fire safety engineering may also be suitable for solving a problem with an aspect of the building design which otherwise follows the provisions in this document

British Standard BS 7974:2001 Application of fire safety engineering principles to the design of buildings and supporting published documents (PDs) provide a framework and guidance on the design and assessment of fire safety measures in buildings. Following the discipline of BS 7974 should enable designers and Building Control Bodies to be aware of the relevant issues, the need to consider the complete fire safety system, and to follow a disciplined analytical framework.

**0.26** Factors that should be taken into account include:

a.    the anticipated probability of a fire occurring;

b.    the anticipated fire severity;

c.    the ability of a structure to resist the spread of fire and smoke; and

d.    the consequential danger to people in and around the building.

**0.27** A wide variety of measures could be considered and incorporated to a greater or lesser extent, as appropriate in the circumstances. These include.

a.    the adequacy of means to prevent fire;

b.    early fire warning by an automatic detection and warning system;

c.    the standard of means of escape;

d.    provision of smoke control;

e.    control of the rate of growth of a fire;

f.    the adequacy of the structure to resist the effects of a fire;

g.    the degree of fire containment;

h.    fire separation between buildings or parts of buildings;

i.    the standard of active measures for fire extinguishment or control;

j.    facilities to assist the fire and rescue service;

k.    the availability of powers to require staff training in fire safety and fire routines;

l.    consideration of the availability of any continuing control under other legislation that could ensure continued maintenance of such systems; and

m.    management.

**0.28** It is possible to use quantitative techniques to evaluate risk and hazard. Some factors in the measures listed above can be given numerical values in some circumstances. The assumptions made when quantitative methods are used need careful assessment.

### Buildings of special architectural or historic interest

**0.29** Some variation of the provisions set out in this document may also be appropriate where Part B applies to existing buildings, particularly in buildings of special architectural or historic interest, where adherence to the guidance in this document might prove unduly restrictive. In such cases it would be appropriate to take into account a range of fire safety features, some of which are dealt with in this document, and some of which are not addressed in any detail, and to set these against an assessment of the hazard and risk peculiar to the particular case.

# B1 MEANS OF WARNING AND ESCAPE

This Approved Document deals with the following Requirement from Part B of Schedule 1 to the Building Regulations 2000 (as amended).

| Requirement | Limits on application |
|---|---|
| **Means of warning and escape** | |
| B1. The building shall he designed and constructed so that there are appropriate provisions for the early warning of fire, and appropriate means of escape in case of fire from the building to a place of safety outside the building capable of being safely and effectively used at all material times. | Requirement B1 does not apply to any prison provided under Section 33 of the Prison Act 1952 (power to provide prisons, etc.). |

## Guidance

### Performance

In the Secretary of State's view the Requirement B1 will be met if:

a.    there is sufficient means for giving early warning of fire for persons in the building;

b.    there are routes of sufficient number and capacity, which are suitably located to enable persons to escape to a place of safety in the event of fire; and

c.    the routes are sufficiently protected from the effects of fire, where necessary.

### Introduction

**B1.i** These provisions relate to building work and material changes of use which are subject to the functional requirement B1; they may therefore affect new or existing buildings. They are concerned with the measures necessary to ensure reasonable facilities for means of warning and escape in case of fire. They are only concerned with fire precautions where these are necessary to safeguard escape routes.

They assume that in the design of the building, reliance should not be placed on external rescue by the fire and rescue service nor should it be based on a presumption that they will attend an incident within a given time. This Approved Document has been prepared on the basis that, in an emergency, the occupants of any part of a building should be able to escape safely without any external assistance.

It should also be noted that the guidance for a typical one or two storey dwellinghouse is limited to the provision of smoke alarms and to the provision of openable windows for emergency egress.

## Analysis of the problem

**B1 .ii** The design of means of escape and the provision of other fire safety measures, such as smoke alarms, should be based on an assessment of the risk to the occupants in the event of fire. The assessment should take into account the nature of the building structure; the use of the building; the potential of fire spread through the building; and the standard of fire safety management proposed. Where it is not possible to identify with any certainty any of these elements, a judgement as to the likely level of provision must be made.

**Bl.iii** Fires do not normally start in two different places in a building at the same time. Initially, a fire will create a hazard only in the part in which it starts and it is unlikely, at this stage, to involve a large area. The fire may subsequently spread to other parts of the building, usually along the circulation routes. The items that are the first to be ignited are often furnishings and other items not controlled by the Building Regulations. It is less likely that the fire will originate in the structure of the building itself and the risk of it originating accidentally in circulation areas is limited, provided that the combustible content of such areas is restricted.

**B1.iv** The primary danger associated with fire in its early stages is not flame but the smoke and noxious gases produced by the fire. They cause most of the casualties and may also obscure the way to escape routes and exits. Measures designed to provide safe means of escape must therefore provide appropriate arrangements to limit the rapid spread of smoke and fumes.

### Criteria for means of escape

**B1 .v** The basic principles for the design of means of escape are:

a.    that there should be alternative means of escape from most situations;

b.    where direct escape to a place of safety is not possible, it should be possible to reach a place of relative safety, such as a protected stairway, which is on a route to an exit, within a reasonable travel distance; and

c.    in certain conditions, a single direction of escape (a dead end) can be accepted as providing reasonable safety. These conditions depend on the use of the building and its associated fire risk, the size and height of the building, the extent of the dead end and the numbers of persons accommodated within the dead end.

The ultimate place of safety is the open air clear of the effects of the fire.

**B1 .vi** For the purposes of Building Regulations, the following are not acceptable as means of escape:

a.    lifts (except for a suitably designed and installed evacuation lift);

b.    portable ladders and throw-out ladders; and

c.    manipulative apparatus and appliances, e.g. fold-down ladders and chutes.

**Note:** The regulations would not prohibit the use of such measures as an additional feature but they are not considered suitable as an alternative to adequate means of escape.

### Unprotected and protected escape routes

**Bl.vii** The unprotected part of an escape route is that part which a person has to traverse before reaching either the safety of a final exit or the comparative safety of a protected escape route, i.e. a protected corridor or protected stairway.

Unprotected escape routes should be limited in extent so that people do not have to travel excessive distances while exposed to the immediate danger of fire and smoke.

Even with protected horizontal escape routes the distance to a final exit or protected stairway needs to be limited because the structure does not give protection indefinitely*

**Bl.viii** Protected stairways are designed to provide virtually 'fire sterile* ar'as which lead to places of safety outside the building. Once inside a protected stairway, a person can be considered to be safe from immediate danger from flame and smoke. They can then proceed to a place of safety at their own pace. To enable this to be done, flames, smoke and gases must be excluded from these escape routes, as far as is reasonably possible, by fire-resisting construction and doors or by an appropriate smoke control system, or by a combination of both of these methods.

## Security

**Bl.ix** The need for easy and rapid evacuation of a building in case of fire may conflict with the control of entry and exit in the interest of security. Measures intended to prevent unauthorised access can also hinder entry of the fire and rescue service to rescue people trapped by fire.

Potential conflicts should be identified and resolved at the design stage and not left until after completion of the work. The architectural liaison officers attached to most police forces are a valuable source of advice.

This document does not intend for the types of lock used on windows (see paragraph 2.8) and entrance doors to dwelling houses to be controlled under the Building Regulations.

## General
### Use of the document
**B1.x**  Section 1 deals with fire detection and alarm systems. Section 2 deals with means of escape.

# Section 1: Fire detection and fire alarm systems

## Introduction
**1.1**    Provisions are made in this section for suitable arrangements to be made in dwellinghouses to give early warning in the event of fire.

## General
**1.2**    The installation of smoke alarms, or automatic fire detection and alarm systems can significantly increase the level of safety by automatically giving an early warning of fire. The following guidance is appropriate for most dwellinghouses. However, where it is known that the occupants of a proposed dwellinghouse are at a special risk from fire, it may be more appropriate to provide a higher standard of protection, e.g. additional detectors.

**1.3**    All new dwellinghouses should be provided with a fire detection and fire alarm system in accordance with the relevant recommendations of BS 5839-6:2004 to at least a Grade D Category LD3 standard.

**1.4**    The smoke and heat alarms should be mains-operated and conform to BS 5446-1:2000 or BS 5446-2:2003, respectively: Fire detection and fire alarm devices for dwellinghouses, Part 1 Specification for smoke alarms; or Part 2 Specification for heat alarms. They should have a standby power supply, such as a battery (either rechargeable or non-rechargeable) or capacitor. More information on power supplies is given in clause 15 of BS 5839-6:2004.

**Note:** BS 5446-1 covers smoke alarms based on ionization chamber smoke detectors and optical (photo-electric) smoke detectors. The different types of detector respond differently to smouldering and fast-flaming fires. Either type of detector is generally suitable. However, the choice of detector type should, if possible, take into account the type of fire that might be expected and the need to avoid false alarms. Optical detectors tend to be less affected by low levels of 'invisible* particles, such as fumes from kitchens, that often cause false alarms. Accordingly, they are generally more suitable than ionization chamber detectors for installation in circulation spaces adjacent to kitchens.

## Large houses
**1.5**    A dwellinghouse is regarded as large if it has more than one storey and any of those storeys exceed 200m².

**1.6**    A large dwellinghouse of 2 storeys (excluding basement storeys) should be fitted with a fire detection and fire alarm system of Grade B category LD3 as described in BS 5839-6:2004.

**1.7**    A large dwellinghouse of 3 or more storeys (excluding basement storeys) should be fitted with a Grade A Category LD2 system as described in BS 5839-6:2004, with detectors sited in accordance with the recommendations of BS 5839-1:2002 for a Category L2 system.

## Material alterations
**1.8**    Where new habitable rooms are provided above the ground floor level, or where they are provided at ground floor level and there is no final exit from the new room, a fire detection and fire alarm system should be installed. Smoke alarms should be provided in the circulation spaces of the dwellinghouse in accordance with paragraphs 1.10 to 1.18 to ensure that any occupants of the new rooms are warned of any fire that may impede their escape.

## Sheltered housing
**1.9**    The detection equipment in a sheltered housing scheme with a warden or supervisor should have a connection to a central monitoring point (or alarm receiving centre) so that the person in charge is aware that a fire has been detected in one of the dwellinghouses and can identify the dwelling house concerned. These provisions are not intended to be applied to the common parts of a sheltered housing development, such as communal lounges, or to sheltered accommodation in the Institutional or Other residential purpose groups (see Approved Document B Volume 2).

## Positioning of smoke and heat alarms

**1.10**   Detailed guidance on the design and installation of fire detection and alarm systems in dwellinghouses is given in BS 5839-6:2004. However, the following guidance is appropriate to most common situations.

**1.11**   Smoke alarms should normally be positioned in the circulation spaces between sleeping spaces and places where fires are most likely to start (e.g. kitchens and living rooms) to pick up smoke in the early stages of a fire.

**1.12**   There should be at least one smoke alarm on every storey of a dwellinghouse.

**1.13**   Where the kitchen area is not separated from the stairway or circulation space by a door, there should be a compatible interlinked heat detector or heat alarm in the kitchen, in addition to whatever smoke alarms are needed in the circulation space(s).

**1.14**   Where more than one alarm is installed they should be linked so that the detection of smoke or heat by one unit operates the alarm signal in all of them. The manufacturers instructions about the maximum number of units that can be linked should be observed.

**1.15**   Smoke alarms / detectors should be sited so that:

a.    there is a smoke alarm in the circulation space within 7.5m of the door to every habitable room;

b.    they are ceiling-mounted and at least 300mm from walls and light fittings (unless, in the case of light fittings, there is test evidence to prove that the proximity of the light fitting will not adversely affect the efficiency of the detector). Units designed for wall-mounting may also be used provided that the units are above the level of doorways opening into the space and they are fixed in accordance with manufacturers' instructions; and

c.    the sensor in ceiling-mounted devices is between 25mm and 600mm below the ceiling (25-150mm in the case of heat detectors or heat alarms).

**Note:** This guidance applies to ceilings that are predominantly flat and horizontal.

**1.16**   It should be possible to reach the smoke alarms to carry out routine maintenance, such as testing and cleaning, easily and safely. For this reason smoke alarms should not be fixed over a stair or any other opening between floors.

**1.17**   Smoke alarms should not be fixed next to or directly above heaters or air-conditioning outlets. They should not be fixed in bathrooms, showers, cooking areas or garages, or any other place where steam, condensation or fumes could give false alarms.

**1.18**   Smoke alarms should not be fitted in places that get very hot (such as a boiler room) or very cold (such as an unheated porch). They should not be fixed to surfaces which are normally much warmer or colder than the rest of the space, because the temperature difference might create air currents which move smoke away from the unit.

## Power supplies

**1.19**   The power supply for a smoke alarm system should be derived from the dwellinghouse's mains electricity supply. The mains supply to the smoke alarm(s) should comprise a single independent circuit at the dwellinghouse's main distribution board (consumer unit) or a single regularly used local lighting circuit. This has the advantage that the circuit is unlikely to be disconnected for any prolonged period. There should be a means of isolating power to the smoke alarms without isolating the lighting.

**1.20**   The electrical installation should comply with Approved Document P (Electrical safety).

**1.21**   Any cable suitable for domestic wiring may be used for the power supply and interconnection to smoke alarm systems, it does not need any particular fire survival properties except in large houses (BS 5839-6:2004 specifies fire resisting cables for Grade A and B systems). Any conductors used for interconnecting alarms (signalling) should be readily distinguishable from those supplying mains power, e.g. by colour coding.

**Note:** Mains-powered smoke alarms may be interconnected using radio-links, provided that this does not reduce the lifetime or duration of any standby power supply below 72 hours. In this case, the smoke alarms may be connected to separate power circuits (see paragraph 1.19)

**1.22**   Other effective options exist and are described in BS 5839-1:2002 and BS 5839-6:2004. For example, the mains supply may be reduced to extra low voltage in a control unit incorporating a standby trickle-charged battery, before being distributed at that voltage to the alarms.

## Design and installation of systems

**1.23**  It is essential that fire detection and fire alarm systems are properly designed, installed and maintained. Where a fire alarm system is installed, an installation and commissioning certificate should be provided. Third party certification schemes for fire protection products and related services are an effective means of providing the fullest possible assurances, offering a level of quality, reliability and safety.

**1.24**  A requirement for maintenance cannot be made as a condition of passing plans by the Building Control Body. However, the attention of developers and builders is drawn to the importance of providing the occupants with information on the use of the equipment, and on its maintenance (or guidance on suitable maintenance contractors). See paragraph 0.11.

**Note:** BS 5839-1 and BS 5839-6 recommend that occupiers should receive the manufacturers' instructions concerning the operation and maintenance of the alarm system.

# Section 2: Means of escape

## Introduction

**2.1** The means of escape from a typical one or two storey dwellinghouse is relatively simple to provide. Few provisions are specified in this document beyond ensuring that means are provided for giving early warning in the event of fire (see Section 1) and that suitable means are provided for emergency egress from each storey via windows or doors.

With increasing height more complex provisions are needed because emergency egress through upper windows becomes increasingly hazardous. It is then necessary to protect the internal stairway. If there are floors more than 7.5m above ground level, the risk that the stairway will become impassable before occupants of the upper parts of the dwellinghouse have escaped is appreciable, and an alternative route from those parts should be provided. See Diagram 1.

**Note:** Ground level is explained in Appendix C, Diagram C1.

---

**Diagram 1 Means of escape from dwellinghouses**

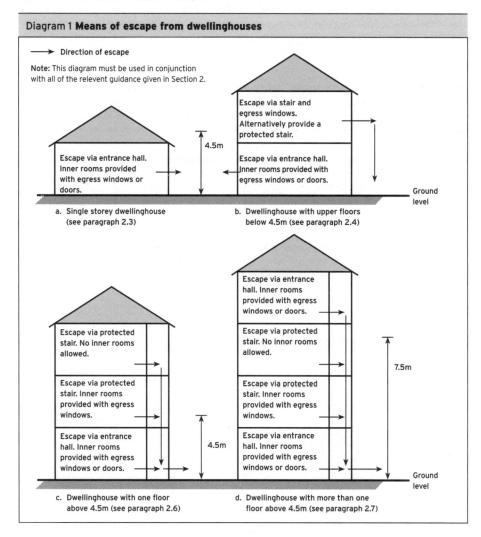

a. Single storey dwellinghouse (see paragraph 2.3)

b. Dwellinghouse with upper floors below 4.5m (see paragraph 2.4)

c. Dwellinghouse with one floor above 4.5m (see paragraph 2.6)

d. Dwellinghouse with more than one floor above 4.5m (see paragraph 2.7)

**2.2**  In providing any kind of fire protection in houses it should be recognised that measures which significantly interfere with the day-to-day convenience of the occupants may be less reliable in the long term.

## Provisions for escape from the ground storey

**2.3**  Except for kitchens, all habitable rooms in the ground storey should either:

a.    open directly onto a hall leading to the entrance or other suitable exit; or

b.    be provided with a window (or door) which complies with paragraph 2.8.

**Note:** See also General Provisions.

## Provisions for escape from upper floors not more than 4.5m above ground level

**2.4**  Except for kitchens, all habitable rooms in the upper storey(s) of a dwellinghouse served by only one stair should be provided with:

a.    a window (or external door) which complies with paragraph 2.8; or

b.    direct access to a protected stairway (as described in 2.6 (a) or (b)),

**Note:** A single window can be accepted to serve two rooms provided both rooms have their own access to the stairs. A communicating door between the rooms should also be provided so that it is possible to gain access to the window without passing through the stair enclosure.

**Note:** See also General Provisions.

## Provisions for escape from upper floors more than 4.5m above ground level

**2.5**  The provisions described in 2.6 and 2.7 need not be followed if the dwellinghouse has more than one internal stairway, which afford effective alternative means of escape and are physically separated from each other.

**Note:** The necessary degree of separation is a matter of judgement, eg. stairs may be separated by fire-resisting construction or by a number of rooms.

### Dwellinghouses with one floor more than 4.5m above ground level

**2.6**  The dwellinghouse may either have a protected stairway as described in (a) below, or the top floor can be separated and given its own alternative escape route as described in (b).

a.    The upper storeys (those above ground storey) should be served by a protected stairway (protected at all levels) which should either:

   i. extend to a final exit, see Diagram 2(a); or

   ii. give access to at least two escape routes at ground level, each delivering to final exits and separated from each other by fire-resisting construction and fire doors, see Diagram 2(b); or

b.    The top storey should be separated from the lower storeys by fire-resisting construction and be provided with an alternative escape route leading to its own final exit. See Diagram 3.

**Note:** See also General Provisions.

---

### Diagram 2 **Alternative arrangements for final exits**

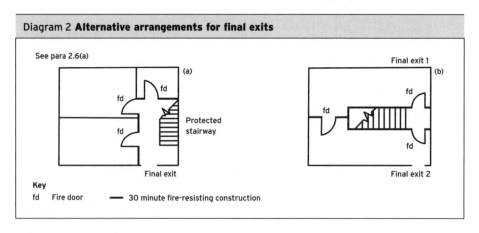

See para 2.6(a)

(a)    fd    fd    Protected stairway    Final exit

Final exit 1    (b)    fd    fd    fd    Final exit 2

Key
fd    Fire door    —— 30 minute fire-resisting construction

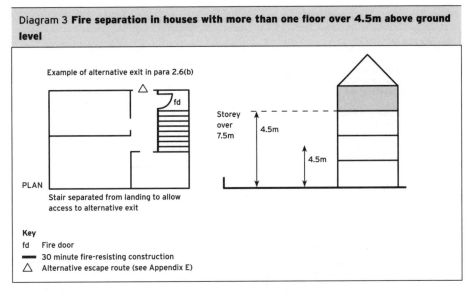

Diagram 3 **Fire separation in houses with more than one floor over 4.5m above ground level**

Example of alternative exit in para 2.6(b)

fd

PLAN

Stair separated from landing to allow
access to alternative exit

Storey
over
7.5m

4.5m

4.5m

**Key**
fd    Fire door
━━    30 minute fire-resisting construction
△    Alternative escape route (see Appendix E)

## Dwellinghouses with more than one floor over 4.5m above ground level

**2.7**    Where a dwellinghouse has two or more storeys with floors more than 4.5m above ground level (typically a dwellinghouse of four or more storeys) then, in addition to meeting the provisions in paragraph 2.6:

a.    an alternative escape route should be provided from each storey or level situated 7.5m or more above ground level. Where the access to the alternative escape route is via:

i. the protected stairway to an upper storey; or

ii. a landing within the protected stairway enclosure to an alternative escape route on the same storey; then

iii. the protected stairway at or about 7.5m above ground level should be separated from the lower storeys or levels by fire-resisting construction, see Diagram 3; or

b.    the dwellinghouse should be fitted throughout with a sprinkler system designed and installed in accordance with BS 9251:2005.

**Note:** See also General Provisions.

## General provisions
### Emergency egress windows and external doors

**2.8**    Any window provided for emergency egress purposes and any external door provided for escape should comply with the following conditions:

a.    the window should have an unobstructed openable area that is at least 0.33m$^2$ and at least 450mm high and 450mm wide (the route through the window may be at an angle rather than straight through). The bottom of the openable area should be not more than 1100mm above the floor; and

b.    the window or door should enable the person escaping to reach a place free from danger from fire. This is a matter for judgement in each case, but, in general, a courtyard or back garden from which there is no exit other than through other buildings would have to be at least as deep as the dwellinghouse is high to be acceptable, see Diagram 4.

**Note 1:** Approved Document K Protection from falling, collision and impact specifies a minimum guarding height of 800mm, except in the case of a window in a roof where the bottom of the opening may be 600mm above the floor.

**Note 2:** Locks (with or without removable keys) and stays may be fitted to egress windows, subject to the stay being fitted with a release catch, which may be child resistant.

**Note 3:** Windows should be designed such that they will remain in the open position without needing to be held by a person making their escape.

---

Diagram 4 **Ground or basement storey exit into an enclosed space**

See para 2.8(b)

For an escape route to be acceptable into an enclosed courtyard or garden, the depth of back garden should exceed:

a.  the height of the house above ground level (X); or

b.  where a rear extension is provided, the height of the extensions (Y)

whichever is greater.

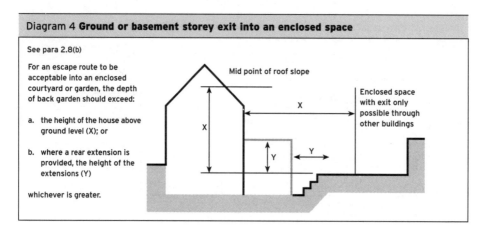

---

### Inner rooms

**2.9**  A room whose only escape route is through another room is termed an inner room and is at risk if a fire starts in that other room (access room). This situation may arise with open-plan layouts and galleries. Such an arrangement is only acceptable where the inner room is:

a.  a kitchen;

b.  a laundry or utility room;

c.  a dressing room;

d.  a bathroom, WC, or shower room;

e.  any other room on a floor, not more than 4.5m above ground level, provided with an emergency egress window which complies with paragraph 2.8; or

f.  a gallery which complies with paragraph 2.12.

**Note:** A room accessed only via an inner room (an inner-inner room) may be acceptable if it complies with the above, not more than one door separates the room from an interlinked smoke alarm and none of the access rooms is a kitchen.

### Balconies and flat roofs

**2.10**  A flat roof forming part of a means of escape should comply with tie following provisions:

a.  the roof should be part of the same building from which escape is being made;

b.  the route across the roof should lead to a storey exit or external escape route; and

c.  the part of the roof forming the escape route and its supporting structure, together with any opening within 3m of the escape route, should provide 30 minutes fire resistance (see Appendix A, Table A1).

**2.11**  Where a balcony or flat roof is provided for escape purposes guarding may be needed, in which case it should meet the provisions in Approved Document K Protection from falling, collision and impact.

### Galleries

**2.12**  A gallery should be provided with an alternative exit or, where the gallery floor is not more than 4.5m above ground level, an emergency egress window which complies with paragraph 2.8. Alternatively, where the gallery floor is not provided with an alternative exit or escape window, it should comply with the following;

a.  the gallery should overlook at least 50% of the room below (see Diagram 5);

b.  the distance between the foot of the access stair to the gallery and the door to the room containing the gallery should not exceed 3m;

c.  the distance from the head of the access stair to any point on the gallery should not exceed 7.5m; and

d.  any cooking facilities within a room containing a gallery should either:

i. be enclosed with fire-resisting construction; or

ii. be remote from the stair to the gallery and positioned such that they do not prejudice the escape from the gallery.

---

### Diagram 5 **Gallery floors with no alternative exit**

See para 2.12

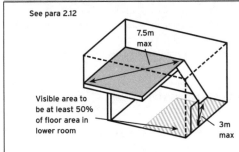

7.5m max

Visible area to be at least 50% of floor area in lower room

3m max

**Notes:**
1   This diagram does not apply where the gallery to
    i. provided with an alternative escape route; or
    ii. provided with an emergency egress window
    (where the gallery floor is not more than 4.6m
    above ground level).
2   Any cooking facilities within a room containing a
    gallery should either:
    i. be enclosed with fire-resisting construction; or
    ii. be remote from the stair to the gallery and
    positioned such that they do not prejudice the
    escape from the gallery.

---

### Basements

**2.13** Because of the risk that a single stairway may be blocked by smoke from a fire in the basement or ground storey, if the basement storey contains any habitable room, the dwellinghouse should be provided with either

a.   an external door or window suitable for egress from the basement (see paragraph 2.8); or

b.   a protected stairway leading from the basement to a final exit.

### Cavity barriers

**2.14** Cavity barriers should be provided above the enclosures to a protected stairway in a dwellinghouse with a floor more than 4.5m above ground level (see Diagram 6).

### Diagram 6 **Alternative cavity barrier arrangements in roof space over protected stairway in a house with a floor more than 4.5m above ground level**

See para 2.14

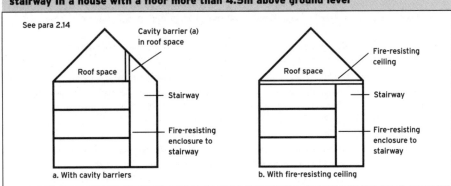

a. With cavity barriers

b. With fire-resisting ceiling

### External escape stairs

**2.15** Where an external escape stair is provided, it should meet the following provisions:

a.   All doors giving access to the stair should be fire-resisting, except that a fire-resisting door is not required at the head of any stair leading downwards where there is only one exit from the building onto the top landing.

b.   Any part of the external envelope of the building within 1800mm of (and 9m vertically below) the flights and landings of an external escape stair should be of fire-resisting construction, except that the 1800mm dimension may be reduced to 1100mm above the top level of the stair if it is not a stair up from a basement to ground level (see Diagram 7).

c.   There is protection by fire-resisting construction for any part of the building (including any doors) within 1800mm of the escape route from the stair to a place of safety, unless there is a choice of routes from the foot of the stair that would enable the people escaping to avoid exposure to the effects of the fire in the adjoining building.

d.   Any stair more than 6m in vertical extent is protected from the effects of adverse weather conditions. (This should not be taken to imply a full enclosure. Much will depend on the location of the stair and the degree of protection given to the stair by the building itself).

e.   Glazing in areas of fire-resisting construction mentioned above should also be fire-resisting (integrity but not insulation) and fixed shut.

---

Diagram 7 **Fire resistance of areas adjacent to external stairs**

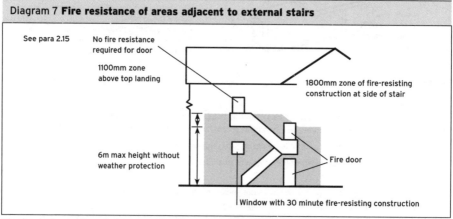

See para 2.15

No fire resistance required for door

1100mm zone above top landing

1800mm zone of fire-resisting construction at side of stair

6m max height without weather protection

Fire door

Window with 30 minute fire-resisting construction

---

**Air circulation systems in houses with a floor more than 4.5m above ground level**

**2.16** Air circulation systems which circulate air within an individual dwellinghouse with a floor more than 4.5m above ground level should meet the guidance given in paragraph 2.17. Where ventilation ducts pass through compartment walls into another building then the guidance given in Approved Document B Volume 2 should be followed.

**2.17** With these types of systems, the following precautions are needed to avoid the possibility of the system allowing smoke or fire to spread into a protected stairway:

Transfer grilles should not be fitted in any wall, door, floor or ceiling enclosing a protected stairway.

a.   Any duct passing through the enclosure to a protected stairway or entrance hall should be of rigid steel construction and all joints between the ductwork and the enclosure should be fire-stopped.

b.   Ventilation ducts supplying or extracting air directly to or from a protected stairway, should not serve other areas as well.

c.   Any system of mechanical ventilation which recirculates air and which serves both the stairway and other areas should be designed to shut down on the detection of smoke within the system.

d.   A room thermostat for a ducted warm air heating system should be mounted in the living room, at a height between 1370mm and 1830mm, and its maximum setting should not exceed 27°C.

e.   Passenger lifts

**2.18** Where a passenger lift is provided in the dwellinghouse and it serves any floor more than 4.5m above ground level, it should either be located in the enclosure to the protected stairway (see paragraph 2.6) or be contained in a fire-resisting lift shaft.

## WORK ON EXISTING HOUSES

### Replacement windows

**2.19** Regulation 4(1) requires that all "building work", as defined by Regulation 3, complies with the applicable requirements of Schedule 1 to the Building Regulations. The definition of building work in Regulation 3(1) includes the provision or extension of a "controlled service or fitting" in or in connection with a building. The definition of controlled service or fitting is given in Regulation 2(1), and includes a replacement window.

Where windows are to be replaced (but not where they are to be repaired only, as repair work to windows does not fall within the definition of building work) the replacement work should comply with the requirements of Parts L and N of

Schedule 1. In addition, the building should not have a lesser level of compliance, after the work has been completed, with other applicable Parts of Schedule 1.

For the purposes of Part B1, where a window is located such that, in a new dwellinghouse, an escape window would be necessary and the window is of sufficient size that it could be used for the purposes of escape then:

a. the replacement window opening should be sized to provide at least the same potential for escape as the window it replaces; or

b. where the original window is larger than necessary for the purposes of escape, the window opening could be reduced down to the minimum specified in paragraph 2.8.

**Note:** Part B3 makes provisions for cavity barriers around window openings in some forms of construction. Where windows are replaced it may be necessary to consider if adequate protection is maintained.

### Material alterations

**2.20** Paragraph 0.20 sets out the requirements relating to material alterations. What constitutes reasonable provision where undertaking material alterations would depend on the circumstances in the particular case and would need to take account of historic value (see paragraph 0.29). Possible ways of satisfying the requirements include:

a. Smoke alarms

Where new habitable rooms are provided then smoke alarms should be provided in accordance with paragraph 1.8.

b. Loft conversions

Where a new storey is to be added by converting an existing roof space, the provisions for escape need to be considered throughout the full extent of the escape route. For example, a loft conversion to a two-storey house will result in the need to protect the stairway (by providing fire-resisting doors and partitions) where previously no protection may have existed (see paragraph 2.6a).

**Note:** If it is considered undesirable to replace existing doors (e.g. if they are of historical or architectural merit) it may be possible to retain the doors or upgrade them to an acceptable standard.

**Note:** Where an 'open-plan' arrangement exists at ground level it may be necessary to provide a new partition to enclose the escape route (see Diagram 2).

Alternatively, it may be possible to provide sprinkler protection to the open-plan area, in conjunction with a fire-resisting partition and door (E20), in order to separate the ground floor from the upper storeys. This door should be so arranged to allow the occupants of the loft room to access an escape window at first floor level (in accordance with paragraph 2.8) in the event of a fire in the open-plan area. Cooking facilities should be separated from the open-plan area with fire-resisting construction.

# B2 INTERNAL FIRE SPREAD (LININGS) - THE REQUIREMENT

This Approved Document deals with the following Requirement from Part B of Schedule 1 to the Building Regulations 2000 (as amended).

| Requirement | Limits on application |
|---|---|
| **Internal fire spread (linings)** | |
| B2. (1) To inhibit the spread of fire within the building, the internal linings shall: | |
| (a) adequately resist the spread of flame over their surfaces; and | |
| (b) have, if ignited, a rate of heat release or a rate of fire growth, which is reasonable in the circumstances. | |
| (2) to this paragraph 'intemal linings' mean the materials or products used in lining any partition, wall, ceiling or other internal structure. | |

## Guidance

### Performance

In the Secretary of State's view the Requirements of B2 will be met if the spread of flame over the internal linings of the building is restricted by making provision for them to have low rates of surface spread of flame and, in some cases, to have a low rate of heat release, so as to limit the contribution that the fabric of the building makes to fire growth. In relation to the European fire tests and classification system, the requirements of B2 will be met if the heat released from the internal linings is restricted by making provision for them to have a resistance to ignition and a rate of fire growth which are reasonable in the circumstances.

The extent to which this is necessary is dependent on the location of the lining.

### Introduction

#### Fire spread and internal linings

**B2.i** The choice of materials for walls and ceilings can significantly affect the spread of a fire and its rate of growth, even though they are not likely to be the materials first ignited.

It is particularly important in circulation spaces where linings may offer the main means by which fire spreads and where rapid spread is most likely to prevent occupants from escaping.

Several properties of lining materials influence fire spread. These include the ease of ignition and the rate at which the lining material gives off heat when burning. The guidance relating to the European fire tests and classification provides for control of internal fire spread through control of these properties. This document does not give detailed guidance on other properties, such as the generation of smoke and fumes.

#### Floors and stairs

**B2.ii** The provisions do not apply to the upper surfaces of floors and stairs because they are not significantly involved in a fire until it is well developed, and thus do not play an important part in fire spread in the early stages of a fire that are most relevant to the safety of occupants.

#### Other controls on internal surface properties

**B2.iii** In Section 7 there is guidance on enclosures to above ground drainage system pipes.

**Note:** External flame spread is dealt with in Sections 8 to 10.

### Furniture and fittings

**B2.iv** Furniture and fittings can have a major effect on fire spread but it is not possible to control them through Building Regulations. They are therefore not dealt with in this Approved Document.

### Classification of performance

**B2.v** Appendix A describes the different classes of performance and the appropriate methods of test (see paragraphs 7-20).

The national classifications used are based on tests in BS 476 *Fire tests on building materials and structures,* namely BS 476-6:1989 *Method of test for fire propagation for products* and BS 476-7:1997 Method of test to determine the classification of the surface spread of flame of products. However, BS 476-4:1970 *Non-combustibility test for materials* and BS 476-11:1982 *Method for assessing the heat emission from building products* are also used as one method of meeting Class 0. Other tests are available for classification of thermoplastic materials if they do not have the appropriate rating under BS 476: Part 7; three ratings, referred to as TP(a) rigid and TP(a) flexible and TP(b), are used.

The European classifications are described in BS EN 13501-1:2002 *Fire classification of construction products and building elements,* Part 1 *Classification using data from reaction to fire tests.* They are based on a combination of four European test methods, namely:

- BS EN ISO 1182:2002. *Reaction to fire tests for building products – Non combustibility test*
- BS EN ISO 1716:2002. *Reaction to fire tests for building products – Determination of the gross calorific value*
- BS EN 13823:2002. *Reaction to fire tests for building products – Building products excluding floorings exposed to the thermal attack by a single burning item*
- BS EN ISO 11925-2:2002. *Reaction to fire tests for building products. Part 2 Ignitability when subjected to direct impingement of flame.*

For some building products, there is currently no generally accepted guidance on the appropriate procedure for testing and classification in accordance with the harmonised European fire tests. Until such a time that the appropriate European test and classification methods for these building products are published classification may only be possible using existing national test methods.

Table A8, in Appendix A, gives typical performance ratings which may be achieved by some generic materials and products.

# Section 3: Wall and ceiling linings

### Classification of linings

**3.1**   Subject to the variations and specific provisions described in paragraphs 3.2 to 3.16, the surface linings of walls and ceilings should meet the following classifications:

| Table 1 **Classification of linings** | | |
|---|---|---|
| **Location** | **National class** [1] | **European class** [1][3][4] |
| Small rooms [2] of area not more than 4m² | 3 | D-s3, d2 |
| Domestic garages of area not more than 40m² | | |
| Other rooms [2] (including garages) | 1 | C-s3, d2 |
| Circulation spaces within dwellinghouses | | |

Notes:

1.   See paragraph B2.v.

2.   For moaning of room, see definition in Appendix E.

3.   The National classifications do not automatically equate with the equivalent classifications in the European column, therefore products cannot typically assume a European data, unless they have been tested accordingly.

4.   When a classification includes 's3, d2', this means that there is no limit set for smoke production and/or flaming droplets/ particles.

### Definition of walls

**3.2**  For the purpose of the performance of wall linings, a wall includes:

a.    the surface of glazing (except glazing in doors); and

b.    any part of a ceiling which slopes at an angle of more than 70° to the horizontal.

But a wall does not include:

c.    doors and door frames;

d.    window frames and frames in which glazing is fitted;

e.    architraves, cover moulds, picture rails, skirtings and similar narrow members; or

f.    fireplace surrounds, mantle shelves and fitted furniture.

### Definition of ceilings

**3.3**  For the purposes of the performance of ceiling linings, a ceiling includes:

a.    the surface of glazing;

b.    any part of a wall which slopes at an angle of 70° or less to the horizontal;

c.    the underside of a gallery; and

d.    the underside of a roof exposed to the room below.

But a ceiling does not include:

e.    trap doors and their frames;

f.    the frames of windows or roof lights (see Appendix E) and frames in which glazing is fitted; or

g.    architraves, cover moulds, picture rails, exposed beams and similar narrow members.

## Variations and special provisions

### Walls

**3.4**  Parts of walls in rooms may be of a poorer performance than specified in paragraph 3.1 (but not poorer than Class 3 (National class) or Class D-s3, d2 (European class) provided the total area of those parts in any one room does not exceed one half of the floor area of the room, subject to a maximum of 20m².

### Fire-protecting suspended ceilings

**3.5**  A suspended ceiling can contribute to the overall fire resistance of a floor/ceiling assembly. Such a ceiling should satisfy paragraph 3.1. It should also meet the provisions of Appendix A, Table A3.

### Fire-resisting ceilings

**3.6**  Cavity barriers are needed in some concealed floor or roof spaces (see Section 6), however, this need can be reduced by the use of a fire-resisting ceiling below the cavity.

### Rooflights

**3.7**  Rooflights should meet the relevant classification in 3.1. However, plastic rooflights with at least a Class 3 rating may be used where 3.1 calls for a higher standard, provided the limitations in Table 2 and in Table 6 are observed.

**Note:** No guidance is currently possible on the performance requirements in the European fire tests as there is no generally accepted test and classification procedure.

## Thermoplastic materials

### General

**3.8**  Thermoplastic materials (see Appendix A, paragraph 17) which cannot meet the performance given in Table 1, can nevertheless be used in windows, rooflights and lighting diffusers in suspended ceilings if they comply with the provisions described in paragraphs 3.10 to 3.14. Flexible thermoplastic material may be used in panels to form a suspended ceiling if it complies with the guidance in paragraph 3.16. The classifications used in paragraphs 3.11 to 3.16, Table 2 and Diagram 9 are explained in Appendix A, paragraph 20.

**Note:** No guidance is currently possible on the performance requirements in the European fire tests as there is no generally accepted test and classification procedure.

### Windows and internal glazing

**3.9**  External windows to rooms (though not to circulation spaces) may be glazed with thermoplastic materials, if the material can be classified as a TP(a) rigid product.

Internal glazing should meet the provisions in paragraph 3.1.

**Notes:**

1.    A "wall' does not include glazing in a door (see paragraph 3.2).

2.    Attention is drawn to the guidance on the safety of glazing in Approved Document N *Glazing - safety in relation to impact, opening and cleaning.*

## Rooflights

**3.10**   Rooflights to rooms and circulation spaces (with the exception of protected stairways) may be constructed of a thermoplastic material if:

a.    the lower surface has a TP(a) (rigid) or TP(b) classification

b.    the size and disposition of the roof lights accords with the limits in Table 2 and with the guidance to B4 in Table 7.

## Lighting diffusers

**3.11**   The following provisions apply to lighting diffusers which form part of a ceiling. They are not concerned with diffusers of light fittings which are attached to the soffit of, or suspended beneath a ceiling (see Diagram 8).

Lighting diffusers are translucent or open- structured elements that allow light to pass through. They may be part of a luminaire or used below roof lights or other sources of light.

**3.12**   Thermoplastic lighting diffusers should not be used in fire-protecting or fire-resisting ceilings, unless they have been satisfactorily tested as part of the ceiling system that is to be used to provide the appropriate fire protection.

**3.13**   Subject to the above paragraphs, ceilings to rooms and circulation spaces (but not protected stairways) may incorporate thermoplastic lighting diffusers if the following provisions are observed:

a.    Wall and ceiling surfaces exposed within the space above the suspended ceiling (other than the upper surfaces of the thermoplastic panels) should comply with the general provisions of paragraph 3.1, according to the type of space below the suspended ceiling;

b.    If the diffusers are of classification TP(a) (rigid), there are no restrictions on their extent;

c.    If the diffusers are of classification TP(b), they should be limited in extent as indicated in Table 2 and Diagram 9.

## Suspended or stretched-skin ceilings

**3.14**   The ceiling of a room may be constructed either as a suspended or stretched-skin membrane from panels of a thermoplastic material of the TP(a) flexible classification, provided that it is not part of a fire-resisting ceiling. Each panel should not exceed 5m² in area and should be supported on all its sides.

---

### Diagram 8 **Lighting diffuser in relation to ceiling**

See para 3.11

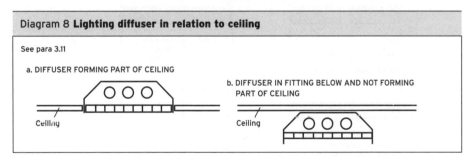

a. DIFFUSER FORMING PART OF CEILING

b. DIFFUSER IN FITTING BELOW AND NOT FORMING PART OF CEILING

Ceiling

Ceiling

**Table 2 Limitations applied to thermoplastic rooflights and lighting diffusers in suspended ceilings and Class 3 plastic rooflights**

| Minimum classification of lower surface | Use of space below the diffusers or rooflight | Maximum area of each diffuser panel or rooflight [1] (m²) | Max total area of diffuser panels and rooflights as percentage of floor area of the space in which the ceiling is located (%) | Minimum separation distance between diffuser panels or rooflights [1] (m) |
|---|---|---|---|---|
| TP(a) | Any except protected stairway | No limit [2] | No limit | No limit |
| Class 3 [3] or TP(b) | Rooms | 5 | 50 [4] | 3 |
| | Circulation spaces except protected stairways | 5 | 15 [4] | 3 |

Notes:
1. Smaller panels can be grouped together provided that the overall size of the group and the space between one group and any others satisfies the dimensions shown in Diagram 9.
2. Lighting diffusers of TP(a) flexible rating should be restricted to panels of not more than 5m² each, see paragraph 3.14.
3. There are no limits on Class 3 material in small rooms see Table 1.
4. The minimum 3m separation specified in Diagram 9 between each 5m² must be maintained. Therefore, in some cases it may not also be possible to use the maximum percentage quoted.

**Diagram 9 Layout restrictions on Class 3 plastic rooflights, TP(b) rooflights and TP(b) lighting diffusers**

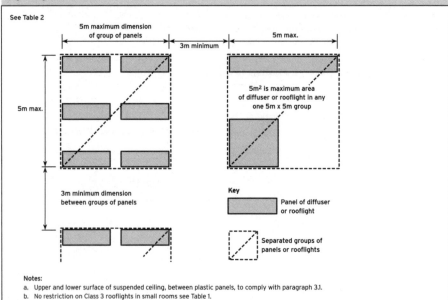

See Table 2

5m maximum dimension of group of panels

3m minimum

5m max.

5m max.

5m² is maximum area of diffuser or rooflight in any one 5m x 5m group

3m minimum dimension between groups of panels

Key

Panel of diffuser or rooflight

Separated groups of panels or rooflights

Notes:
a. Upper and lower surface of suspended ceiling, between plastic panels, to comply with paragraph 3.1.
b. No restriction on Class 3 rooflights in small rooms see Table 1.

# B3 INTERNAL FIRE SPREAD (STRUCTURE) - THE REQUIREMENT

This Approved Document deals with the following Requirement from Part B of Schedule 1 to the Building Regulations 2000 (as amended).

| Requirement | Limits on application |
| --- | --- |
| **Internal fire spread (linings)** | |
| B3. (1) The building shall be designed and constructed so that, in the event of fire, its stability will be maintained for a reasonable period. | |
| (2) A wall common to two or more buildings shall be designed and constructed so that it adequately resists the spread of fire between those buildings. For the purposes of this sub-paragraph a house in a terrace and a semi-detached house are each to be treated as a separate building. | |
| (3) Where reasonably necessary to inhibit the spread of fire within the building, measures shall be taken, to an extent appropriate to the size and intended use of the building, comprising either or both of the following: | Requirement B3(3) does not apply to material alterations to any prison provided under Section 33 of the Prison Act 1952. |
| (a) sub-division of the building with fire-resisting construction; | |
| (b) installation of suitable automatic fire suppression systems. | |
| (4) The building shall be designed and constructed so that the unseen spread of fire and smoke within concealed spaces in its structure and fabric is inhibited. | |

## Guidance

### Performance

In the Secretary of State's view the Requirements of B3 will be met:

a.  if the loadbearing elements of structure of the building are capable of withstanding the effects of fire for an appropriate period without loss of stability;

b.  if the building is sub-divided by elements of fire-resisting construction into compartments;

c.  if any openings in fire-separating elements (see Appendix E) are suitably protected in order to maintain the integrity of the element (i.e. the continuity of the fire separation); and

d.  if any hidden voids in the construction are sealed and sub-divided to inhibit the unseen spread of fire and products of combustion, in order to reduce the risk of structural failure and the spread of fire, in so far as they pose a threat to the safety of people in and around the building.

The extent to which any of these measures are necessary is dependent on the use of the building and, in some cases, its size, and on the location of the element of construction.

### Introduction

**B3.i**  Guidance on loadbearing elements of structure is given in Section 4. Section 5 is concerned with the sub-division of a building into compartments, and Section 6 makes provisions about concealed spaces (or cavities).

Section 7 gives information on the protection of openings and on fire-stopping which relates to compartmentation and to fire spread in concealed spaces. Common to all these sections and to other provisions of Part B, is the property of fire resistance.

### Fire resistance

**B3.ii** The fire resistance of an element of construction is a measure of its ability to withstand the effects of fire in one or more ways, as follows:

a.    resistance to collapse, i.e. the ability to maintain loadbearing capacity (which applies to loadbearing elements only);

b.    resistance to fire penetration, i.e. an ability to maintain the integrity of the element; and

c.    resistance to the transfer of excessive heat, i.e. an ability to provide insulation from high temperatures.

**B3.iii** 'Elements of structure' is the term applied to the main structural loadbearing elements, such as structural frames, floors and loadbearing walls. Compartment walls are treated as elements of structure although they are not necessarily loadbearing. Roofs, unless they serve the function of a floor, are not treated as elements of structure. External walls, such as curtain walls or other forms of cladding which transmit only self weight and wind loads and do not transmit floor load, are not regarded as loadbearing for the purposes of B3.ii(a), although they may need fire resistance to satisfy requirement B4 (see Sections 8 to 9).

Loadbearing elements may or may not have a fire-separating function. Similarly, fire-separating elements may or may not be loadbearing.

### Guidance elsewhere in the Approved Document concerning fire resistance

**B3.iv** There is guidance in Section 2 concerning the use of fire-resisting construction to protect means of escape. There is guidance in Section 9 about fire resistance of external walls to restrict the spread of fire between buildings. Appendix A gives information on methods of test and performance for elements of construction. Appendix B gives information on fire doors. Appendix C gives information on methods of measurement. Appendix D gives information on purpose group classification. Appendix E gives definitions.

## Section 4: Loadbearing elements of structure

### Introduction

**4.1**    Premature failure of the structure can be prevented by provisions for loadbearing elements of structure to have a minimum standard of fire resistance, in terms of resistance to collapse or failure of loadbearing capacity. The purpose in providing the structure with fire resistance is threefold, namely:

a.    to minimise the risk to the occupants, some of whom may be unable to make their own escape if they have become trapped or injured;

b.    to reduce the risk to firefighters, who may be engaged in search or rescue operations; and

c.    to reduce the danger to people in the vicinity of the building, who might be hurt by falling debris or as a result of the impact of the collapsing structure on other buildings.

### Fire resistance standard

**4.2**    Elements of structure such as structural frames, beams, columns, loadbearing walls (internal and external), floor structures and gallery structures should have at least the fire resistance given in Appendix A, Table A1.

### Application of the fire resistance standards for loadbearing elements

**4.3**    The measures set out in Appendix A include provisions to ensure that where one element of structure supports or gives stability to another element of structure, the supporting element has no less fire resistance than the other element (see notes to Table A2). The measures also provide for elements of structure that are common to more than one building or compartment, to be constructed to the standard of the greater of the relevant provisions. Special provisions about fire resistance of elements of structure in single storey buildings are also given and there are concessions in respect of firs resistance of elements of structure in basements where at least one side of the basement is open at ground level.

### Exclusions from the provisions for elements of structure

**4.4**    The following are excluded from the definition of element of structure for the purposes of these provisions:

a.    structure that only supports a roof, unless:

i. the roof performs the function of a floor, such as a roof terrace, or as a means of escape (see Section 2), or

ii. the structure is essential for the stability of an external wall which needs to have fire resistance; and

b.    the lowest floor of the building.

Additional guidance

**4.5**   Guidance in other sections of this Approved Document may also apply if a loadbearing wall is:

a.    a compartment wall (this includes a wall common to two buildings), (see Section 5);

b.    a wall between a dwellinghouse and an integral garage, (see Section 5, paragraph 5.4);

c.    protecting a means of escape, (see Section 2); or

d.    an external wall, (see Sections 8 to 9).

**4.6**   If a floor is also a compartment floor, see Section 5.

### Floors in loft conversions

**4.7**   In altering an existing two-storey single family dwellinghouse to provide additional storeys, the provisions in this Approved Document are for the floor(s), both old and new, to have the full 30 minute standard of fire resistance shown in Appendix A, Table A1. However, provided that the following conditions are satisfied, namely:

a.    only one storey is being added;

b.    the new storey contains no more than 2 habitable rooms; and

c.    the total area of the new storey does not amount to more than 50m²;

then the existing first floor construction may bs accepted if it has at least a modified 30 minute standard of fire resistance, in those places where the floor separates only rooms (and not circulation spaces). **Notes:**

1.    The 'modified 30 minute' standard satisfies the test criteria for the full 30 minutes in respect of loadbearing capacity, but allows reduced performances for integrity and insulation (see Appendix A, Table A1, item 3(a)).

2.    A floor which forms part of the enclosure to the circulation space between the loft conversion and the final exit needs a full 30 minute standard.

### Conversion to flats

**4.8**   Where an existing dwellinghouse or other building is converted into flats the guidance in Volume 2 should be followed.

# Section 5: Compartmentation

## Introduction

**5.1**   The spread of fire within a building can be restricted by sub-dividing it into compartments separated from one another by walls and/or floors of fire-resisting construction. The object is twofold:

a.    to prevent rapid fire spread which could trap occupants of the building; and

b.    to reduce the chance of fires becoming large, on the basis that large fires are more dangerous, not only to occupants and fire and rescue service personnel, but also to people in the vicinity of the building. Compartmentation is complementary to provisions made in Section 2 for the protection of escape routes, and to provisions made in Sections 8 to 10 against the spread of fire between buildings.

## Provision of Compartmentation

**5.2**   Compartment walls and compartment floors should be provided in the circumstances described below, with the proviso that the lowest floor in a building does not need to be constructed as a compartment floor. Provisions for the protection of openings in compartment walls and compartment floors are given in paragraph 5.13 and Section 7.

**5.3**   Every wall separating semi-detached houses, or houses in terraces, should be constructed as a compartment wall and the houses should be considered as separate buildings.

**5.4**   If a domestic garage is attached to (or forms an integral part of) a dwelling house, the garage should be separated from the rest of the dwellinghouse, as shown in Diagram 10.

**5.5**   Where a door is provided between a dwellinghouse and the garage, the floor of the garage should be laid to fall to allow fuel spills to flow away from the door to the outside. Alternatively, the door opening should be positioned at least 100mm above garage floor level.

## Construction of compartment walls and compartment floors
### General
5.6    Every compartment wall and compartment floor should:

a.    form a complete barrier to fire between the compartments they separate; and

b.    have the appropriate fire resistance as indicated in Appendix A, Tables A1 and A2.

---

Diagram 10 **Separation between garage and dwellinghouse**

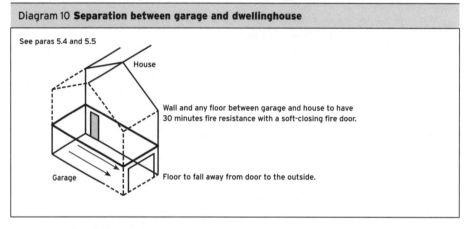

See paras 5.4 and 5.5

House

Wall and any floor between garage and house to have
30 minutes fire resistance with a soft-closing fire door.

Garage

Floor to fall away from door to the outside.

---

**Note:** Timber beams, joists, purlins and rafters may be built into or carried through a masonry or concrete compartment wall if the openings for them are kept as small as practicable and then fire-stopped. If trussed rafters bridge the wall, they should be designed so that failure of any part of the truss due to a fire in one compartment will not cause failure of any part of the truss in another compartment.

### Compartment walls between buildings

**5.7**    Compartment walls that are common to two or more buildings should run the full height of the building in a continuous vertical plane. Thus adjoining buildings should only be separated by walls, not floors.

**5.8**    Compartment walls in a top storey beneath a roof should be continued through the roof space (see definition of compartment in Appendix E).

### Junction of compartment wall or compartment floor with other walls
**5.9**    Where a compartment wall or compartment floor meets another compartment wall, or an external wall, the junction should maintain the fire resistance of the Compartmentation. Fire-stopping should meet the provisions of paragraphs 7.12 to 7.14.

**5.10**    At the junction of a compartment floor with an external wall that has no fire resistance (such as a curtain wall) the external wall should be restrained at floor level to reduce the movement of the wall away from the floor when exposed to fire.

### Junction of compartment wall with roof
**5.11**    A compartment wall should be taken up to meet the underside of the roof covering or deck, with fire-stopping where necessary at the wall/roof junction to maintain the continuity of fire resistance. The compartment wall should also be continued across any eaves.

**5.12**    If a fire penetrates a roof near a compartment wall there is a risk that it will spread over the roof to the adjoining compartment. To reduce this risk either

a.    the wall should be extended up through the roof for a height of at least 375mm above the top surface of the adjoining roof covering (see Diagram 11a). Where there is a height difference of at least 375mm between two roofs or where the roof coverings on either side of the wall are AA, AB or AC this height may be reduced to

200mm; or

b.   a zone of the roof 1500mm wide on either side of the wall should have a covering of designation AA, AB or AC. Any combustible boarding used as a substrate to the roof covering, wood wool slabs, or timber tiling battens that are carried over the compartment wall should be fully bedded in mortar or other suitable material over the width of the wall (see Diagram 11 b).

**Note:** Double-skinned insulated roof sheeting with a thermoplastic core should incorporate a band of material of limited combustibility at least 300mm wide centred over the wall.

## Openings in compartmentation
### Openings in compartment walls separating buildings or occupancies
**5.13**  Any openings in a compartment wall which is common to two or more buildings should be limited to those for

a.   a door which is needed to provide a means of escape in case of fire and which has the same fire resistance as that required for the wall (see Appendix B, Table B1) and is fitted in accordance with the provisions of Appendix B; and

b.   the passage of a pipe which meets the provisions in Section 7.

### Doors
**5.14**  Information on fire doors may be found in Appendix B.

---

### Diagram 11 **Junction of compartment wall with roof**

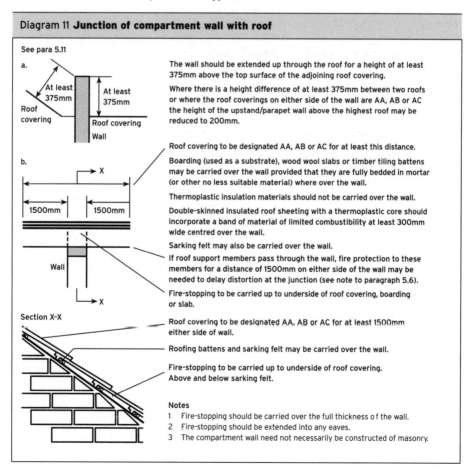

See para 5.11

a.

At least 375mm
Roof covering

At least 375mm
Roof covering
Wall

The wall should be extended up through the roof for a height of at least 375mm above the top surface of the adjoining roof covering.

Where there is a height difference of at least 375mm between two roofs or where the roof coverings on either side of the wall are AA, AB or AC the height of the upstand/parapet wall above the highest roof may be reduced to 200mm.

b.

X

1500mm   1500mm

Wall

X

Roof covering to be designated AA, AB or AC for at least this distance.

Boarding (used as a substrate), wood wool slabs or timber tiling battens may be carried over the wall provided that they are fully bedded in mortar (or other no less suitable material) where over the wall.

Thermoplastic insulation materials should not be carried over the wall.

Double-skinned insulated roof sheeting with a thermoplastic core should incorporate a band of material of limited combustibility at least 300mm wide centred over the wall.

Sarking felt may also be carried over the wall.

If roof support members pass through the wall, fire protection to these members for a distance of 1500mm on either side of the wall may be needed to delay distortion at the junction (see note to paragraph 5.6).

Fire-stopping to be carried up to underside of roof covering, boarding or slab.

Section X-X

Roof covering to be designated AA, AB or AC for at least 1500mm either side of wall.

Roofing battens and sarking felt may be carried over the wall.

Fire-stopping to be carried up to underside of roof covering. Above and below sarking felt.

Notes
1   Fire-stopping should be carried over the full thickness of the wall.
2   Fire-stopping should be extended into any eaves.
3   The compartment wall need not necessarily be constructed of masonry.

# Section 6: Concealed spaces (cavities)

## Introduction

**6.1**    Concealed spaces or cavities in the construction of a building provide a ready route for smoke and flame spread e.g. in walls, floors, ceilings and roofs. As any spread is concealed, it presents a greater danger than would a more obvious weakness in the fabric of the building.

## Provision of cavity barriers

**6.2**    Provisions are given below for cavity barriers in specified locations. The provisions necessary to restrict the spread of smoke and flames through cavities are broadly for the purpose of sub-dividing cavities, which could otherwise form a pathway around a fire separating element, and closing the edges of cavities; therefore reducing the potential for unseen fire spread. See also paragraph 2.14.

**Note:** These should not be confused with fire stopping details, see Sections 5 and 7.

Consideration should also be given to the construction and fixing of cavity barriers provided for these purposes and the extent to which openings in them should be protected. For guidance on these issues, see paragraphs 6.6 to 6.9 respectively.

**6.3**    Cavity barriers should be provided at the edges of cavities, including around openings (such as window and door openings). Additionally, cavity barriers should be provided at the junction between an external cavity wall and a compartment wall that separates buildings, see Diagram 12; and at the top of such an external cavity wall, except where the cavity wall complies with Diagram 13.

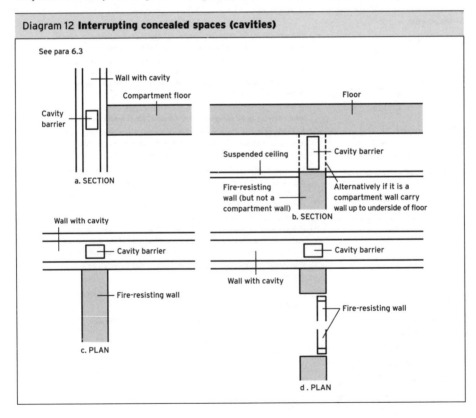

Diagram 12 **Interrupting concealed spaces (cavities)**

It is important to continue any compartment wall up through a ceiling or roof cavity to maintain the standard of fire resistance – therefore compartment walls should be carried up to the roof, see paragraph 5.11. It is not appropriate to complete a line of compartment walls by fitting cavity barriers above them.

### Double-skinned insulated roof sheeting

**6.4**  Cavity barriers need not be provided between double-skinned corrugated or profiled insulated roof sheeting, if the sheeting is a material of limited combustibility; and both surfaces of the insulating layer have a surface spread of flame of at least Class 0 or 1 (National class) or Class C-s3, d2 or better (European class) (see Appendix A); and make contact with the inner and outer skins of cladding.

**Note:** When a classification includes "s3, d2", this means that there is no limit set for smoke production and/or flaming droplets/particles.

---

### Diagram 13 **Cavity walls excluded from provisions for cavity barriers**

See para 6.3

SECTION THROUGH CAVITY WALL

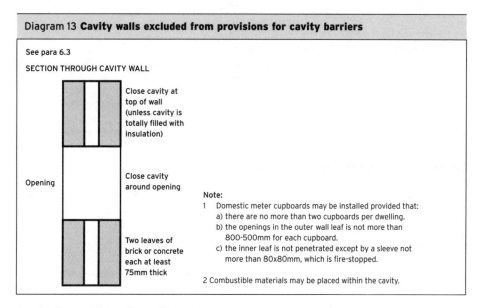

Close cavity at top of wall (unless cavity is totally filled with insulation)

Opening

Close cavity around opening

Two leaves of brick or concrete each at least 75mm thick

Note:
1   Domestic meter cupboards may be installed provided that:
   a) there are no more than two cupboards per dwelling.
   b) the openings in the outer wall leaf is not more than 800-500mm for each cupboard.
   c) the inner leaf is not penetrated except by a sleeve not more than 80x80mm, which is fire-stopped.

2 Combustible materials may be placed within the cavity.

---

### Construction and fixings for cavity barriers

**6.5**  Every cavity barrier should be constructed to provide at least 30 minutes fire resistance and may be formed by any construction provided for another purpose if it meets the provisions for cavity barriers (see Appendix A, Table A1, item 10).

However, cavity barriers in a stud wall or partition, or provided around openings may be formed of:

a.     steel at least 0.5mm thick; or

b.     timber at least 38mm thick; or

c.    polythene-sleeved mineral wool, or mineral wool slab, in either case under compression when installed in the cavity; or

d.    calcium silicate, cement-based or gypsum-based boards at least 12mm thick.

**Note:** Cavity barriers provided around openings may be formed by the window or door frame if the frame is constructed of steel or timber of the minimum thickness in (a) or (b) above as appropriate.

**6.6**  A cavity barrier should, wherever possible, be tightly fitted to a rigid construction and mechanically fixed in position. Where this is not possible (for example, in the case of a junction with slates, tiles, corrugated sheeting or similar materials) the junction should be fire-stopped. Provisions for fire-stopping are set out in Section 7.

**6.7**  Cavity barriers should also be fixed so that their performance is unlikely to be made ineffective by:

a.    movement of the building due to subsidence, shrinkage or temperature change; and movement of the external envelope due to wind; and

b.    collapse in a fire of any services penetrating them; and

c.    failure in a fire of their fixings (but see note below); and

d.    failure in a fire of any material or construction which they abut. (For example, if a suspended ceiling is continued over the top of a fire-resisting wall or partition, and direct connection is made between the ceiling and the cavity barrier above the line of the wall or partition, premature failure of the cavity barrier can occur when the ceiling collapses. However, this may not arise if the ceiling is designed to provide fire resistance of 30 minutes or more.)

**Note:** Where cavity barriers are provided in roof spaces, the roof members to which they are fitted are not expected to have any fire resistance (for the purpose of supporting the cavity barrier(s)).

## Openings in cavity barriers

**6.8**  Any openings in a cavity barrier should be limited to those for:

a.    doors which have at least 30 minutes fire resistance (see Appendix B, Table B1, item 1(a)) and are fitted in accordance with the provisions of Appendix B;

b.    the passage of pipes which meet the provisions in Section 7;

c.    the passage of cables or conduits containing one or more cables;

d.    openings fitted with a suitably mounted automatic fire damper; and

e.    ducts which are fire-resisting or are fitted with a suitably mounted automatic fire damper where they pass through the cavity barrier.

# Section 7: Protection of openings and fire-stopping

## Introduction

**7.1**   Sections 7 and 8 make provisions for fire-separating elements and set out the circumstances in which there may be openings in them. This section deals with the protection of openings in such elements.

**7.2**   If a fire-separating element is to be effective, then every joint, or imperfection of fit, or opening to allow services to pass through the element, should be adequately protected by sealing or fire-stopping so that the fire resistance of the element is not impaired.

**7.3**   The measures in this section are intended to delay the passage of fire. They generally have the additional benefit of retarding smoke spread but the test specified in Appendix A for integrity does not directly stipulate criteria for the passage of smoke.

**7.4**   Consideration should also be given to the effect of services that may be built into the construction that could adversely affect its fire resistance. For instance, where downlighters, loudspeakers and other electrical accessories are installed, additional protection may be required to maintain the integrity of a wall or floor.

**7.5**   Detailed guidance on door openings and fire doors is given in Appendix B.

## Openings for pipes

**7.6**   Pipes which pass through fire-separating elements (unless the pipe is in a protected shaft), should meet the appropriate provisions in alternatives A, B or C below.

### Alternative A: Proprietary seals (any pipe diameter)

**7.7**   Provide a proprietary sealing system which has been shown by test to maintain the fire resistance of the wall, floor or cavity barrier.

### Alternative B: Pipes with a restricted diameter

**7.8**   Where a proprietary sealing system is not used, fire-stopping may be used around the pipe, keeping the opening as small as possible. The nominal internal diameter of the pipe should not be more than the relevant dimension given in Table 3.

**Table 3 Maximum nominal internal diameter of pipes passing through a fire separating element (see paragraph 7.6 to 7.9)**

| | Pipe material and maximum nominal internal diameter (mm) | | |
|---|---|---|---|
| **Situation** | **(a)** <br> **Non-combustible materials** [1] | **(b)** <br> **Lead, aluminium, aluminium alloy, uPVC** [2]**. fibre cement** | **(c)** <br> **Any other material** |
| 1. Wall separating dwellinghouses | 160 | 160 (stack pipe) [3] <br><br> 110 (branch pipe) [3] | 40 <br><br> 40 |
| 2. Wall or floor separating a dwellinghouse from an attached garage | 160 | 110 | 40 |
| 3. Any other situation | 160 | 40 | 40 |

**Notes:**

1. Any non-combustible material (such as cast iron, copper or steel) which, if exposed to a temperature of 800°C, will not soften or fracture to the extent that flame or hot gas will pass through the wall of the pipe.

2. uPVC pipes complying with BS 4514 and uPVC pipes complying with BS 5255.

3. These diameters are only in relation to pipes forming part of an above-ground drainage system and enclosed as shown in Diagram 15. In other cases the maximum diameters against situation 3 apply.

### Alternative C: sleeving

**7.9**  A pipe of lead, aluminium, aluminium alloy, fibre-cement or uPVC, with a maximum nominal internal diameter of 160mm, may be used with a sleeving of non-combustible pipe as shown in Diagram 14. The specification for non-combustible and uPVC pipes is given in the notes to Table 3.

Diagram 14 **Pipes penetrating structure**

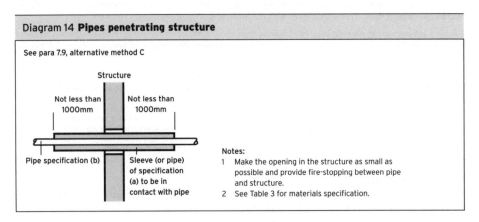

See para 7.9, alternative method C

Structure

Not less than 1000mm · Not less than 1000mm

Pipe specification (b)

Sleeve (or pipe) of specification (a) to be in contact with pipe

**Notes:**

1  Make the opening in the structure as small as possible and provide fire-stopping between pipe and structure.

2  See Table 3 for materials specification.

Diagram 15 **Enclosure for drainage or water supply pipes**

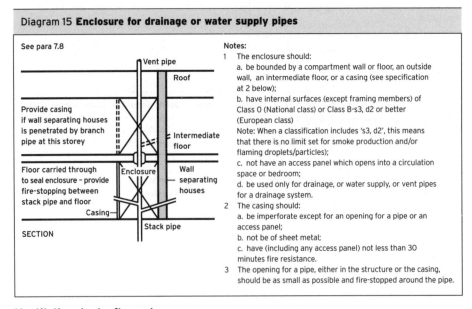

See para 7.8

Vent pipe

Roof

Provide casing if wall separating houses is penetrated by branch pipe at this storey

Intermediate floor

Floor carried through to seal enclosure – provide fire-stopping between stack pipe and floor

Enclosure

Wall separating houses

Casing

Stack pipe

SECTION

**Notes:**

1  The enclosure should:

a. be bounded by a compartment wall or floor, an outside wall,  an intermediate floor, or a casing (see specification at 2 below);

b. have internal surfaces (except framing members) of Class 0 (National class) or Class B-s3, d2 or better (European class)

Note: When a classification includes 's3, d2', this means that there is no limit set for smoke production and/or flaming droplets/particles);

c. not have an access panel which opens into a circulation space or bedroom;

d. be used only for drainage, or water supply, or vent pipes for a drainage system.

2  The casing should:

a. be imperforate except for an opening for a pipe or an access panel;

b. not be of sheet metal;

c. have (including any access panel) not less than 30 minutes fire resistance.

3  The opening for a pipe, either in the structure or the casing, should be as small as possible and fire-stopped around the pipe.

## Ventilation ducts, flues etc.

**7.10**  Air circulation systems which circulate air within an individual dwellinghouse with a floor more than 4.5m above ground level should meet the guidance given in paragraph 2.16. Where ventilation ducts pass through compartment walls into another building then the guidance given in Approved Document B Volume 2 should be followed.

**7.11**  If a flue or duct containing flues or appliance ventilation duct(s), passes through a compartment wall or compartment floor, or is built into a compartment wall, each wall of the flue or duct should have a fire resistance of at least half that of the wall or floor in order to prevent the by-passing of the compartmentation (see Diagram 16).

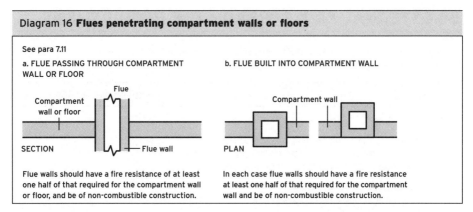

Diagram 16 **Flues penetrating compartment walls or floors**

See para 7.11

a. FLUE PASSING THROUGH COMPARTMENT WALL OR FLOOR

b. FLUE BUILT INTO COMPARTMENT WALL

Flue walls should have a fire resistance of at least one half of that required for the compartment wall or floor, and be of non-combustible construction.

In each case flue walls should have a fire resistance at least one half of that required for the compartment wall and be of non-combustible construction.

## Fire-stopping

**7.12** In addition to any other provisions in this document for fire-stopping:

a. joints between fire-separating elements should be fire-stopped; and

b. all openings for pipes, ducts, conduits or cables to pass through any part of a fire-separating element should be:

i. kept as few in number as possible; kept as small as practicable; and

ii. fire-stopped (which in the case of a pipe or duct should allow thermal movement).

**7.13** To prevent displacement, materials used for fire-stopping should be reinforced with (or supported by) materials of limited combustibility in the following circumstances:

a. in all cases where the unsupported span is greater than 100mm; and

b. in any other case where non-rigid materials are used (unless they have been shown to be satisfactory by test).

**7.14** Proprietary fine-stopping and sealing systems, (including those designed for service penetrations) which have been shown by test to maintain the fire resistance of the wall or other element, are available and may be used.

Other fire-stopping materials include:

- cement mortar;
- gypsum-based plaster;
- cement-based or gypsum-based vermiculite/perlite mixes;
- glass fibre, crushed rock, blast furnace slag or ceramic-based products (with or without resin binders); and
- intumescent mastics.

These may be used in situations appropriate to the particular material. Not all of them will be suitable in every situation.

Guidance on the process of design, installation and maintenance of passive fire protection is available in *Ensuring Best Practice for Passive Fire Protection in Buildings* (ISBN: 1 87040 919 1) produced by the Association for Specialist Fire Protection (ASFP).

Further information on the generic types of systems available, information about their suitability for different applications and guidance on test methods is given in the ASFP Red Book:

*Fire Stopping and Penetration Seals for the Construction Industry – the 'Red Book'* published by the Association for Specialist Fire Protection and freely available from the ASFP website at www.asfp.org.uk.

# B4 EXTERNAL FIRE SPREAD - THE REQUIREMENT

This Approved Document deals with the following Requirement from Part B of Schedule 1 to the Building Regulations 2000 (as amended).

| Requirement | Limits on application |
|---|---|
| **External fire spread** | |
| B4. (1) The external walls of the building shall adequately resist the spread of fire over the walls and from one building to another, having regard to the height, use and position of the building. | |
| (2) The roof of the building shall adequately resist the spread of fire over the roof and from one building to another, having regard to the use and position of the building. | |

## Guidance

### Performance

In the Secretary of State's view the Requirements of B4 will be met:

a.    if the external walls are constructed so that the risk of ignition from an external source, and the spread of fire over their surfaces, is restricted by making provision for them to have low rates of heat release;

b.    if the amount of unprotected area in the side of the building is restricted so as to limit the amount of thermal radiation that can pass through the wall, taking the distance between the wall and the boundary into account; and

c.    if the roof is constructed so that the risk of spread of flame and/or fire penetration from an external fire source is restricted.

In each case so as to limit the risk of a fire spreading from the building to a building beyond the boundary, or vice versa.

The extent to which this is necessary is dependent on the use of the building, its distance from the boundary and, in some cases, its height

### Introduction

#### External walls

**B4.i** The construction of external walls and the separation between buildings to prevent external fire spread are closely related,

The chances of fire spreading across an open space between buildings, and the consequences if it does, depend on:

a.    the size and intensity of the fire in the building concerned;

b.    the distance between the buildings;

c.    the fire protection given by their facing sides; and

d.    the risk presented to people in the other building(8).

**B4.ii** Provisions are made in Section 8 for the fire resistance of external walls and to limit the susceptibility of the external surface of walls to ignition and to fire spread.

**B4.iii** Provisions are made in Section 9 to limit the extent of openings and other unprotected areas in external walls in order to reduce the risk of fire spread by radiation,

#### Roofs

**B4.iv** Provisions are made in Section 10 for reducing the risk of fire spread between roofs and over the surfaces of roofs.

# Section 8: Construction of external walls

## Introduction

**8.1**   Provisions are made in this section for the external walls of the building to have sufficient fire resistance to prevent fire spread across the relevant boundary. The provisions are closely linked with those for space separation in Section 9 which sets out limits on the amount of unprotected area of wall. As the limits depend on the distance of the wall from the relevant boundary, it is possible for some or all of the walls to have no fire resistance, except for any parts which are loadbearing (see paragraph B3.iii).

External walls are elements of structure and the relevant period of fire resistance (specified in Appendix A) depends on the use, height and size of the building concerned. If the wall is 1000mm or more from the relevant boundary, a reduced standard of fire resistance is accepted in most cases and the wall only needs fire resistance from the inside.

**8.2**   Provisions are also made to restrict the combustibility of external walls of buildings that are less than 1000mm from the relevant boundary. This is in order to reduce the surface's susceptibility to ignition from an external source.

In the guidance to Requirement B3, provisions are made in Section 4 for internal and external loadbearing walls to maintain their loadbearing function in the event of fire.

## Fire resistance standard

**8.3**   The external walls of the building should have the appropriate fire resistance given in Appendix A, Table A1, unless they form an unprotected area under the provisions of Section 9.

## External surfaces

**8.4**   The external surfaces of walls within 1000mm of the relevant boundary should meet Class 0 (National Class) or Class B-s3,d2 or better (European class). The total amount of combustible material on walls more than 1000mm from the relevant boundary may be limited in practice by the provisions for space separation in Section 9 (see paragraphs 9.7 to 9.17.).

# Section 9: Space separation

## Introduction

**9.1**   The provisions in this Section are based on a number of assumptions and, whilst some of those may differ from the circumstances of a particular case, together they enable a reasonable standard of space separation to be specified. The provisions limit the extent of unprotected areas in the sides of a building (such as openings and areas with a combustible surface) which will not give adequate protection against the external spread of fire from one building to another.

A roof is not subject to the provisions in this Section unless it is pitched at an angle greater than 70° to the horizontal (see definition for 'external wall' in Appendix E). Similarly, vertical parts of a pitched roof such as dormer windows (which taken in isolation might be regarded as a wall), would not need to meet the following provisions unless the slope of the roof exceeds 70°. It is a matter of judgement whether a continuous run of dormer windows occupying most of a steeply pitched roof should be treated as a wall rather than a roof.

**9.2**   The assumptions are:

a.   that the size of a fire will depend on the compartmentation of the building, so that a fire may involve a complete compartment, but will not spread to other compartments;

b.   that the intensity of the fire is related to the use of the building (i.e. purpose group), but that it can be moderated by a sprinkler system;

c.   that Residential (1 and 2) and Assembly and Recreation (5) Purpose Groups represent a greater life risk than other uses;

d.   that there is a building on the far side of the boundary that has a similar elevation to the one in question and that it is at the same distance from the common boundary; and

e.   that the amount of radiation that passes through any part of the external wall that has fire resistance may be discounted.

**9.3**   Where a reduced separation distance is desired (or an increased amount of unprotected area) it may be advantageous to introduce additional compartment walls and/or floors.

## Boundaries

**9.4**  The use of the distance to a boundary, rather than to another building, in measuring the separation distance, makes it possible to calculate the allowable proportion of unprotected areas, regardless of whether there is a building on an adjoining site and regardless of the site of that building and the extent of any unprotected areas that it might have.

A wall is treated as facing a boundary if it makes an angle with it of 80° or less (see Diagram 17).

Usually only the distance to the actual boundary of the site needs to be considered. But, in some circumstances, when the site boundary adjoins a space where further development is unlikely, such as a road, then part of the adjoining space may be included as falling within the relevant boundary for the purposes of this section. The meaning of the term boundary is explained in Diagram 17.

### Relevant boundaries

**9.5**  The boundary which a wall faces, whether it is the actual boundary of the site or a notional boundary, is called the relevant boundary (see Diagrams 17 and 18).

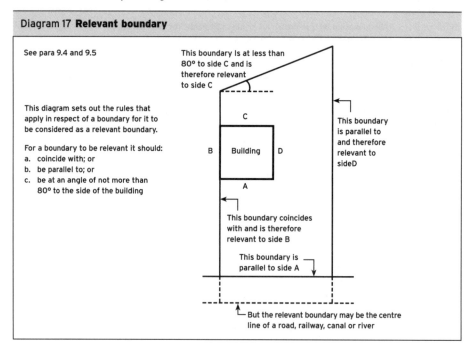

Diagram 17 **Relevant boundary**

See para 9.4 and 9.5

This diagram sets out the rules that apply in respect of a boundary for it to be considered as a relevant boundary.

For a boundary to be relevant it should:
a. coincide with; or
b. be parallel to; or
c. be at an angle of not more than 80° to the side of the building

This boundary Is at less than 80° to side C and is therefore relevant to side C

This boundary is parallel to and therefore relevant to sideD

This boundary coincides with and is therefore relevant to side B

This boundary is parallel to side A

But the relevant boundary may be the centre line of a road, railway, canal or river

### Notional boundaries

**9.6**  The distances to other buildings on the same site also need to be considered. This is done by assuming that there is a boundary between those buildings. This assumed boundary is called a notional boundary. The appropriate rules are given in Diagram 18.

## Unprotected areas

### Unprotected areas and fire resistance

**9.7**  Any part of an external wall which has less fire resistance than the appropriate amount given in Appendix A, Table A2, is considered to be an unprotected area.

### Status of combustible surface materials as unprotected area

**9.8**  If an external wall has the appropriate fire resistance, but has combustible material more than 1mm thick as its external surface, then that wall is counted as an unprotected area amounting to half the actual area of the combustible material, see Diagram 19. (For the purposes of this provision, a material with a Class 0 rating (National class) or Class B-s3, d2 rating (European class) (see Appendix A, paragraphs 7 and 13) need not be counted as unprotected area.)

Diagram 18 **Notional boundary**

See para 9.6

This diagram sets out the rules that apply where there there is a building on the same site that a notional boundary needs to be assumed between the buildings.

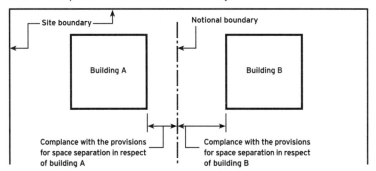

The notional boundary should be set in the area between the two buildings using the following rules:

1.  The notional boundary is assumed to exist in the space between the buildings and is positioned so that one of the buildings would comply with the provisions for space separation having regard to the amount of its unprotected area. In practice, if one of the buildings is existing, the position of the boundary will be set by the space separation factors for that building.
2.  The siting of the new building, or the second building if both are new, can then be checked to see that it also compiles, using the notional boundary as the relevant boundary for the second building.

**Note:** When a classification includes 's3, d2', this means that there is no limit set for smoke production and/or flaming droplets/particles.

Diagram 19 **Status of combustible surface material as unprotected area**

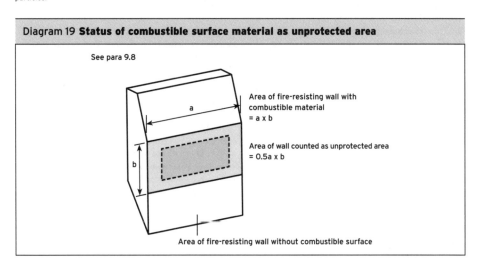

### Small unprotected areas

**9.9** Small unprotected areas in an otherwise protected area of wall are considered to pose a negligible risk of fire spread and may be disregarded. Diagram 20 shows the constraints that apply to the placing of such areas in relation to each other and to lines of compartmentation inside the building. These constraints vary according to the size of each unprotected area.

### Canopies

**9.10**  Some canopy structures would be exempt from the application of the Building Regulations by falling within Class VI or Class VII of Schedule 2 to the Regulations (Exempt buildings and works). Many others may not meet the exemption criteria and, in such cases, the provisions in this section about limits of unprotected areas could be onerous.

In the case of a canopy attached to the side of a building, provided that the edges of the canopy are at least 2m from the relevant boundary, separation distance may be determined from the wall rather than the edge of the canopy (see Diagram 21).

### External walls within 1000mm of the relevant boundary

**9.11**  A wall situated within 1000mm from any point on the relevant boundary, including a wall coincident with the boundary, will meet the provisions for space separation if:

a.   the only unprotected areas are those shown in Diagram 20; and

b.   the rest of the wall is fire-resisting from both sides.

### External walls 1000mm or more from the relevant boundary

**9.12**  A wall situated at least 1000mm from any point on the relevant boundary will meet the provisions for space separation if:

a.   the extent of unprotected area does not exceed that given by one of the methods referred to in paragraph 9.13; and

b.   the rest of the wall (if any) is fire-resisting.

## Methods for calculating acceptable unprotected area

**9.13**  Two simple methods are given in this Approved Document for calculating the acceptable amount of unprotected area in an external wall that is at least 1000mm from any point on the relevant boundary. (For walls within 1000mm of the boundary see paragraph 9.11 above.)

Method 1 may be used for small residential buildings and is set out in paragraph 9.16.

Method 2 may be used for most buildings or compartments for which Method 1 is not appropriate, and is set out in paragraph 9.17.

There are other more precise methods, described in a BRE report *External fire spread: Building separation and boundary distances* (BR 187, BRE 1991), which may be used instead of Methods 1 and 2. The 'Enclosing Rectangle' and 'Aggregate Notional Area' methods are included in the BRE report.

### Basis for calculating acceptable unprotected area

**9.14**  The basis of Methods 1 and 2 was originally set out in Fire Research Technical Paper No 5, 1963. This has been reprinted as part of the BRE report referred to in paragraph 9.13. The aim is to ensure that the building is separated from the boundary by at least half the distance at which the total thermal radiation intensity received from all unprotected areas in the wall would be 12.6 kw/m$^2$ (in still air), assuming the radiation intensity at each unprotected area is 84 kw/m$^2$.

### Sprinkler systems

**9.15**  If a building is fitted throughout with a sprinkler system, it is reasonable to assume that the intensity and extent of a fire will be reduced. The sprinkler system should meet the relevant recommendations of BS 9251 *Sprinkler systems for residential and domestic occupancies. Code of practice.* In these circumstances the boundary distance may be half that for an otherwise similar, but unsprinklered, building, subject to there being a minimum distance of 1000mm. Alternatively, the amount of unprotected area may be doubled if the boundary distance is maintained.

**Note:** The presence of sprinklers may be taken into account in a similar way when using the BRE report referred to in paragraph 9.14.

### Method 1

**9.16**  This method applies only to a building, which is 1000mm or more from any point on the relevant boundary and meets the following rules for determining the maximum unprotected area, which should be read with Diagram 22:

a.   The building should not exceed 3 storeys in height (basements are not counted) or be more than 24m in length; and

b.    Each side of the building will meet the provisions for space separation if:

    i. the distance of the side of the building from the relevant boundary; and

    ii. the extent of the unprotected area, are within the limits given in Diagram 22; and

**Note:** In calculating the maximum unprotected area, any areas falling within the limits shown in Diagram 20, and referred to in paragraph 9.9, can be disregarded.

c.    Any parts of the side of the building in excess of the maximum unprotected area should be fire-resisting.

### Diagram 20 **Unprotected areas which may be disregarded in assessing the separation distance from the boundary**

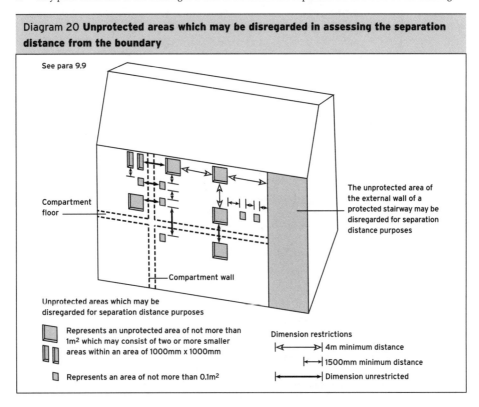

See para 9.9

Compartment floor

Compartment wall

The unprotected area of the external wall of a protected stairway may be disregarded for separation distance purposes

Unprotected areas which may be disregarded for separation distance purposes

Represents an unprotected area of not more than 1m² which may consist of two or more smaller areas within an area of 1000mm x 1000mm

Represents an area of not more than 0.1m²

Dimension restrictions

4m minimum distance

1500mm minimum distance

Dimension unrestricted

### Diagram 21 **The effect of a canopy on separation distance**

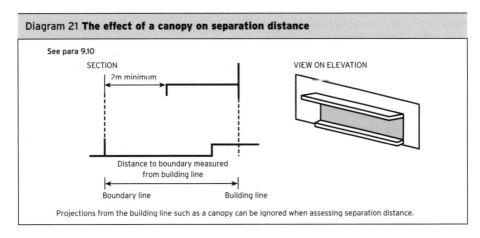

See para 9.10

SECTION

2m minimum

VIEW ON ELEVATION

Distance to boundary measured from building line

Boundary line          Building line

Projections from the building line such as a canopy can be ignored when assessing separation distance.

## Diagram 22 **Permitted unprotected areas for Method 1**

See para 9.16

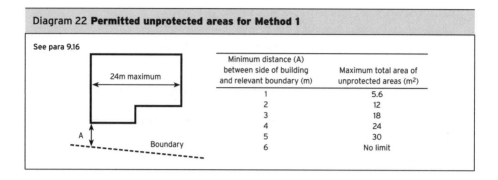

| Minimum distance (A) between side of building and relevant boundary (m) | Maximum total area of unprotected areas (m²) |
|---|---|
| 1 | 5.6 |
| 2 | 12 |
| 3 | 18 |
| 4 | 24 |
| 5 | 30 |
| 6 | No limit |

## Table 4 **Permitted unprotected areas for Method 2**

| Minimum distance between side of building and relevant boundary (m) | Maximum total percentage of unprotected areas % |
|---|---|
| 1 | 8 |
| 2.5 | 20 |
| 5 | 40 |
| 7.5 | 60 |
| 10 | 80 |
| 12.5 | 100 |

Notes:

a.   Intermediate values may be obtained by interpolation.

b.   For buildings which are fitted throughout with an automatic sprinkler system, see para 9.15.

c.   The total percentage of unprotected area is found by dividing the total unprotected area by the area of rectangle that encloses all the unprotected areas and multiplying the result by 100.

## Method 2

**9.17** This method applies to a dwellinghouse which is more than 1000mm from any point on the relevant boundary. The following rules for determining the maximum unprotected area should be read with Table 4.

a.   The building or compartment should not exceed 10m in height.

**Note:** For any building or compartment more than 10m in height, the methods set out in the BRE report *External fire spread: Building separation and boundary distances* can be applied.

b.   Each side of the building will meet the provisions for space separation if either

   i. the distance of the side of the building from the relevant boundary; or

   ii. the extent of unprotected area, are within the appropriate limits given in Table 4.

**Note:** In calculating the maximum unprotected area, any areas shown in Diagram 20, and referred to in paragraph 9.9, can be disregarded.

c.   Any parts of the side of the building in excess of the maximum unprotected area should be fire-resisting.

# Section 10: Roof coverings

## Introduction

**10.1** The provisions in this section limit the use, near a boundary, of roof coverings which will not give adequate protection against the spread of fire over them. The term roof covering is used to describe constructions which may consist of one or more layers of material, but does not refer to the roof structure as a whole. The provisions in this Section are principally concerned with the performance of roofs when exposed to fire from the outside.

**10.2** The circumstances when a roof is subject to the provisions in Section 9 for space separation are explained in paragraph 9.1.

### Other controls on roofs

**10.3** There are provisions concerning the fire properties of roofs in other Sections of this document In the guidance to B1 (paragraph 2.10) there are provisions for roofs that are part of a means of escape. In the guidance to B2 there are provisions for the internal surfaces of roof lights as part of the internal lining of a room or circulation space. In the guidance to B3 there are provisions in Section 4 for roofs which are used as a floor and in Section 6 for roofs that pass over the top of a compartment wall.

## Classification of performance

**10.4** The performance of roof coverings is designated by reference to the test methods specified in BS 476-3:2004 *Fire tests on building materials and structures. Classification and method of test for external fire exposure to roofs* or determined in accordance with BS EN 13501 -5:2005 *Fire classification of construction products and building elements. Classification using data from external fire exposure to roof tests,* as described in Appendix A. The notional performance of some common roof coverings is given in Table A5 of Appendix A.

Rooflights are controlled on a similar basis, and plastic rooflights described in paragraphs 10.6 and 10.7 may also be used.

## Separation distances

**10.5** The separation distance is the minimum distance from the roof (or part of the roof) to the relevant boundary, which may be a notional boundary.

Table 5 sets out separation distances according to the type of roof covering and the size and use of the building. There are no restrictions on the use of roof coverings designated AA. AB or AC (National class) or $B_{ROOF}(t4)$ (European class) classification. In addition, roof covering products (and/or materials) as defined in Commission Decision 2000/553/EC of 6 September 2000 implementing Council Directive 89/106/EEC as regards the external fire performance of roof coverings can be considered to fulfil all of the requirements for performance characteristic 'external fire performance' without the need for testing provided that any national provisions on the design and execution of works are fulfilled.

**Note:** The boundary formed by the wall separating a pair of semi-detached houses may be disregarded for the purposes of this Section (but see Section 5, Diagram 11(b), which deals with roofs passing over the top of a compartment wall).

### Plastic rooflights

**10.6** Table 6 sets out the limitations on the use of plastic rooflights which have at least a Class 3 (National class) or Class D-s3, d2 (European class) lower surface, and Table 7 sets out the limitations on the use of thermoplastic materials with a TP(a) rigid or TP(b) classification (see also Diagram 23). The method of classifying thermoplastic materials is given in Appendix A.

**10.7** When used in roof lights, a rigid thermoplastic sheet product made from polycarbonate or from unplasticised PVC, which achieves a Class 1 (National class) rating for surface spread of flame when tested to BS 476-7:1997 (or 1987 or 1971), or Class C-s3,d2 (European class) can be regarded as having an AA (National class) designation or $B_{ROOF}(t4)$ (European class) classification, other than for the purposes of Diagram 11.

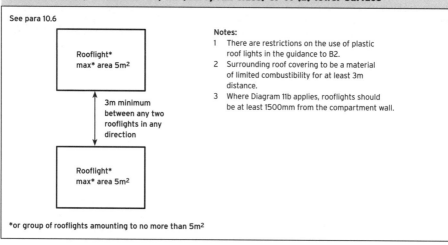

Diagram 23 **Limitations on spacing and size of plastic rooflights having a Class 3 (National class) or Class D-s3, d2 (European class) or TP(b) lower surface**

See para 10.6

Rooflight*
max* area 5m²

3m minimum
between any two
rooflights in any
direction

Rooflight*
max* area 5m²

**Notes:**
1   There are restrictions on the use of plastic roof lights in the guidance to B2.
2   Surrounding roof covering to be a material of limited combustibility for at least 3m distance.
3   Where Diagram 11b applies, rooflights should be at least 1500mm from the compartment wall.

*or group of rooflights amounting to no more than 5m²

### Unwired glass in rooflights

**10.8** When used in rooflights, unwired glass at least 4mm thick can be regarded as having an AA designation (National class) or $B_{ROOF}$(t4) (European class) classification.

### Thatch and wood shingles

**10.9** Thatch and wood shingles should be regarded as having an AD/BD/CD designation or $E_{ROOF}$(t4) (European class) classification in Table 5 if performance under BS 476-3:2004 (or 1958) or BS EN 1187:xxxx cannot be established.

**Note:** Consideration can be given to thatched roofs being closer to the boundary than shown in Table 5 if, for example, the following precautions (based on *Thatched buildings. New properties and extensions* [the 'Dorset Model']) are incorporated in the design:

a.   the rafters are overdrawn with construction having not less than 30 minutes fire resistance;

b.   the guidance given in Approved Document J Combustion appliances and fuel storage is followed; and

c.   the smoke alarm installation (see Section 1) extends to the roof space.

### Table 5 **Limitations on roof coverings***

| Designation† of covering of roof or part of roof | | Minimum distance from any point on relevant boundary | | | |
|---|---|---|---|---|---|
| National Class | European Class | Less than 6m | At least 6m | At least 12m | At least 20m |
| AA, AB or AC | $B_{ROOF}$(t4) | ● | ● | ● | ● |
| BA, BB or BC | $C_{ROOF}$(t4) | ○ | ● | ● | ● |
| CA, CB or CC | $D_{ROOF}$(t4) | ○ | ● (1)(2) | ● (1) | ● |
| AD, BD or CD | $E_{ROOF}$(t4) | ○ | ● (1)(2) | ● (1) | ● (1) |
| DA, DB, DC or DD | $F_{ROOF}$(t4) | ○ | ○ | ○ | ● (1)(2) |

Notes for table 5 (above):

\* See paragraph 10.8 for limitations on glass; paragraph 10.9 for limitations on thatch and wood shingles; and paragraphs 10.6 and 10.7 and Tables 6 and 7 for limitations on plastic rooflights.

† The designation of external roof surfaces is explained in Appendix A. (See Table A5 for notional designations of roof coverings.)

Separation distances do not apply to the boundary between roofs of a pair of semi-detached houses (see para 10.5) and to enclosed/ covered walkways. However, see Diagram 11 if the roof passes over the top of a compartment wall.

Openable polycarbonate and PVC rooflights which achieve a Class1 (National class) or Class C-s3, d2 (European class) rating by test, see paragraph 10.7, may be regarded as having an AA (National class) designation or $B_{ROOF}$(t4) (European class) classification.

The National classification do not automatically equate with the equivalent classifications in the European column, therefore products cannot typically assume a European class unless they have been tested accordingly.

● Acceptable

○ Not acceptable.

1. Not acceptable on any of the following buildings:
   a. Houses in terraces of three or more houses.
   b. Any other buildings with a cubic capacity of more than 1500m².

2. Acceptable on buildings not listed in Note 1, provided that part of the roof is no more than 3m² in area and is at least 1500mm from any similar part, with the roof between the parts covered with a material of limited combustibility.

### Table 6 Class 3 (National class) or Class D-s3, d2 (European class) plastic rooflights: limitations on use and boundary distance

| Minimum classification on lower surface [1] | Space which rooflight can serve | Minimum distance from any point on relevant boundary to rooflight with an external designation† of: | |
| --- | --- | --- | --- |
| | | AD BD CD (National class) or $E_{ROOF}$(t4) (European class) CA CB CC or $D_{ROOF}$(t4) (European class) | DA DB DC DD (National class) or $F_{ROOF}$(t4) (European class) |
| Class 3 (National class) or Class D-s3, d2 (European class) | a. Balcony, verandah, carport or covered way. which has at least one longer side wholly or permanently open<br><br>b. Detached swimming pool<br><br>c. Conservatory, garage or outbuilding, with a maximum floor area of 40m² | 6m | 20m |
| | d. Circulation space [2] (except 0m on a protected stairway)<br><br>e. Room [2] | 6m [3] | 20m [3] |

**Notes:**

† The designation of external roof surfaces is explained in Appendix A.
None of the above designations are suitable for protected stairways.
Polycarbonate and PVC rooflights which achieve a Class 1 (National classy or class C-s3, d2 (European class) rating by test, see paragraph 10.7, may be regarded as having an AA designation (National class) or $B_{ROOF}$(t4) (European class) classification.

The National classifications do not automatically equate with the equivalent classifications in the European column, therefore products cannot typically assume a European class unless they have been tested accordingly.

Where Diagram 11 b applies, rooflights should be at least 1.5m from the compartment wall.

Products may have upper and lower surfaces with different properties if they have double skins or are laminates of different materials; in which case the more onerous distance (from Tables 6 and 7) applies.

1. See also the guidance to B2.

2.  Single akin rooflight only, in the case of non-thermoplastic material.
3.  The rooflight should also meet the provisions of Diagram 23.

Table 7 **TP(a) and TP(b) plastic rooflights: limitations on use and boundary distance**

| Minimum classification on lower surface [1] | Space which rooflight can serve | Minimum distance from any point on relevant boundary to rooflight with an external surface classification [1] of: | |
| --- | --- | --- | --- |
| | | TP(a) | TP(b) |
| 1.TP(a) rigid | Any space except a protected stairway | 6m [2] | Not applicable |
| 2.TP(b) | a. Balcony, verandah, carport or covered way, which has at least one longer side wholly or permanently open | Not applicable | 6m |
| | b. Detached swimming pool | | |
| | c. Conservatory, garage or outbuilding, with a maximum floor area of 40m² | | |
| | d. Circulation space (except a protected stairway) | Not applicable | 6m [4] |
| | e. Room [3] | | |

**Notes:**

None of the above designations are suitable for protected stairways.

Polycarbonate and PVC rooflights which achieve a Class 1 (National classy or class C-s3, d2 (European class) rating by test, see paragraph 10.7, may be regarded as having an AA designation (National class) or $B_{ROOF}$(t4) (European class) classification.

Where Diagram 11 b applies, rooflights should be at least 1.5m from the compartment wall.

Products may have upper and lower surfaces with different properties if they have double skins or are laminates of different materials; in which case the more onerous distance (from Tables 6 and 7) applies.

The National classifications do not automatically equate with the equivalent classifications in the European column, therefore products cannot typically assume a European class unless they have been tested accordingly.

1.  See also the guidance to B2.
2.  No limit in the case of any space described in 2a, b & c.
3.  Single akin rooflight only, in the case of non-thermoplastic material.
4.  The rooflight should also meet the provisions of Diagram 23.

# B5 ACCESS AND FACILITIES FOR THE FIRE AND RESCUE SERVICE - THE REQUIREMENT

This Approved Document deals with the following Requirement from Part B of Schedule 1 to the Building Regulations 2000 (as amended).

| Requirement | Limits on application |
| --- | --- |
| **Access and facilities for the fire service** | |
| B5. (1) The building shall be designed and constructed so as to provide reasonable facilities to assist firefighters in the protection of life. | |
| (2) Reasonable provision shall be made within the site of the building to enable fire appliances to gain access to the building. | |

## Guidance

### Performance

In the Secretary of State's view the Requirements of B5 will be met:

a.   if there is sufficient means of external access to enable fire appliances to be brought near to the building for effective use;

b.   if there is sufficient means of access into, and within, the building for firefighting personnel to effect search and rescue and fight fire;

c.   if the building is provided with sufficient internal fire mains and other facilities to assist firefighters in their tasks; and

d.   if the building is provided with adequate means for venting heat and smoke from a fire in a basement.

These access arrangements and facilities are only required in the interests of the health and safety of people in and around the building. The extent to which they are required will depend on the use and size of the building in so far as it affects the health and safety of those people.

### Introduction

**B5.i**  The main factor determining the facilities needed to assist the fire and rescue service is the size of the building. Generally speaking firefighting is carried out within the building.

For dwellinghouses, it is usually only necessary to ensure that the building is sufficiently close to a point accessible to fire and rescue service vehicles (see paragraph 11.2). For very large houses additional measures may be necessary. The guidance given in Approved Document B Volume 2 *(Buildings other than dwellinghouses)* may be applicable.

If it is proposed to deviate from the general guidance in Section 11 then it would be advisable to seek advice from the Fire and Rescue Service at the earliest opportunity.

## Section 11: Vehicle access

### Introduction

**11.1**   For the purposes of this Approved Document, vehicle access to the exterior of a building is needed to enable high reach appliances, such as turntable ladders and hydraulic platforms, to be used and to enable pumping appliances to supply water and equipment for firefighting, search and rescue activities.

Vehicle access routes and hard-standings should meet the criteria described in paragraph 11.4 where they are to be used by fire and rescue service vehicles.

**Note:** Requirements cannot be made under the Building Regulations for work to be done outside the site of the works shown on the deposited plans, building notice or initial notice. In this connection it may not always be reasonable to upgrade an existing route across a site to a small building such as a single dwellinghouse. The options in such a case, from doing no work to upgrading certain features of the route, e.g. a sharp bend, should be considered by the Building Control Body in consultation with the fire and rescue service.

**11.2**   There should be vehicle access for a pump appliance to within 45m of all points within the dwellinghouse.

**11.3**   Every elevation to which vehicle access is provided in accordance with paragraph 11.2 should have a suitable door(s), not less than 750mm wide, giving access to the interior of the building.

## Design of access routes and hard-standings

**11.4**   A vehicle access route may be a road or other route which, including any inspection covers and the like, meets the standards in Table 8 and paragraph 11.5.

**11.5**   Turning facilities should be provided in any dead end access route that is more than 20m long (see Diagram 24). This can be by a hammerhead or turning circle, designed on the basis of Table 8.

Table 8 **Typical fire and rescue service vehicle access route specification**

| Appliance type | Minimum width of road between kerbs (m) | Minimum width of gateways (m) | Minimum turning circle between kerbs (m) | Minimum turning circle between walls (m) | Minimum clearance height (m) | Minimum carrying capacity (tonnes) |
|---|---|---|---|---|---|---|
| Pump | 3.7 | 3.1 | 16.8 | 19.2 | 3.7 | 12.5 |
| High reach | 3.7 | 3.1 | 26.0 | 29.0 | 4.0 | 17.0 |

Notes:

1.   Fire appliances are not standardised. Some fire and rescue services have appliances of greater weight or different size. In conjunction with the Fire and Rescue Authority, the Building Control Body may adopt other dimensions in such circumstances.

2.   Because the weight of high reach appliances is distributed over a number of axles, it is considered that their infrequent use of a carriageway or route designed to 12.5 tonnes should not cause damage. It would therefore be reasonable to design the roadbase to 12.5 tonnes, although structures such as bridges should have the full 17 tonnes capacity.

Diagram 24 **Turning facilities**

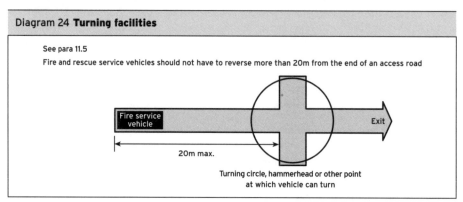

See para 11.5

Fire and rescue service vehicles should not have to reverse more than 20m from the end of an access road

Fire service vehicle

Exit

20m max.

Turning circle, hammerhead or other point at which vehicle can turn

# Appendix A: Performance of materials, products and structures

## Introduction

**1.**   Much of the guidance in this document is given in terms of performance in relation to British or European Standards for products or methods of test or design or in terms of European Technical Approvals. In such cases the material, product or structure should:

a.   be in accordance with a specification or design which has been shown by test to be capable of meeting that performance; or

**Note:** For this purpose, laboratories accredited by the United Kingdom Accreditation Service (UKAS) for conducting the relevant tests would be expected to have the necessary expertise.

b.    have been assessed from test evidence against appropriate standards, or by using relevant design guides, as meeting that performance; or

**Note:** For this purpose, laboratories accredited by UKAS for conducting the relevant tests and suitably qualified fire safety engineers might be expected to have the necessary expertise.

For materials/products where European standards or approvals are not yet available and for a transition period after they become available, British standards may continue to be used. Any body notified to the UK Government by the Government of another Member State of the European Union as capable of assessing such materials/products against the relevant British Standards, may also be expected to have the necessary expertise. Where European materials/products standards or approvals are available, any body notified to the European Commission as competent to assess such materials or products against the relevant European standards or technical approval can be considered to have the appropriate expertise.

c.    where tables of notional performance are included in this document, conform with an appropriate specification given in these tables; or

d.    in the case of fire-resisting elements:

i. conform with an appropriate specification given in Part II of the Building Research Establishments' Report *Guidelines for the construction of fire-resisting structural elements* (BR 128, BRE 1988); or

ii. be designed in accordance with a relevant British Standard or Eurocode.

**Note 1:** Different forms of construction can present different problems and opportunities for the provision of structural fire protection. Further information on some specific forms of construction can be found in:

• Timber – BRE 454 *Multi-storey timber frame buildings – a design guide* 2003 ISBN: 1 86081 605 3

• Steel – SCI P197 *Designing for structural fire safety: A handbook for architects and engineers* 1999 ISBN: 1 85942 074 5

**Note 2:** Any test evidence used to substantiate the fire resistance rating of a construction should be carefully checked to ensure that it demonstrates compliance that is adequate and applicable to the intended use. Small differences in detail (such as fixing method, joints, dimensions and the introduction of insulation materials etc.) may significantly affect the rating.

**2.**    Building Regulations deal with fire safety in buildings as a whole. Thus they are aimed at limiting fire hazard.

The aim of standard fire tests is to measure or assess the response of a material, product, structure or system to one or more aspects of fire behaviour. Standard fire tests cannot normally measure fire hazard. They form only one of a number of factors that need to be taken into account Other factors are set out in this publication.

## Fire resistance

**3.**    Factors having a bearing on fire resistance, that are considered in this document, are:

a.    fire severity;

b.    building height; and c. building occupancy.

**4.**    The standards of fire resistance given are based on assumptions about the severity of fires and the consequences should an element fail. Fire severity is estimated in very broad terms from the use of the building (its purpose group), on the assumption that the building contents (which constitute the fire load) are similar for buildings in the same use.

A number of factors affect the standard of fire resistance specified. These are:

a.    the amount of combustible material per unit of floor area in various types of building (the fire load density);

b.    the height of the top floor above ground, which affects the ease of escape and of firefighting operations, and the consequences should large scale collapse occur;

c.    occupancy type, which reflects the ease with which the building can be evacuated quickly;

d.    whether there are basements, because the lack of an external wall through which to vent heat and smoke may increase heat build-up and thus affect the duration of a fire, as well as complicating firefighting; and

e.    whether the building is of single storey construction (where escape is direct and structural failure is unlikely to precede evacuation)*

Because the use of buildings may change, a precise estimate of fire severity based on the fire load due to a particular use may be misleading. Therefore, if a fire engineering approach of this kind is adopted, the likelihood that the fire load may change in the future needs to be considered.

**5.**    Performance in terms of the fire resistance to be met by elements of structure, doors and other forms of construction is determined by reference to either

a.    (National tests) BS 476 Fire tests on building materials and structures. Parts 20-24:1987, i.e. Part 20 Method for determination of the fire resistance of elements of construction (general principles), Part 21 Methods for determination of the fire resistance of loadbearing elements of construction, Part 22 Methods for determination of the fire resistance of non-loadbearing elements of construction, Part 23 Methods for determination of the contribution of components to the fire resistance of a structure, and Part 24 Method for determination of the fire resistance of ventilation ducts (or to BS 476-8:1972 in respect of items tested or assessed prior to 1 January 1988); or

b.    (European tests) Commission Decision 2000/367/EC of 3 May 2000 implementing Council Directive 89/106/EEC as regards the classification of the resistance to fire performance of construction products, construction works and parts thereof.

**Note:** The designation of xxxx is used for the year reference for standards that are not yet published. The latest version of any standard may be used provided that it continues to address the relevant requirements of the Regulations.

All products are classified in accordance with BBS EN 13501 -2:2003 Fire classification of construction products and building elements. Classification using data from fire resistance tests, excluding ventilation services (excluding products for use in ventilation systems).

BS EN 13501-3:2005 Fire classification of construction products and building elements. Classification using data from fire resistance tests on products and elements used in building service installations: fire resisting ducts and fire dampers (other than smoke control systems).

BS EN 13501-4:xxxx, Fire classification of construction products and building elements, Part 4 – Classification using data from fire resistance tests on smoke control systems.

The relevant European test methods under BS EN 1364, 1365,1366 and 1634 are listed in Appendix F.

**Table A1 gives the specific requirements for each element in terms of one or more of the following performance criteria:**

a.    **resistance to collapse** (loadbearing capacity), which applies to loadbearing elements only, denoted R in the European classification of the resistance to fire performance;

b.    **resistance to fire penetration** (integrity), denoted E in the European classification of the resistance to fire performance; and

c.    **resistance to the transfer of excessive heat** (insulation), denoted I in the European classification of the resistance to fire performance.

**Table A2 sets out the minimum periods of fire resistance for elements of structure.**

**Table A3 sets out criteria appropriate to the suspended ceilings that can be accepted as contributing to the fire resistance of a floor.**

**Table A4 sets out limitations on the use of uninsulated fire-resisting glazed elements. These limitations do not apply to the use of insulated fire-resisting glazed elements.**

Information on tested elements is frequently given in literature available from manufacturers and trade associations.

Information on tests on fire-resisting elements is also given in such publications as:

Association for Specialist Fire Protection Yellow Book – Fire protection for structural steel in buildings, 4th edition. See Appendix F.

## Roofs

**6.** Performance in terms of the resistance of roofs to external fire exposure is determined by reference to either:

a.  (National tests) BS 476-3:2004 *External fire exposure roof tests*; or

b.  (European tests) Commission Decision XXXX/YYY/EC amending Decision 2001/671/EC *Establishing a classification system for the external fire performance of roofs and roof coverings.*

Constructions are classified within the National system by two letters in the range A-D, with an AA designation being the best. The first letter indicates the time to penetration; the second letter a measure of the spread of flame.

Constructions are classified within the European system as $B_{ROOF}(t4)$, $C_{ROOF}(t4)$. $D_{ROOF}(t4)$, $E_{ROOF}(t4)$ or $F_{ROOF}(t4)$ (with $B_{ROOF}(t4)$ being the highest performance and $F_{ROOF}(t4)$ being the lowest) in accordance with BS EN 13501-5:2005 Fire classification of construction products and building elements – Classification using data from external fire exposure to roof tests.

BS EN 13501-5 refers to four separate tests. The suffix (t4) used above indicates that Test 4 is to be used for the purposes of this Approved Document.

Some roof covering products (and/or materials) can be considered to fulfil all of the requirements for the performance characteristic "external fire performance" without the need for testing, subject to any national provisions on the design and execution of works being fulfilled. These roof covering products are listed in Commission Decision 2000/553/EC of 6th September 2000 implementing Council Directive 89/106/EEC as regards the external fire performance of roof coverings.

In some circumstances roofs, or parts of roofs, may need to be fire-resisting, for example if used as an escape route or if the roof performs the function of a floor. Such circumstances are covered in Sections 2, 4 and 6.

**Table A5 gives notional designations of some generic roof coverings.**

## Reaction to fire

**7.** Performance in terms of reaction to fire to be met by construction products is determined by Commission Decision 200/147/EC of 8 February 2000 implementing Council Directive 89/106/EEC as regards the classification of the reaction to fire performance of construction products.

**Note:** The designation of xxxx is used for the year reference for standards that are not yet published. The latest version of any standard may be used provided that it continues to address the relevant requirements of the Regulations.

All products, excluding floorings, are classified as †A1, A2, B, C, D, E or F (with class A1 being the highest performance and F being the lowest) in accordance with BS EN 13501 -1:2002 *Fire classification of construction products and building elements, Part 1 – Classification using data from reaction to fire tests.*

†    The classes of reaction to fire performance ofA2, B, C, D and E are accompanied by additional classifications related to the production of smoke (s1, s2, s3) and/or flaming droplets/particles (dO, d1, d2).

The relevant European test methods are specified as follows:

- BS EN ISO 1182:2002 Reaction to fire tests for building products – Non-combustibility test

- BS EN ISO 1716:2002 Reaction to fire tests for building products – Determination of the gross calorific value

- BS EN 13823:2002 Reaction to fire tests for building products – Building products excluding floorings exposed to the thermal attack by a single burning item

- BS EN ISO 11925-2:2002 Reaction to fire tests for building products, Part 2 – Ignitability when subjected to direct impingement of a flame.

- BS EN 13238:2001 Reaction to fire tests for building products – conditioning procedures and general rules for selection of substrates.

## Non-combustible materials

**8.** Non-combustible materials are defined in Table A6 either as listed products, or in terms of performance:

a.  (National classes) when tested to BS 476-4:1970 *Fire tests on building materials and structures – Non-cornbustibility test for materials* or BS 476-11:1982 *Fire tests on building materials and structures – Method for assessing the heat emission from building materials.*

b.    (European classes) when classified as class A1 in accordance with BS EN 13501-1:2002 *Fire classification of construction products and building elements. Classification using data from reaction to fire tests* when tested to BS EN ISO 1182:2002 *Reaction to fire tests for building products – Non-combustibility test* and BS EN ISO 1716:2002 *Reaction to fire tests for building products – Determination of the gross calorific value.*

**Table A6 identifies non-combustible products and materials, and lists circumstances where their use is necessary.**

## Materials of limited combustibility

**9.**    Materials of limited combustibility are defined in Table A7:

a.    (National classes) by reference to the method specified in BS 476-11:1982;

b.    (European classes) in terms of performance when classified as class A2-s3, d2 in accordance with BS EN 13501-1:2002 *Fire classification of construction products and building elements. Classification using data from reaction to fire tests* when tested to BS EN ISO 1182:2002 *Reaction to fire tests for building products – Non-combustibility test* or BS EN ISO 1716:2002 *Reaction to fire tests for building products – Determination of the gross calorific value* and BS EN 13823:2002 *Reaction to fire tests for building products – Building products excluding floorings exposed to the thermal attack by a single burning item.*

**Table A7 also includes composite products (such as plasterboard) which are considered acceptable, and where these are exposed as linings they should also meet any appropriate flame spread rating.**

## Internal linings

**10.**    Flame spread over wall or ceiling surfaces is controlled by providing for the lining materials or products to meet given performance levels in tests appropriate to the materials or products involved.

**11.**    Under the National classifications, lining systems which can be effectively tested for 'surface spread of flame' are rated for performance by reference to the method specified in BS 476- 7:1997 (or 1987 or 1971) *Fire tests on building materials and structures. Method of test to determine the classification of the surface spread of flame of products* under which materials or products are classified 1, 2, 3 or 4 with Class 1 being the highest.

Under the European classifications, lining systems are classified in accordance with BS EN 13501-1:2002 *Fire classification of construction products and building elements, Part 1 – Classification using data from reaction to fire tests*. Materials or products are classified as A1, A2, B, C, D, E or F, with A1 being the highest. When a classification includes 's3, d2', it means that there is no limit set for smoke production and/or flaming droplets/particles.

**12.**    To restrict the use of materials which ignite easily, which have a high rate of heat release and/or which reduce the time to flashover, maximum acceptable 'fire propagation' indices are specified, where the National test methods are being followed. These are determined by reference to the method specified in BS 476-6:1989 or 1981. Index of performance (I) relates to the overall test performance, whereas sub-index (i1) is derived from the first three minutes of test.

**13.**    The highest National product performance classification for lining materials is Class 0. This is achieved if a material or the surface of a composite product is either:

a.    composed throughout of materials of limited combustibility; or

b.    a Class 1 material which has a fire propagation index (I) of not more than 12 and sub-index (i1) of not more than 6.

**Note:** Class 0 is not a classification identified in any British Standard test.

**14.**    Composite products defined as materials of limited combustibility (see paragraph 9 and Table AT) should in addition comply with the test requirement appropriate to any surface rating specified in the guidance on requirements B2, B3 and B4.

**15.**    The notional performance ratings of certain widely used generic materials or products are listed in Table A8 in terms of their performance in the traditional lining tests BS 476-6:1989 and BS 476-7:1997 or in accordance with BS EN 13501-1:2002.

**16.**    Results of tests on proprietary materials are frequently given in literature available from manufacturers and trade associations.

Any reference used to substantiate the surface spread of flame rating of a material or product should be carefully checked to ensure that it is suitable, adequate and applicable to the construction to be used. Small differences in detail, such as thickness, substrate, colour, form, fixings, adhesive etc, may significantly affect the rating.

## Thermoplastic Materials

**17.** A thermoplastic material means any synthetic polymeric material which has a softening point below 200°C if tested to BS EN ISO 306:2004 method A120 *Plastics – Thermoplastic materials – Determination of Vicat softening temperature*. Specimens for this test may be fabricated from the original polymer where the thickness of material of the end product is less than 2.5mm.

**18.** A thermoplastic material in isolation can not be assumed to protect a substrate when used as a lining to a wall or ceiling. The surface rating of both products must therefore meet the required classification. If, however, the thermoplastic material is fully bonded to a non-thermoplastic substrate, then only the surface rating of the composite will need to comply.

**19.** Concessions are made for thermoplastic materials used for window glazing, roof lights, and lighting diffusers within suspended ceilings, which may not comply with the criteria specified in paragraphs 11 to 16. They are described in the guidance on requirements B2 and B4.

**20.** For the purposes of the requirements B2 and B4 thermoplastic materials should either be used according to their classification 0-3, under the BS 476-6:1989 and B8 476-7:1997 tests as described in paragraphs 11 to 16, (if they have such a rating), or they may be classified TP(a) rigid, TP(a) flexible, or TP(b) according to the following methods:

### TP(a) rigid:

    i. Rigid solid pvc sheet;

    ii. Solid (as distinct from double- or multiple-skin) polycarbonate sheet at least 3mm thick;

    iii. Multi-skinned rigid sheet made from unplasticised pvc or polycarbonate which has a Class 1 rating when tested to BS 476-7:1997 or 1971 or 1987; and

    iv. Any other rigid thermoplastic product, a specimen of which (at the thickness of the product as put on the market), when tested to BS 2782:1970 as amended in 1974: Method 508A *Rate of burning (Laboratory method)*, performs so that the test flame extinguishes before the first mark and the duration of flaming or afterglow does not exceed five seconds following removal of the burner-

### TP(a) flexible:

Flexible products not more than 1 mm thick which comply with the Type C requirements of BS 5867-2:1980 Specification for fabrics for curtains and drapes – Flammability requirements when tested to BS 5438:1989 Methods of test for flammability of textile fabrics when subjected to a small igniting flame applied to the face or bottom edge of vertically oriented specimens Test 2, with the flame applied to the surface of the specimens for 5,15, 20 and 30 seconds respectively, but excluding the cleansing procedure; and

### TP(b):

    i. Rigid solid polycarbonate sheet products less than 3mm thick, or multiple-skin polycarbonate sheet products which do not qualify as TP(a) by test; or

    ii. Other products which, when a specimen of the material between 1.5 and 3mm thick is tested in accordance with BS 2782:1970, as amended in 1974: Method 508A, has a rate of burning which does not exceed 50mm / minute.

**Note:** If it is not possible to cut or machine a 5mm-thick specimen from the product then a 3mm test specimen can be moulded from the same material as that used for the manufacture of the product.

**Note:** Currently, no new guidance is possible on the assessment or classification of thermoplastic materials under the European system since there is no generally accepted European test procedure and supporting comparative data.

## Fire test methods

**21.** A guide to the various test methods in BS 476 and BS 2782 is given in PD 6520 Guide to fire test methods for building materials and elements of construction (available from the British Standards Institution).

A guide to the development and presentation of fire tests and their use in hazard assessment is given in BS 6336:1998 Guide to development and presentation of fire tests and their use in hazard assessment

Table A1 **Specific provisions of test for fire resistance of elements of structure etc**

| Part of building | Minimum provisions when tested to the relevant part of BS 476 [1] (minutes) | | | Minimum provisions when tested to the relevant European standard (minutes) [9] | Method of exposure |
|---|---|---|---|---|---|
| | Load-bearing capacity [2] | Integrity | Insulation | | |
| 1. Structural frame, beam or column. | See Table A2 | Not applicable | Not applicable | R see Table A2 | Exposed faces |
| 2. Loadbearing wall (which is not also a wall described in any of the following items). | See Table A2 | Not applicable | Not applicable | R see Table A2 | Each side separately |
| 3. Floor [3] | | | | | |
| a. In upper storey of 2-storey dwellinghouse (but not over garage or basement); | 30 | 15 | 15 | R 30 and REI15 | From underside |
| b. Any other floor-including compartment floors. | See Table A2 | See Table A2 | See Table A2 | REI see Table A2 | From underside |
| 4. Roof any part forming an escape route; | 30 | 30 | 30 | REI 30 | From underside [4] |
| 5. External walls | | | | | |
| a. any part less than 1000mm from any point on the relevant boundary; | See Table A2 | See Table A2 | See Table A2 | REI see Table A2 | Each side separately |
| b. any part 1000mm or more from the relevant boundary [5]; | See Table A2 | See Table A2 | 15 | RE see Table A2 and REI 15 | From inside the building |
| c. any part adjacent to an external escape route (see paragraph 2.10 and 2.15 and Diagram 7). | 30 | 30 | No provision [6] [7] | RE 30 | From inside the building |
| 6. Compartment walls (other than in item 8) | See Table A2 | See Table A2 | See Table A2 | REI see Table A2 | Each side separately |
| 7. Enclosure (which does not form part of a compartment wall or a protected shaft) to a: | | | | | |
| a. protected stairway; | 30 | 30 | 30 [8] | REI 30 [8] | Each side separately |
| b. lift shaft. | 30 | 30 | 30 | REI 30 | Each side separately |
| 8. Wall or floor separating an attached or integral garage from a dwellinghouse | 30 | 30 | 30 [8] | REI 30 [8] | From garage side |

Table A1 **Specific provisions of test for fire resistance of elements of structure etc**

| Part of building | Minimum provisions when tested to the relevant part of BS 476 [1] (minutes) | | | Minimum provisions when tested to the relevant European standard (minutes) [9] | Method of exposure |
|---|---|---|---|---|---|
| | Load-bearing capacity [2] | Integrity | Insulation | | |
| 9. Fire-resisting construction: in dwelling-houses not described elsewhere | 30 | 30 | 30 [8] | REI 30 [8] | |
| 10. Cavity barrier | Not applicable | 30 | 15 | E 30 and EI 15 | Each side separately |
| 11. Ceiling described in paragraph 2.14, Diagram 6 | Not applicable | 30 | 30 | EI 30 | From underside |
| 12. Duct described in paragraph 6.8e | Not applicable | 30 | No provision | E30 | From outside |
| 13. Casing around a drainage system described in paragraph 7.8, Diagram 15 | Not applicable | 30 | No provision | E30 | From outside |
| 14. Fluewalls described in paragraph 7.11, Diagram 16 | Not applicable | Half the period specified In Table A2 for the | Half the period specified In Table A2 for the | EL half the period specified in Table A2 for the compartment wall/ floor | From outside |
| 15. Construction described in | Not applicable | 30 | 30 | EL 30 | From underside |
| 16. Fire doors | | See Table B1 | | See Table B1 | |

**Notes:**
1. Part 21 for loadbearing elements, Part 22 for non-loadbaring elements, Part 23 for fire-protecting suspended ceilings, and Part 24 for ventilation ducts. BS 476-8 results are acceptable for items tested or assessed before 1 January 1988.
2. Applies to loadbaring elements only (see B3.ii and Appendix E).
3. Guidance on increasing the fire resistance of existing timber floors is given in BRE Digest 208 Increasing the fire resistance of existing timber floors (BRE 1988).
4. A suspended ceiling should only be relied on to contribute to the fire resistance of the floor if the ceiling meets the appropriate provisions given in Table A
5. The guidance in Section 9 allows such walls to contain areas which need not be fire-resisting (unprotected areas).
6. Unless needed as part of a wall in item 5a or 5b.
7. Except for any limitations on glazed elements given in Table A4.
8. See Table A4 for permitted extent of uninsulated glazed elements.
9. The National classifications do not automatically equate with the equivalent classifications in the European column, therefore products cannot typically assume a European class unless they have been tested accordingly.
   'R' is the European classification of the resistance to fire performance in respect of loadbearing capacity; 'E' is the European classification of the resistance to Km performance in respect of integrity; and 'I' is the European classification of the resistance to fire performance in respect of insulation.

## Table A2 Minimum periods of fire resistance for dwellinghouses

Minimum periods (minutes) for elements of structure in a:

| Basement storey [1] inducting floor over | Ground or upper storey | |
|---|---|---|
| | Height (m) of top floor above ground | |
| | Not more than 5 | Not more than 5 |
| 30 [2] | 30 [2] | 60 [3] |

**Notes:**

Modifications referred to in Table A2:

1.  The floor over a basement (or if there is more than one basement, the floor over the topmost basement) should meet the provisions for the ground and upper storeys if that period is higher.
2.  Increased to a minimum of 60 minutes for compartment walls separating buildings.
3.  30 minutes in the case of three storey dwellinghouses, increased to 60 minutes minimum for compartment walls separating buildings.
4.  Refer to table A1 for the specific provisions of test.

### Application of the fire resistance standards in table A2:

a.  Where one element of structure supports or carries or gives stability to another, the fire resistance of the supporting element should be no less than the minimum period of fire resistance for the other element (whether that other element is load bearing or not).

There are circumstances where it may be reasonable to vary this principle, for example:

i. where the supporting structure is in the open air, and is not likely to be affected by the fire in the building; or

ii. where the supporting structure is in a different compartment, with a fire-separating element (which has the higher standard of fire resistance) between the supporting and the separated structure; or

iii. where a plant room on the roof needs a higher fire resistance than the elements of structure supporting it.

b.  Where an element of structure forms part of more than one building or compartment, that element should be constructed to the standard of the greater of the relevant provisions.

c.  Although most elements of structure in a single storey building may not need fire resistance (see the guidance on requirement B3, paragraph 4.4(a)), fire resistance will be needed if the element:

i. is part of (or supports) an external wall and there is provision in the guidance on requirement B4 to limit the extent of openings and other unprotected areas in the wall; or

ii. is part of (or supports) a compartment wall, including a wall common to two or more buildings, or a wall between a dwellinghouse and an attached or integral garage; or

iii. supports a gallery.

For the purposes of this paragraph, the ground storey of a building which has one or more basement storeys and no upper storeys, may be considered as a single-storey building. The fire resistance of the basement storeys should be that appropriate to basements.

## Table A3 Limitations on fire-protecting suspended ceilings (see Table A1, Note 4)

| Height of building or separated part (m) | Type of floor | Provision for fire resistance of floor (minutes) | Description of suspended ceiling |
|---|---|---|---|

| Less than 18 | Not compartment | 60 or less | Type W, X, Y or Z |
|---|---|---|---|
| | Compartment | less than 60 | |
| | | 60 | Type X, Y or Z |
| 18 or more | any | 60 or less | Type Y or Z |
| No limit | any | More than 60 | Type Z |

**Notes:**

1. Ceiling type and description (the change from Types A-D to Types W-Z is to avoid confusion with Classes A-D (European)):

    W. Surface of ceiling exposed to the cavity should be Class 0 or Class 1 (National) or Class C-s3. d2 or better (European).

    X. Surface of ceiling exposed to the cavity should be Class 0 (National) or Class B-s3, d2 or better (European).

    Y. Surface of ceiling exposed to the cavity should be Class 0 (National) or Class B-s3, d2 or better (European). Ceiling should not contain easily openable access panels.

    Z. Ceiling should be of a material of limited combustibility (National) or of Class A2-s3, d2 or better (European) and not contain easily openable access panels. Any insulation above the ceiling should be of a material of limited combustibility (National) or Class A2-s3, d2 or better (European).

2. Any access panels provided in fire protecting suspended ceilings of type Y or Z should be secured in position by releasing devices or screw fixings, and they should be shown to have been tested in the ceiling assembly in which they are incorporated.

3. The National classifications do not automatically equate with the equivalent European classifications, therefore products cannot typically assume a European class unless they have been tested accordingly.

    When a classification includes 's3, d2', this means that there is no limit set for smoke production and/or flaming droplets/particles.

### Table A4 **Limitations on the use of uninsulated glazed elements on escape routes** (These limitations do not apply to glazed elements which satisfy the relevant insulation criterion, see Table A1)

| Position of glazed element | Maximum total glazed area in parts of a building with access to: | | | |
|---|---|---|---|---|
| | A single stairway | | More than one stairway | |
| | Walls | Door leaf | Walls | Door leaf |
| 1. Within the enclosures of a protected stairway, or within fire-resisting separation shown in Section 2 Diagram 2; | Unlimited above 1100mm from floor or pitch of the stair | Unlimited | Unlimited above 1100mm from floor or pitch of the stair | Unlimited |
| 2. Within fire-resisting separation: i. shown in Section 2 Diagram 4; or ii. described in para 2.13b. | Unlimited above 100mm from floor | Unlimited above 100mm from floor | Unlimited above 100mm from floor | Unlimited above 100mm from floor |
| 3. Existing window between an attached/integral garage and the dwellinghouse. | Unlimited | Not applicable | Unlimited | Not applicable |
| 4. Adjacent to an external escape stair (see para 2.16 and Diagram 7) or roof escape (see para 2.10). | Unlimited | Unlimited | Unlimited | Unlimited |

**Notes:**

1. The 100mm limit is intended to reduce the risk of fire spread from a floor covering.
2. Fire-resisting glass should be marked with the manufacturer and product name.

3.    Good guidance can be found in A guide to beat practice in the specification and use of fire-resistant glazed systems published by the Glass and Glazing Federation.

## Table A5 Notional designations of roof coverings

### Part i: Pitched roofs covered with slates or tiles

| Covering material | Supporting structure | Designation |
|---|---|---|
| 1. Natural slates<br><br>2. Fibre reinforced cement slates<br><br>3. Clay tiles<br><br>4. Concrete tiles | Timber rafters with or without underfelt, sarking, boarding, woodwool slabs, compressed straw slabs, plywood, wood chipboard, or fibre insulating board | AA (National class) or $B_{ROOF}$(t4) (European class) |

**Note:** Although the Table does not include guidance for roofs covered with bitumen felt, it should be noted that there is a wide range of materials on the market and information on specific products is readily available from manufacturers.

### Part ii: Pitched roofs covered with self-supporting sheet

| Roof covering material | Construction | Supporting structure | Designation |
|---|---|---|---|
| 1. Profiled sheet of galvanised steel, aluminium, fibre reinforced cement, or pre-painted (coil coated) steel or aluminium with a pvc or pvf2 coating | Single skin without underlay, or with underlay or plasterboard, fibre insulating board, or woodwool slab | Structure of timber, steel or concrete | AA (National class) or $B_{ROOF}$(t4) (European class) |
| 2. Profiled sheet of galvanised steel, aluminium, fibre reinforced cement, or pre-painted (coil coated) steel or aluminium with a pvc or pvf2 coating | Double skin without interlayer, or with interlayer of resin bonded glass fibre, mineral wool slab, polystyrene, or polyurethane | Structure of timber, steal or concrete | AA (National class) or $B_{ROOF}$(t4) (European class) |

### Part ill. Flat roofs covered with bitumen felt

A flat roof comprising bitumen felt should (irrespective of the felt specification) be deemed to be of designation AA (National class) or $B_{ROOF}$(t4) (European class) if the felt is laid on a deck constructed of 6mm plywood, 12.5mm wood chipboard, 16mm (finished) plain edged timber boarding, compressed straw slab, screeded wood wool slab. profiled fibre reinforced cement or steel deck (single or double skin) with or without fibre insulating board overlay, profiled aluminium deck (single or double skin) with or without fibre insulating board overlay, or concrete or clay pot slab (insitu or pre cast), and has a surface finish of:

a. bitumen-bedded stone chippings covering the whole surface to a depth of at least 12.5mm;

b. bitumen-bedded tiles of a non-combustible material;

c. sand and cement screed; or

d. macadam

## Table A5 Notional designations of roof coverings

**Part iv. Pitched or flat roofs covered with fully supported material**

| Covering material | Supporting structure | Designation |
|---|---|---|
| 1. Aluminium sheet<br><br>2. Copper sheet<br><br>3. Zinc sheet<br><br>4. Lead sheet<br><br>5. Mastic asphalt | timber joists and:<br><br>tongued and grooved boarding, or plain edged boarding | AA* (National class) or $B_{ROOF}(t4)$ (European class) |
| 6. Vitreous enamelled steel<br><br>7. Lead/tin alloy coated steel sheet<br><br>8. Zinc/aluminium alloy coated steel sheet | steel or timber joists with deck of:<br><br>woodwool slabs, compressed straw slab, wood chipboard, fibre insulating board, or 9.5mm plywood | AA (National class) or $B_{ROOF}(t4)$ (European class) |
| 9. Pre-painted (coil coated) steel sheet including liquid-applied pvc coatings | concrete or clay pot slab (insitu or pre-cast) or non-combustible deck of steel, aluminium, or fibre cement (with or without insulation) | AA (National class) or $B_{ROOF}(t4)$ (European class) |

Notes:
* Lead sheet supported by timber joists and plain edged boarding should be regarded as having a BA designation and is deemed to be designated class $C_{ROOF}(t4)$ (European class).

The National classifications do not automatically equate with the equivalent classifications in the European column; therefore, products cannot typically assume a European class unless they have been tested accordingly.

### Table A6 Use and definitions of non-combustible materials

| References in AD B guidance to situations where such materials should be used | Definitions of non-combustible materials | |
|---|---|---|
| | National class | European class |
| 1. Pipes meeting the provisions in the guidance to B3, Table 3.<br><br>2. Flue walls meeting the provisions in the guidance to B3, Diagram 16. | a. Any material which when tested to BS 476-11:1982 does not flame nor cause any rise in temperature on either the centre (specimen) or furnace thermocouples<br><br>b. Totally inorganic materials such as concrete, fired clay, ceramics, metals, plaster and masonry containing not more than 1% by weight or volume of organic material. (Use in buildings of combustible metals such as magnesium/ aluminium alloys should be assessed in each individual case).<br><br>c. Concrete bricks or blocks meeting B8 EN 771-1:2003<br><br>d. Products classified as non-combustible under BS 476-4:1970 | a. Any material classified as class A1 in accordance with BS EN 13501-1:2002 Fire classification of construction products and building elements, Part 1 - Classification using data from reaction to fire tests.<br><br>b. Products made from one or more of the materials considered as Class A1 without the need for testing as defined in Commission Decision 2003/424/EC of 6th June 2003 amending Decision 96/603/EC establishing the list of products belonging to Classes A1 "No contribution to fire" provided for in the Decision 94/611/EC implementing Article 20 of the Council Directive 89/106/EEC on construction products. None of the materials shall contain more than 1 % by weight or volume (whichever is the more onerous) of homogeneously distributed organic material. |

**Note:**

National classifications do not automatically equate with the equivalent classifications in the European column, therefore products cannot typically assume a European class unless they have been tested accordingly.

**Table A7 Use and definitions of materials of limited combustibility**

| References in AD B guidance to situations where such materials should be used | Definitions of materials of limited combustibility | |
|---|---|---|
| | **National class** | **European class** |
| 1. Reinforcement/support for fire-stopping referred to in the guidance to B3. see 7.13.<br><br>2. Roof coverings meeting provisions:<br><br>a. in the guidance to B4, Table 5 or<br><br>b. in the guidance to B4, Diagram 23.<br><br>3. Class 0 materials meeting the provisions in Appendix A, paragraph 13(a).<br><br>4. Ceiling tiles or panels of any fire-protecting suspended ceiling (Type Z) in Table A3. | a. Any non-combustible material listed in Table A6.<br><br>b. Any material of density 300/kg/m² or more, which when tested to BS 476-11:1982. does not flame and the rise in temperature on the furnace thermocouple is not more than 20°C.<br><br>c. Any material with a non-combustible core at least 8mm thick having combustible facings (on one or both sides) not more than 0.5mm thick. (Where a flame spread rating is specified, these materials must also meet the appropriate test requirements). | a. Any material listed in Table A6.<br><br>b. Any material/product classified as Class A2-s3, d2 or better in accordance with BS EN 13501 -1:2002 Fire classification of construction products and bulking elements. Classification using date from reaction to fire tests. |
| 5. Insulation above any fire-protecting suspended ceiling (Type Z) in Table A3. | Any of the materials (a), (b) or (c) above, or:<br><br>d. Any material of density less than 300kg/m³, which when tested to BS 476-11:1982, does not flame for more than 10 seconds and the rise in temperature on the centre (specimen) thermocouple is not more than 35°C and on the furnace thermocouple is not more than 25°C. | Any of the materials/products (a) or (b) above. |

Notes:

1. The National classifications do not automatically equate with the equivalent classifications in the European column, therefore, products cannot typically assume a European class unless they have been tested accordingly.

2. When a classification includes 's3, d21', this means that there is no limit set for smoke production and/or flaming droplets/particles.

## Table A8 Typical performance ratings of some generic materials and products

| Rating | Material or product |
|---|---|
| Class 0 (National) | 1. Any non-combustible material or material of limited combustibility, (composite products listed in Table A7 must meet test requirements given in Appendix A, paragraph 13(b)). |
| | 2. Brickwork, blockwork, concrete and ceramic tiles. |
| | 3. Plasterboard (painted or not with a PVC facing not more than 0.5mm thick) with or without an air gap or fibrous or cellular insulating material behind. |
| | 4. Woodwool cement slabs. |
| | 5. Mineral fibre tiles or sheets with cement or resin binding. |
| Class 3 (National) | 6. Timber or plywood with a density more than 400kg/m$^3$, painted or unpainted. |
| | 7. Wood particle board or hardboard, either untreated or painted. |
| | 8. Standard glass reinforced polyesters. |
| Class A1 (European) | 9. Any material that achieves this class or is defined as 'classified without further test' in a published Commission Decision. |
| Class A2-s3, d2 (European) | 10. Any material that achieves this class or is defined as 'classified without further test' in a published Commission Decision. |
| Class B-s3, d2 (European) | 11. Any material that achieves this class or is defined as 'classified without further test' in a published Commission Decision. |
| Class C-s3, d2 (European) | 12. Any material that achieves this class or is defined as 'classified without further test' in a published Commission Decision. |
| Class D-s3, d2 (European) | 13. Any material that achieves this class or is defined as 'classified without further test' in a published Commission Decision. |

**Notes** (National):
1. Materials and products listed under Class 0 also meet Class 1.
2. Timber products listed under Class 3 can be brought up to Class 1 with appropriate proprietary treatments.
3. The following materials and products may achieve the ratings listed below. However, as the properties of different products with the same generic description vary, the ratings of these materials/products should be substantiated by test evidence.
   Class 0 - aluminium faced fibre insulating board, flame retardant decorative laminates on a calcium silicate board, thick polycarbonate sheet, phenolic sheet and UPVC.
   Class 1 - phenolic or melamine laminates on a calcium silicate substrate and flame-retardant decorative laminates on a combustible substrate.

**Notes** (European):
For the purposes of the Building Regulations:
1. Materials and products listed under Class A1 also meet Classes A2-s3. d2, B-s3, d2, C-s3, d2 and D-s3. d2.
2. Materials and products listed under Class A2-s3, d2 also meet Classes B-s3, d2. C-s3. d2 and D-s3, d2.
3. Materials and products listed under Class B-s3, d2 also meet Classes C-s3, d2 and D-s3, d2.
4. Materials and products listed under Class C-s3. d2 also meet Class D-s3, d2.
5. The performance of timber products listed under Class D-s3, d2 can be improved with appropriate proprietary treatments.
6. Materials covered by the CWFT process (classification without further testing) can be found by accessing the European Commission's website via the link on the CLG website www.communities.gov.uk
7. The national classifications do not automatically equate with the equivalent classifications in the European column, therefore products cannot typically assume a European class unless they have boon tested accordingly.
8. When a classification includes 's3, d2', that means that there to no limit sot for smoke production and/or flaming droplets/ particles.

# Appendix B: Fire doors

1.  All fire doors should have the appropriate performance given in Table B1 either:

a.  by their performance under test to BS 476- 22:1987 *Fire tests on building materials and structures – Methods for determination of the fire resistance of non-loadbearing elements of construction,* in terms of integrity for a period of minutes, e.g. FD30. A suffix (S) is added for doors where restricted smoke leakage at ambient temperatures is needed; or

b.  as determined with reference to Commission Decision 2000/367/EC of 3 May 2000 implementing Council Directive 89/106/EEC as regards the classification of the resistance to fire performance of construction products, construction works and parts thereof. All fire doors should be classified in accordance with BS EN 13501-2:2003 *Fire classification of construction products and building elements. Classification using data from fire resistance tests, excluding ventilation services.*

They are tested to the relevant European method from the following:

BS EN 1634-1:2000 Fire resistance tests for door and shutter assemblies – Fire doors and shutters;

BS EN 1634-2:xxxx Fire resistance tests for door and shutter assemblies – Fire door hardware;

BS EN 1634-3:2001 Fire resistance tests for door and shutter assemblies – Smoke control doors.

The performance requirement is in terms of integrity (E) for a period of minutes. An additional classification of $S_a$ is used for all doors where restricted smoke leakage at ambient temperatures is needed.

The requirement (in either case) is for test exposure from each side of the door separately, except in the case of lift doors which are tested from the landing side only.

Any test evidence used to substantiate the fire resistance rating of a door or shutter should be carefully checked to ensure that it adequately demonstrates compliance that is applicable to the complete installed assembly. Small differences in detail (such as glazing apertures, intumescent strips, door frames and ironmongery etc.) may significantly affect the rating.

**Note 1:** The designation of xxxx is used for standards that are not yet published. The latest version of any standard may be used provided that it continues to address the relevant requirements of the Regulations.

**Note 2:** Until such time that the relevant harmonised product standards are published, for the purposes of meeting the Building Regulations, products tested in accordance with BS EN 1634-1:2000 (with or without pre firetest mechanical conditioning) will be deemed to have satisfied the provisions provided that they achieve the minimum fire resistance in terms of integrity, as detailed in Table B1.

2.  Fire doors serving an attached or integral garage should be fitted with a self-closing device.

3.  Unless shown to be satisfactory when tested as part of a fire door assembly, the essential components of any hinge on which a fire door is hung should be made entirely from materials having a melting point of at least 800°C.

4.  Tables A1 and A2 set out the minimum periods of fire resistance for the elements of structure to which performance of some doors is linked. Table A4 sets out limitations on the use of uninsulated glazing in fire doors.

5.  BS 8214:1990 gives recommendations for the specification, design, construction, installation and maintenance of fire doors constructed with non-metallic door leaves.

Guidance on timber fire-resisting door-sets, in relation to the new European test standard, may be found in *Timber fire-resisting doorsets: maintaining performance under the new European test standard* published by TRADA (Timber Research and Development Association).

Guidance for metal doors is given in *Code of practice for fire-resisting metal doorsets* published by the DSMA poor and Shutter Manufacturers' Association) in 1999.

6.  Hardware used on fine doors can significantly affect performance in fire. Notwithstanding the guidance in this Approved Document guidance is available in *Hardware for fire and escape doors* published by the Builders' Hardware Industry Federation.

### Table B1 **Provision for fire doors**

| Position of door | Minimum fire resistance of door in terms of integrity (minutes) when tested to BS 476-22:1987 [1] | Minimum fire resistance of door in terms of integrity (minutes) when tested to the relevant European standard [3] |
| --- | --- | --- |
| 1. Any door: | | |
| a. within a cavity barrier | FD 30 | E30 |
| b. between a dwellinghouse and a garage | FD 30Sa [2] | E30Sa [2] |
| c. forming part of the enclosures to a protected stairway in a single family dwellinghouse | FD 20 | E20 |
| d. within any other fire-resisting construction in a dwellinghouse not described elsewhere in this table | FD 20 | E20 |

**Notes:**

1. To BS 476-22:1987 (or BS 476-8:1972 subject to paragraph 5 in Appendix A).
2. Unless pressurization techniques complying with BS EN 12101 -6:2005 *Code of practice for smoke control using pressure differentials* are used, these doors should also either
   (a) have a leakage rate not exceeding 3m³/m/bour (head and Jambs only) when tested at 25 Pa under BS 476 *Fire tests on building materials and structures. Section 31.1 Methods for measuring smoke penetration through doorsets and shutter assemblies, Method of measurement under ambient temperature conditions'*, or
   (b) meet the additional classification requirement of Sa when tested to BS EN 1634-3:2001 *Fire resistance tests for door and shutter assemblies, Part 3-Smoke control doors.*
3. The National classifications do not automatically equate with the equivalent classifications in the European column, therefore products cannot typically assume a European class unless they have been tested accordingly.

## Appendix C: Methods of measurement

**1.** Some form of measurement is an integral part of many of the provisions in this document. Diagram C1 shows how the height of the top storey should be measured.

### Diagram C1 **Height of top storey in building**

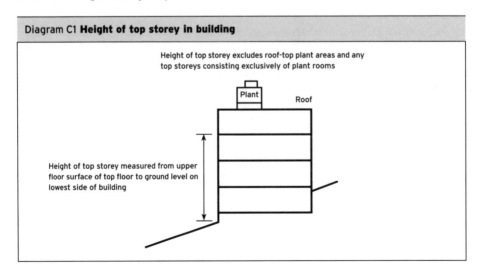

Height of top storey excludes roof-top plant areas and any top storeys consisting exclusively of plant rooms

Plant

Roof

Height of top storey measured from upper floor surface of top floor to ground level on lowest side of building

# Appendix D: Purpose groups

**1.**    Many of the provisions in this document are related to the use of the building. The use classifications are termed purpose groups and represent different levels of hazard. They can apply to a whole building, or (where a building is compartmented) to a compartment in the building, and the relevant purpose group should be taken from the main use of the building or compartment.

**2.**    Table D1 sets out the purpose group classification.

**Note:** This is only of relevance to this Approved Document.

**Table D1 Classification of Purpose Groups**

| Title | Group | Purpose for which the building or compartment of a building is intended to be used |
|-------|-------|------------------------------------------------------------------------------------|
| Residential (dwellings) | 1(a)* | Flat. |
| | 1(b)† | Dwellinghouse which contains a habitable storey with a floor level which is more than 4.5m above ground level. |
| | 1(c)+ | Dwellinghouse which does not contain a habitable storey with a floor level which is more than 4.5m above ground level. |
| Residential (Institutional) | 2(a) | Hospital, home, school or other similar living accommodation for, or for the treatment, care or maintenance of persons suffering from disabilities due to illness or old age or other physical or mental incapacity, or under the age of 5 years, or place of lawful detention, where such persons sleep on the premises. |
| (Other) | 2(b) | Hotel, boarding house, residential cottage, hall of residence, hostel, and any other residential purpose not described above. |
| Office | 3 | Offices or premises used for the purpose of administration, clerical work (including writing, book keeping, sorting papers, filing, typing, duplicating, machine calculating, drawing and the editorial preparation of matter for publication, police and fire and rescue service work), handling money (including banking and building society work), and communications (including postal, telegraph and redo communications) or radio, television, film, audio or video recording, or performance (not open to the public) and their control. |
| Shop and commercial | 4 | Shops or premises used for a retail trade or business (including the sale to members of the public of food or drink for immediate consumption and retail by auction, self-selection and over-the-counter wholesale trading, the business of lending books or periodicals for gain and the business of a banker or hairdresser and the rental of storage space to the public) and premises to which the public is invited to deliver or collect goods in connection with their hire repair or other treatment, or (except in the case of repair of motor vehicles) where they themselves may carry out such repairs or other treatments. |

## Table D1 Classification of Purpose Groups

| Title | Group | Purpose for which the building or compartment of a building is intended to be used |
|---|---|---|
| Assembly and recreation | 5 | Place of assembly, entertainment or recreation; including bingo halls, broadcasting, recording and film studios open to the public, casinos, dance halls; entertainment, conference, exhibition and leisure centres; funfairs and amusement arcades; museums and art galleries; non-residential clubs, theatres, cinemas and concert halls; educational establishments, dancing schools, gymnasia, swimming pool buildings, riding schools, skating rinks, sports pavilions, sports stadia; law courts; churches and other buildings of worship, crematoria; libraries open to the public, non-residential day centres, clinics, health centres and surgeries; passenger stations and termini for air, rail, road or sea travel; public toilets; zoos and menageries. |
| Industrial | 6 | Factories and other premises used for manufacturing, altering, repairing, cleaning, washing, breaking-up, adapting or processing any article; generating power or slaughtering livestock. |
| Storage and other nonresidential + | 7(a) | Place for the storage or deposit of goods or materials (other than described under 7(b)) and any building not within any of the Purpose Groups 1 to 6. |
| | 7(b) | Car parks designed to admit and accommodate only cars, motorcycles and passenger or light goods vehicles weighing no more than 2500kg gross. |

**Notes:**

This table only apply to Part B.

* Includes live/work units that meet the provisions of paragraph 2.52 of Volume 2.

† Includes any surgeries, consulting rooms, offices or other accommodation, not exceeding 50m$^2$ in total, forming part of a dwelling and used by an occupant of the dwelling in a professional or business capacity.

+ A detached garage not more than 40m$^2$ in area is included in Purpose Group 1(c); as in a detached open carport of not more than 40m$^2$, or a detached building which consists of a garage and open carport where neither the garage nor open carport exceeds 40m$^2$ in area.

# Appendix E: Definitions

**Note:** Except for the items marked * (which are from the Building Regulations), these definitions apply only to Part B.

**Access room** A room through which the only escape route from an inner room passes.

**Accommodation stair** A stair, additional to that or those required for escape purposes, provided for the convenience of occupants.

**Alternative escape routes** Escape routes sufficiently separated by either direction and space, or by fire-resisting construction, to ensure that one is still available should the other be affected by fire- Note: A second stair, balcony or flat roof which enables a person to reach a place free from danger from fire, is considered an alternative escape route for the purposes of a dwelling house.

**Alternative exit** One of two or more exits, each of which is separate from the other.

**Appliance ventilation duct** A duct provided to convey combustion air to a gas appliance.

**Automatic release mechanism** A device which will allow a door held open by it to close automatically in the event of each or any one of the following:

a.    detection of smoke by automatic apparatus suitable in nature, quality and location;

b.    operation of a hand-operated switch fitted in a suitable position;

c.    failure of electricity supply to the device, apparatus or switch;

d.    operation of the fire alarm system if any.

**Basement storey** A storey with a floor which at some point is more than 1200mm below the highest level of ground adjacent to the outside walls.

**Boundary** The boundary of the land belonging to the building, or where the land abuts a road, railway, canal or river, the centre line of that road, railway, canal or river (See Diagram 17.)

**\* Building** Any permanent or temporary building but not any other kind of structure or erection. A reference to a building includes a reference to part of a building.

**Building Control Body** A term used to include both Local Authority Building Control and Approved Inspectors.

**Cavity barrier** A construction, other than a smoke curtain, provided to close a concealed space against penetration of smoke or flame, or provided to restrict the movement of smoke or flame within such a space.

**Ceiling** A part of a building which encloses and is exposed overhead in a room, protected shaft or circulation space. (The soffit of a rooflight is included as part of the surface of the ceiling, but not the frame. An upstand below a rooflight would be considered as a wall.)

**Circulation space** A space (including a protected stairway) mainly used as a means of access between a room and an exit from the building or compartment.

**Class 0** A product performance classification for wall and ceiling linings. The relevant test criteria are set out in Appendix A, paragraph 13.

**Compartment (fire)** A building or part of a building, comprising one or more rooms, spaces or storeys, constructed to prevent the spread of fire to or from another part of the same building, or an adjoining building. (A roof space above the top storey of a compartment is included in that compartment.) (See also 'Separated part'.)

**Compartment wall or floor** A fire-resisting wall/floor used in the separation of one fire compartment from another. (Constructional provisions are given in Section 5.)

**Concealed space or cavity** A space enclosed by elements of a building (including a suspended ceiling) or contained within an element, but not a room, cupboard, circulation space, protected shaft or space within a flue, chute, duct, pipe or conduit.

**Dead end** Area from which escape is possible in one direction only.

**Direct distance** The shortest distance from any point within the floor area, measured within the external enclosures of the building, to the nearest storey exit ignoring walls, partitions and fittings, other than the enclosing walls/ partitions to protected stairways.

**Dwellinghouse** A unit of residential accommodation occupied (whether or not as a sole or main residence):

a.    by a single person or by people living together as a family

b.    by not more than six residents living together as a single household, including a household where care is provided for residents. (See also paragraphs 0.22 and 0.23.)

**\* Dwellinghouse** does not include a flat or a building containing a flat.

### Element of structure:

a.    a member forming part of the structural frame of a building or any other beam or column;

b.    a load bearing wall or loadbearing part of a wall;

c.    a floor;

d.    a gallery (but not a loading gallery, fly gallery, stage grid, lighting bridge, or any gallery provided for similar purposes or for maintenance and repair);

e.    an external wall;

f.    a compartment wall (including a wall common to two or more buildings). (However, see the guidance to B3, paragraph 4.4, for exclusions from the provisions for elements of structure.)

**Escape lighting** That part of the emergency lighting which is provided to ensure that the escape route is illuminated at all material times.

**Escape route** Route forming that part of the means of escape from any point in a building to a final exit.

**European Technical Approval** A favourable technical assessment of the fitness for use of a construction product for an intended use, issued for the purposes of the Construction Products Directive by a body authorised by a Member State to issue European Technical Approvals for those purposes and notified by that Member State to the European Commission.

**European Technical Approvals issuing body** A body notified under Article 10 of the Construction Products Directive. The details of these institutions are published in the 'C' series of the Official Journal of the European Communities.

**Evacuation lift** A lift that may be used for the evacuation of people in a fire.

**Exit passageway** A protected passageway connecting a protected stairway to a final exit (exit passageways should be protected to the same standard as the stairway that they serve).

**External wall (or side of a building)** Includes a part of a roof pitched at an angle of more than 70° to the horizontal, if that part of the roof adjoins a space within the building to which persons have access (but not access only for repair or maintenance).

**Final exit** The termination of an escape route from a building giving direct access to a street, passageway, walkway or open space, and sited to ensure the rapid dispersal of persons from the vicinity of a building so that they are no longer in danger from fire and/or smoke.

**Note:** Windows are not acceptable as final exits.

**Fire door** A door or shutter, provided for the passage of persons, air or objects, which together with its frame and furniture as installed in a building, is intended (when closed) to resist the passage of fire and/or gaseous products of combustion, and is capable of meeting specified performance criteria to those ends. (It may have one or more leaves, and the term includes a cover or other form of protection to an opening in a fire-resisting wall or floor, or in a structure surrounding a protected shaft.)

**Fire-resisting (fire resistance)** The ability of a component or construction of a building to satisfy, for a stated period of time, some or all of the appropriate criteria specified in the relevant part of BS 476.

**Fire-separating element** A compartment wall, compartment floor, cavity barrier and construction enclosing a protected escape route and/or a place of special fire hazard.

**Fire stop** A seal provided to close an imperfection of fit or design tolerance between elements or components, to restrict the passage of fire and smoke.

**\* Flat** A separate and self-contained premises constructed or adapted for use for residential purposes and forming part of a building from some other part of which it is divided horizontally.

**Gallery** A raised area or platform around the sides or at the back of a room which provides extra space.

**Habitable room** A room used, or intended to be used, for dwellinghouse purposes (including; for the purposes of Part B, a kitchen, but not a bathroom).

**Height (of a building or storey for the purposes of Part B)** Height of the top storey above ground is measured as shown in Appendix C, Diagram C1.

**Inner room** Room from which escape is possible only by passing through another room (the access room).

**Material of limited combustibility** A material performance specification that includes non-combustible materials, and for which the relevant test criteria are set out in Appendix A, paragraph 9.

**Means of escape** Structural means whereby [in the event of fire] a safe route or routes is or are provided for persons to travel from any point in a building to a place of safety.

**Non-combustible material** The highest level of reaction to fire performance. The relevant test criteria are set out in Appendix A, paragraph 8.

**Notional boundary** A boundary presumed to exist between buildings on the same site (see Section 9, Diagram 18).

**Occupancy type** A purpose group identified in Appendix D.

**Pipe (for the purposes of Section 7)** Includes pipe fittings and accessories; and excludes a flue pipe and a pipe used for ventilating purposes (other than a ventilating pipe for an above around drainage system).

**Places of special fire hazard** Oil-filled transformer and switch gear rooms, boiler rooms, storage space for fuel or other highly flammable substances, and rooms housing a fixed internal combustion engine.

**Protected circuit** An electrical circuit protected against fire.

**Protected stairway** A stair discharging through a final exit to a place of safety (including any exit passageway between the foot of the stair and the final exit) that is adequately enclosed with fire-resisting construction.

**Purpose group** A classification of a building according to the purpose to which it is intended to be put. See Appendix D, Table D1.

**Relevant boundary** The boundary which the side of the building faces, (and/or coincides with) and which is parallel, or at an angle of not more than 80°, to the side of the building (see Section 9 Diagram 17). A notional boundary can be a relevant boundary.

**Rooflight** A dome light, lantern light, skylight, ridge light, glazed barrel vault or other element intended to admit daylight through a roof.

**Room (for the purposes of B2)** An enclosed space within a building that is not used solely as a circulation space. (The term includes not only conventional rooms, but also walk-in cupboards that are not fittings, and large spaces such as warehouses and auditoria. The term does not include voids such as ducts, ceiling voids and roof spaces.)

**Sheltered housing** includes:

a.    two or more dwellings in the same building;

b.    two or more dwellings on adjacent sites

where those dwellings are, in each case, designed and constructed for the purpose of providing residential accommodation for vulnerable or elderly people who receive, or who are to receive, a support service.

**Single-storey building** A building consisting of a ground storey only. (A separated part which consists of a ground storey only, with a roof to which access is only provided for repair or maintenance, may be treated as a single storey building.) Basements are not included in counting the number of storeys in a building.

**Site (of a building)** The land occupied by the building, up to the boundaries with land in other ownership.

**Smoke alarm** A device containing within one housing all the components, except possibly the energy source, necessary for detecting smoke and giving an audible alarm.

**Self-closing device** A device which is capable of closing the door from any angle and against any latch fitted to the door.

**Storey** includes:

a.    any gallery if its area is more than half that of the space into which it projects; and

b.    a roof, unless it is accessible only for maintenance and repair.

**Storey exit** A final exit, or a doorway giving direct access into a protected stairway, firefighting lobby or external escape route.

**Suspended ceiling (fire-protecting)** A ceiling suspended below a floor, which contributes to the fire resistance of the floor. Appendix A, Table A3, classifies different types of suspended ceiling.

**Technical specification** A standard or a European Technical Approval Guide. It is the document against which compliance can be shown in the case of a standard and against which an assessment is made to deliver the European Technical Approval.

**Thermoplastic material** See Appendix A, paragraph 17.

**Unprotected area** In relation to a side or external wall of a building means:

a.    window, door or other opening, and

   **Note:** Windows that are not openable and are designed and glazed to provide the necessary level of fire resistance need not be regarded as an unprotected area.

b.    any part of the external wall which has less than the relevant fire resistance set out in Section 8.

c.    any part of the external wall which has combustible material more than 1mm thick attached or applied to its external face, whether for cladding or any other purpose. Combustible material in this context is any material which does not have a Class 0 rating.

# Appendix F: Standards and other publications referred to

## Standards

DD 252:2002

Components for residential sprinkler systems. Specification and test methods for residential sprinklers

BS EN ISO 306:2004

Plastics. Thermoplastic materials. Determination of Vicat softening temperature (VST)

BS 476-3:2004

Fire tests on building materials and structures. Classification and method of test for external fire exposure to roofs

BS 476-4:1970

Fire tests on building materials and structures. Non-combustibility test for materials

BS 476-6:1989

Fire tests on building materials and structures. Method of test for fire propagation for products

BS 476-7:1997

Fire tests on building materials and structures. Method of test to determine the classification of the surface spread of flame of products

BS 476-8:1972

Fire tests on building materials and structures. Test methods and criteria for the fire resistance of elements of building construction (Withdrawn)

BS 476-11:1982

Fire tests on building materials and structures. Method for assessing the heat emission from building materials

BS 476-20:1987

Fire tests on building materials and structures. Method for determination of the fire resistance of elements of construction (general principles)

BS 476-21:1987

Fire tests on building materials and structures. Methods for determination of the fire resistance of loadbearing elements of construction

BS 476-22:1987

Fire tests on building materials and structures. Methods for determination of the fire resistance of non-loadbearing elements of construction

BS 476-23:1987

Fire tests on building materials and structures. Methods for determination of the contribution of components to the fire resistance of a structure

BS 476-24:1987

Fire tests on building materials and structures. Method for determination of the fire resistance of ventilation ducts

BS EN 771-1:2003

Specification for masonry units. Clay masonry units

BS EN ISO 1182:2002

Reaction to fire tests for building products. Non-combustibility test

DDENV 1187:2002

Test methods for external fire exposure to roofs

BS EN ISO 1716:2002

Reaction to fire tests for building products. Determination of the heat of combustion

BS 5438:1989

Methods of test for flammability of textile fabrics when subjected to a small igniting flame applied to the face or bottom edge of vertically oriented specimens

**BS 5446-1:2000**

Fire detection and fire alarm devices for dwellings. Specification for smoke alarms

**BS 5446-2:2003**

Fire detection and fire alarm devices for dwellings. Specification for heat alarms

**BS 5839-1:2002**

Fire detection and fire alarm systems for buildings. Code of practice for system design, installation, commissioning and maintenance

**BS 5839-6:2004**

Fire detection and fire alarm systems for buildings. Code of practice for the design, installation and maintenance of fire detection and fire alarm systems in dwellings

**BS 5867-2:1980**

Specification for fabrics for curtains and drapes. Flammability requirements

**BS 7974:2001**

Application of fire safety engineering principles to the design of buildings. Code of practice

**BS 9251:2005**

Sprinkler systems for residential and domestic occupancies. Code of practice

**BS 8214:1990**

Code of practice for fire door assemblies with non-metallic leaves

**BS EN 1364-1:1999**

Fire resistance tests for non-loadbearing elements. Walls

**BSEN 1364-2:1999**

Fire resistance tests for non-loadbearing elements. Ceilings

**BSEN 1365-1:1999**

Fire resistance tests for loadbearing elements. Walls

**BS EN 1365-2:2000**

Fire resistance tests for loadbearing elements. Floors and roofs

**BS EN 1365-3:2000**

Fire resistance tests for loadbearing elements. Beams

**BS EN 1365-4:1999**

Pre resistance tests for loadbearing elements. Columns

**BS EN 1366-1:1999**

Rre resistance tests for service installations. Ducts

**BS EN 1366-2:1999**

Fire resistance tests for service installations. Fire dampers

**BS EN 1366-3:2004**

Fire resistance tests for service installations. Penetration seals

**BS EN 1366-4:2006**

Fire resistance tests for service installations. Linear joint seals

**BS EN 1366-5:2003**

Fire resistance tests for service installations. Service ducts and shafts

**BS EN 1366-6:2004**

Fire resistance tests for service installations. Raised access and hollow core floors

**BS EN 1634-1:2000**

Fire resistance tests for door and shutter assemblies. Fire doors and shutters

**BS EN 1634-3:2001**

Rre resistance tests for door and shutter assemblies. Smoke control doors and shutters

**BSENISO 11925-2:2002**

Reaction to fire tests. Ignitability of building products subjected to direct impingement of flame. Single-flame source test

**BSEN 13238:2001**

Reaction to fire tests for building products. Conditioning procedures and general rules for selection of substrates

**BSEN 13501-1:2002**

Fire classification of construction products and building elements. Classification using test data from reaction to fire tests

**BSEN 13501-2:2003**

Fire classification of construction products and building elements. Classification using data from fire resistance tests, excluding ventilation services

**BSEN 13501-3:2005**

Fire classification of construction products and building elements. Classification using data from fire resistance tests on products and elements used in building service installations: fire resisting ducts and fire dampers

**BSEN 13501-5:2005**

Fire classification of construction products and building elements. Classification using data from external fire exposure to roof tests

**BS EN 13823:2002**

Reaction to fire tests for building products. Building products excluding floorings exposed to thermal attack by a single burning item

## Publications
### Legislation

Disability Discrimination Act 1995

Education Act 1996

Pipelines Safety Regulations 1996, Sl 1996 No 825 and the Gas Safety (Installation and Use) Regulations 1998 Sl 1998 No 2451

Electromagnetic Compatibility Regulations 1992 (SI 1992 No 2372)

Electromagnetic Compatibility (Amendment) Regulations 1994 (Sl 1994 No 3080)

Electrical Equipment (Safety) Regulations 1994 (Sl 1994 No 3260)

Commission Decision 2000/553/EC of 6th September 2000 implementing Council Directive 89/106/EEC

(European tests) Commission Decision 2000/367/ EC of 3rd May 2000 implementing Council Directive 89/106/EEC

Commission Decision 2001/671/EC of 21 August 2001 implementing Council Directive 89/106/EC as regards the classification of the external fire performance of roofs and roof coverings

Commission Decision 2005/823/EC of 22 November 2005 amending Decision 2001/671/EC regarding the classification of the external fire performance of roofs and roof coverings

Commission Decision 2000/147/EC of 8th February 2000 implementing Council Directive 89/106/EEC

Commission Decision 2000/367/EC of 3rd May 2000 implementing Council Directive 89/106/EEC

Commission Decision 96/603/EC of 4th October 1996

94/61 1/EC implementing Article 20 of the Council Directive 89/106/EEC on construction products

Construction Products Regulations 1991 (SI 1991 No 1620)

Construction Product (Amendment) Regulations 1994 (SI 1994 No 3051)

The Workplace (Health, Safety and Welfare) Regulations 1992

Health and Safety (Safety signs and signals) Regulations 1996

### Association for Specialist Fire Protection (ASFP)

ASFP Red book – Fire stopping and penetration seals for the construction industry 2nd Edition
ISBN:1 87040 923 X

ASFP Yellow book- Fire protection or structural steel in buildings 4th Edition
ISBN: 1 87040 925 6

ASFP Grey book – Fire and smoke resisting dampers

ISBN: 1 87040 924 8

ASFP Blue book – Fire resisting ductwork 2nd Edition

ISBN: 1 87040 926 4

www.asfp.org.uk

### The British Automatic Sprinkler Association (BAFSA)

Sprinklers for Safety: Use and Benefits of Incorporating Sprinklers in Buildings and Structures, (2006)

ISBN: 0 95526280 1

www.bafsa.org.uk

### Building Research Establishment Limited (BRE)

BRE Digest 208 increasing the fire resistance of existing timber floors 1988

ISBN: 978 1 86081 359 7

BRE report (BR 368) Design methodologies for smoke and heat exhaust ventilation 1999

ISBN: 978 1 86081 289 7

BRE report (BR 274) Fire safety of PTFE-based materials used in buildings 1994

ISBN: 978 1 86081 653 6

BRE report (BR 135) Fire performance of external thermal insulation for walls of multi-storey buildings 2003

ISBN: 978 1 86081 622 2

BRE report (BR 187) External fire spread: Building separation and boundary distances 1991

ISBN: 978 1 86081 465 5

BRE report (BR128) Guidelines for the construction of fire resisting structural elements 1988

ISBN: 085125 293 1

BRE 454 Multi-storey timber frame buildings – a design guide 2003

ISBN: 1 86081 605 3

www.bre.co.uk

### Builders Hardware Industry Federation

Hardware for Fire and Escape Doors 2006

ISBN: 095216 422 1

www.firecode.org.uk

### Department for Communities and Local Government

Regulatory Reform (Fire Safety) Order 2005

ISBN: 011072 945 5

Fire safety in adult placements: a code of practice

www.communities.gov.uk

### Department for Education and Skills

Building Bulletin (BB) 100

www.dfes.gov.uk

### Department of Health

HTM 05 – 02 Guidance in support of functional provisions for healthcare premises

www.dh.gov.uk

### Door and Shutter Manufacturers' Association (DSMA)

Code of practice for fire-resisting metal doorsets 1999

www.dhfonline.org.uk

### Environment Agency

Pollution Prevention Guidelines (PPG18) Managing Fire Water and Major Spillages

www.environment-agency.gov.uk

**Football Licensing Authority**

Concourses

ISBN: 0 95462 932 9

www.flaweb.org.uk/home.php

**Fire Protection Association (FPA)**

Design guide

www.thefpa.co.uk

**Glass and Glazing Federation (GGF)**

A guide to best practice in the specification and use of fire-resistant glazed systems

www.ggf.org.uk

**Health and Safety Executive (HSE)**

Workplace health, safety and welfare, The Workplace (Health, Safety and Welfare) Regulations 1992, Approved Code of Practice and Guidance; The Health and Safety Commission, L24; published by HMSO 1992;

ISBN: 011886 333 9

www.hse.gov.uk

**International Association of Cold Storage Contractors (IACSC)**

Design, construction, specification and fire management of insulated envelopes for temperature controlled environments 1999

www.iarw.org/iacsc/european_division

**Passive Fire Protection Federation**

Ensuring best practice for passive fire protection in buildings

ISBN. 1 87040 919 1

www.pfpf.org

**Steel Construction Institute (SCI)**

SC/ P197 Designing for structural fire safety: A handbook for architects and engineers 1999

ISBN: 1 85942 074 5

SC/ Publication 288 Fire safe design: A new approach to multi-storey steel-framed buildings (Second Edition) 2000

ISBN: 1 85942 169 5

SC/ Publication P313 Single storey steel framed buildings in fire boundary conditions 2002

ISBN:1 85942 135 0

www.steel-sci.org

**Timber Research and Development Associations (TRADA)**

Timber Fire-Resisting Doorsets: maintaining performance under the new European test standard

ISBN: 1 90051 035 9

www.trada.co.uk

The Building Regulations 2000

# VENTILATION
## APPROVED DOCUMENT

MEANS OF VENTILATION

Came into effect April 2007

## USE OF GUIDANCE

The Approved Documents Limitation on requirements Materials and workmanship

The workplace (health, safety and welfare) Regulations 1992

Mixed use development

### Means of ventilation - The Requirement F1

#### Section 0: General guidance

Performance

Introduction to the provisions

#### Section 1: Dwellings

Introduction to provisions

Ventilation rates

Ventilation systems for dwellings without basements

Ventilation systems for basements

Ventilation of habitable rooms through another room or a conservatory

#### Section 2: Buildings other than dwellings

General

Access for maintenance

Commissioning

Offices

Introduction to provisions

Ventilation rates

Natural ventilation of rooms

Mechanical ventilation of rooms

Alternative approaches

Ventilation of other types of buildings

Ventilation of car parks

Alternative approaches for ventilation of car parks

#### Section 3: Work on existing buildings

General

Addition of a habitable room (not including a conservatory) to   an existing building

Addition of a wet room to an existing building

Addition of a conservatory to an existing building

Historic buildings

#### Section 4: Standards and publications

Standards referred to

Other publications referred to

#### Glossary

#### Appendix A: Performance-based ventilation

#### Appendix B: Purge ventilation

#### Appendix C: Example calculations for ventilation sizing for dwellings

#### Appendix D: Passive stack ventilation system design and installation guidance

#### Appendix E: Good practice guide to the installation of fans for dwellings

#### Appendix F: Minimising ingress of external pollution into buildings in urban areas1

# Use of guidance

## THE APPROVED DOCUMENTS

This document is one of a series that has been approved and issued by the Secretary of State for the purpose of providing practical guidance with respect to the technical requirements of the Building Regulations 2000 for England and Wales.

At the back of this document is a list of all the documents that have been approved and issued by the Secretary of State for this purpose.

Approved Documents are intended to provide guidance for some of the more common building situations. However, there may well be alternative ways of achieving compliance with the requirements. Thus there is no obligation to adopt any particular solution contained in an Approved Document if you prefer to meet the relevant requirement in some other way.

### Other requirements

The guidance contained in an Approved Document relates only to the particular requirements of the Regulations which the document addresses. The building work will also have to comply with the requirements of any other relevant paragraphs in Schedule 1 to the Regulations.

There are Approved Documents which give guidance on each of the parts of Schedule 1 and on Regulation 7.

## LIMITATION ON REQUIREMENTS

In accordance with Regulation 8, the requirements in Parts A to D, F to K and N (except for paragraphs H2 and J6) of Schedule 1 to the Building Regulations do not require anything to be done except for the purpose of securing reasonable standards of health and safety for persons in or about buildings (and any others who may be affected by buildings or matters connected with buildings). This is one of the categories of purpose for which Building Regulations may be made.

Paragraphs H2 and J6 are excluded from Regulation 8 because they deal directly with prevention of the contamination of water. Parts E and M (which deal, respectively, with resistance to the passage of sound, and access to and use of buildings) are excluded from Regulation 8 because they address the welfare and convenience of building users. Part L is excluded from Regulation 8 because it addresses the conservation of fuel and power. All these matters are amongst the purposes, other than health and safety that may be addressed by Building Regulations.

## MATERIALS AND WORKMANSHIP

Any building work which is subject to the requirements imposed by Schedule 1 to the Building Regulations should, in accordance with Regulation 7, be carried out with proper materials and in a workmanlike manner.

You may show that you have complied with Regulation 7 in a number of ways. These include the appropriate use of a product bearing CE marking in accordance with the Construction Products Directive (89/106/EEC)[1]. the Low Voltage Directive (73/23/EEC and amendment 93/68 EEC)[2] and the EMC Directive (89/336/ EEC)[3] as amended by the CE Marking Directive (93/68/EEC)[4] or a product complying with an appropriate technical specification (as defined in those Directives), a British Standard, or an alternative national technical specification of any state which is a contracting party to the European Economic Area which, in use, is equivalent, or a product covered by a national or European certificate issued by a European Technical Approval issuing body, and the conditions of use are in accordance with the terms of the certificate. You will find further guidance in the Approved Document supporting Regulation 7 on materials and workmanship.

---

[1] As Implemented by the Construction Products Regulations 1991 (SI 1991/1620).

[2] As Implemented by the Electrical Equipment (Safety Regulations 1994 (SI 1994/3260).

[3] As Implemented by the Electromagnetic Compatibility Regulations 1992 (SI 1992/2372).

[4] As Implemented by the Construction Products (Amendment) Regulations 1994 (SI 1994/3051) and the Electromagnetic Compatibility (Amendment) Regulations 1994 (811994/3080).

### Independent certification schemes

There are many UK product certification schemes. Such schemes certify compliance with the requirements of a recognised document which is appropriate to the purpose for which the material is to be used. Materials which are not so certified may still conform to a relevant standard.

Many certification bodies which approve such schemes are accredited by UKAS.

### Technical specifications

Building Regulations are made for specific purposes: health and safety, energy conservation and the welfare and convenience of disabled people. Standards and technical approvals are relevant guidance to the extent that they relate to these considerations. However, they may also address other aspects of performance such as serviceability, or aspects which although they relate to health and safety are not covered by the Regulations.

When an Approved Document makes reference to a named standard, the relevant version of the standard is the one listed at the end of the publication. However, if this version has been revised or updated by the issuing standards body, the new version may be used as a source of guidance provided it continues to address the relevant requirements of the Regulations.

The appropriate use of a product which complies with a European Technical Approval as defined in the Construction Products Directive will meet the relevant requirements.

The Office intends to issue periodic amendments to its Approved Documents to reflect emerging harmonised European Standards. Where a national standard is to be replaced by a harmonised European Standard, there will be a co-existence period during which either standard may be referred to. At the end of the co-existence period the national standard will be withdrawn.

## THE WORKPLACE (HEALTH, SAFETY AND WELFARE) REGULATIONS 1992

The Workplace (Health, Safety and Welfare) Regulations 1992 as amended by The Health and Safety (Miscellaneous Amendments) Regulations 2002 (Sl 2002/2174) contain some requirements which affect building design. The main requirements are now covered by the Building Regulations, but for further information see: Workplace health, safety and welfare: Workplace (Healthy Safety and Welfare) Regulations 1992, Approved Code of Practice, L24, HMSO, 1992 (ISBN 0 71760 413 6).

The Workplace (Health, Safety and Welfare) Regulations 1992 apply to the common parts of flats and similar buildings if people such as cleaners and caretakers are employed to work in these common parts. Where the requirements of the Building Regulations that are covered by this Part do not apply to dwellings, the provisions may still be required in the situations described above in order to satisfy the Workplace Regulations.

## MIXED USE DEVELOPMENT

In mixed use developments part of a building may be used as a dwelling while another part has a non-domestic use. In such cases, if the requirements of this part of the Regulations for dwellings and non-domestic use differ, the requirements for non-domestic use should apply in any shared parts of the building.

# MEANS OF VENTILATION F1

## THE REQUIREMENT

This Approved Document, which takes effect on 6 April 2006, deals with the requirement of Part F of Schedule 1 to the Building Regulations 2000.

This guidance does not apply to building work in circumstances where the amendments to Part L made by the Building and Approved Inspectors (Amendment) Regulations 2006 do not apply to the work.

| Requirement | Limits on application |
|---|---|
| **Means of ventilation** | |
| F1. There shall be adequate means of ventilation provided for people in the building. | Requirement F1 does not apply to a building or space within a building: **a.** into which people do not normally go; or **b.** which is used solely for storage; or **c.** which is a garage used solely in connection with a single dwelling |

## Section 0: General guidance

### Performance

**0.1**    In the Secretary of State's view the Requirement of Part F will be met where a ventilation system is provided that, under normal conditions, is capable of limiting the accumulation of moisture, which could lead to mould growth, and pollutants originating within a building which would otherwise become a hazard to the health of the people in the building.

**0.2**    In general terms, the requirement may be achieved by providing a ventilation system which:

**a.** extracts, before it is generally widespread, water vapour from areas where it is produced in significant quantities (e.g. kitchens, utility rooms and bathrooms);

**b.** extracts, before they are generally widespread, pollutants which are a hazard to health from areas where they are produced in significant quantities (e.g. rooms containing processes or activities which generate harmful contaminants);

**c.** rapidly dilutes, when necessary, pollutants and water vapour produced in habitable rooms, occupiable rooms and sanitary accommodation;

**d.** makes available over long periods a minimum supply of outdoor air for occupants and to disperse, where necessary, residual pollutants and water vapour. Such ventilation should minimise draughts and, where necessary, should be reasonably secure and provide protection against rain penetration;

**e.** is designed, installed and commissioned to perform in a way which is not detrimental to the health of the people in the building; and

**f.** is installed to facilitate maintenance where necessary.

**0.3**    The guidance in this Approved Document has not been formulated to deal with the products of tobacco smoking.

**0.4**    Ventilation systems in buildings result in energy being used to heat fresh air taken in from outside and, in mechanical ventilation systems, to move air into, out of and/or around the building. Energy efficiency is dealt with under Part L of the Building Regulations but consideration should be given to mitigation of ventilation energy use, where applicable, by employing heat recovery devices, efficient types of fan motor and/or energy-saving control devices in the ventilation system.

## Introduction to the provisions

0.5  The purpose of this section is to outline briefly what ventilation in buildings is for and the philosophy behind the guidance for ventilation given in Approved Document R More detail is given in some of the informative appendices at the end of this Approved Document.

## The purpose of ventilation

0.6  Ventilation is simply the removal of 'stale' indoor air from a building and its replacement with 'fresh' outside air. It is assumed within the Approved Document that the outside air is of reasonable quality.

0.7  Ventilation is required for one or more of the following purposes:

  a. provision of outside air for breathing;

  b. dilution and removal of airborne pollutants, including odours;

  c. control of excess humidity (arising from water vapour in the indoor air);

  d. provision of air for fuel-burning appliances (which is covered under Part J of the Building Regulations).

Ventilation also provides a means to control thermal comfort and this, along with other methods, is considered in Part L of the Building Regulations and its supporting Approved Documents.

0.8  The airborne pollutants and water vapour mentioned in 0.7(b) and (c) above include those that are released from materials and products used in the construction, decoration and furnishing of a building, and as a result of the activities of the buildings occupants.

0.9  The pollutant(s) of most importance will vary between building types (e.g. dwelling, office, factory), building uses (e.g. industrial process, shop, commercial kitchen), and even from room to room within a building (e.g. kitchen, shower room, conference room, photocopier room). Common pollutants in a dwelling are moisture and combustion products from unflued appliances (e.g. gas cookers) and chemical emissions from construction and consumer products. In an office building, body odour is often the key pollutant, but there are a number of other pollutant sources including the building itself, furnishings, printers and photocopiers.

## Types of ventilation

0.10 Buildings are ventilated through a combination of infiltration and purpose-provided ventilation.

  • Infiltration is the uncontrollable air exchange between the inside and outside of a building through a wide range of air leakage paths in the building structure.

  • Purpose-provided ventilation is the controllable air exchange between the inside and outside of a building by means of a range of natural and/or mechanical devices.

0.11 It is important to minimise the uncontrollable infiltration and supply sufficient purpose-provided ventilation. Air tightness measures to limit infiltration are covered in Part L of the Building Regulations and its supporting Approved Documents. Approved Document F recommends methods of achieving sufficient purpose-provided ventilation, allowing for a reasonably high level of air tightness.

0.12 For the purposes of Part F, a reasonably high level of air tightness (air permeability) means a level higher than the target value recommended under Part L because all new buildings are expected to better the target value to some degree. Research suggests that the most airtight domestic and non-domestic buildings, using normal (but carefully executed) construction methods, can have an air permeability down to around 3-4m3/h per square metre of envelope area at 50 Pascal pressure difference. Therefore, the ventilation provisions recommended in this Approved Document have been specified to cope with air permeability at these levels or worse in typical building types. Where special measures are to be taken to achieve greater air tightness, additional ventilation provisions may be required.

## The ventilation strategy adopted in Approved Document F

**0.13** Approved Document F adopts the following strategy (systems which comply with the strategy are described in Sections 1 and 2).

- **Extract ventilation** from rooms where most water vapour and/or pollutants are released, e.g. activities such as cooking, bathing or photocopying. This is to minimise their spread to the rest of the building. This extract may be either intermittent or continuous.

- **Whole building** ventilation to provide fresh air to the building and to dilute and disperse residual water vapour and pollutants not dealt with by extract ventilation as well as removing water vapour and other pollutants which are released throughout the building (e.g. by building materials, furnishings, activities and the presence of occupants). Whole building ventilation provides nominally continuous air exchange. The ventilation rate may be reduced or ceased when the building is not occupied. It may be necessary to purge the air when the building is re-occupied.

- **Purge ventilation** throughout the building to aid removal of high concentrations of pollutants and water vapour released from occasional activities such as painting and decorating or accidental releases such as smoke from burnt food or spillage of water. Purge ventilation is intermittent, i.e. only required when such occasional activities occur. Purge ventilation provisions may also be used to improve thermal comfort and/or overheating of buildings in summer: the latter is considered further in Approved Documents L1 (a) (New dwellings) and L2(a) (New buildings other than dwellings). Note that purge ventilation was called 'rapid' ventilation in the 1995 edition of Approved Document F.

**0.14** This ventilation strategy can be delivered by a natural ventilation system or a mechanical ventilation system or a combination of both (i.e. 'mixed-mode' or 'hybrid' ventilation system). For mainly naturally ventilated buildings, it is common to use a combination of ventilators to achieve this strategy (e.g. for dwellings it is common to use intermittent extraction fans for extract ventilation, trickle ventilators for whole building ventilation and windows for purge ventilation). For mechanically ventilated or air-conditioned buildings, it is common for the same ventilators to provide both local extract and whole building ventilation and, for buildings other than dwellings, to provide purge ventilation as well.

**0.15** The ventilation systems and devices mentioned in the preceding paragraph are examples of those commonly in use at the time of writing. Other ventilation systems and devices, perhaps following a different strategy (e.g. positive input ventilation), may provide acceptable solutions, provided it can be demonstrated to the building control body (e.g. by a BBA Certificate) that they meet Requirement F1.

## Control of ventilation

**0.16** It is important that ventilation is controllable so that it can maintain reasonable indoor air quality and avoid waste of energy. These controls can be either manual (i.e. operated by the occupant) or automatic.

**0.17** Manually controlled trickle ventilators (the most common type of background ventilators) can be located over the window frames, in window frames, just above the glass or directly through the wall (see Diagram 5 in the Glossary). They are positioned typically 1.7m above floor level to avoid discomfort due to cold draughts. These ventilators often incorporate a simple flap that allows users to shut off the ventilation provided depending on external weather conditions. Trickle ventilators are normally left open in occupied rooms in dwellings. A window with a night latch position is not recommended because of the difficulty of measuring the equivalent area, the greater likelihood of draughts and the potential increased security risk in some locations.

**0.18** In dwellings, humidity controlled devices are available to regulate the humidity of the indoor air and, hence, minimise the risk of condensation and mould growth. These are best installed as part of an extract ventilator in moisture-generating rooms (e.g. kitchen or bathroom). Humidity control is not appropriate for sanitary accommodation where the dominant pollutant is normally odour. Trickle ventilators are available which 'throttle down' the ventilation flow passage(s) according to the pressure difference across the ventilator to reduce draught risks during windy weather. Manufacturers should be consulted when selecting the correct type of pressure-controlled trickle ventilator.

**0.19** Other types of automatic control may be suitable for regulating ventilation devices (e.g. trickle ventilators, ventilation fans, dampers and air terminal devices) in dwellings. In such cases, it is important that the device controls the ventilation air supply and/or extract according to the need for ventilation in the space to remove or dilute indoor pollutants and water vapour. Trickle ventilators with automatic control should also have manual over-ride, so that the occupant can close the ventilator to avoid draughts and fully open the ventilator to provide maximum airflow when required. For pressure-controlled trickle ventilators that are fully open at typical conditions (e.g. 1Pa pressure difference), only a manual close option is recommended.

**0.20** In buildings other than dwellings, various more sophisticated automatic control systems are available. These may be based on sensors located within the building, e.g. occupancy sensors (using local passive infra-red detectors) or indoor carbon dioxide concentration sensors (using electronic carbon dioxide detectors) as an indicator of occupancy level and, therefore, body odour.

## Performance-based guidance

0.21 This Approved Document focuses on performance-based guidance which suggests to the designer what level of ventilation should be sufficient, rather than how it should be achieved. Therefore, the designer has the freedom to use whatever ventilation provisions suit a particular building, including the use of innovative products and solutions, if it can be demonstrated that they meet the performance standard recommended in this Approved Document.

**0.22** The actual performance criteria for acceptable levels of moisture and pollutants are given in Appendix A. The airflow rates necessary to meet the performance criteria are given in the main guidance.

**0.23** Simple guidance in the form of ventilator sizes for the whole dwelling is also provided to make it easier for designers to meet Building Regulations requirements in common situations.

## Equivalent area and free area of ventilators

**0.24** Equivalent area has been introduced into the Approved Document instead of free area for the sizing of background ventilators (including trickle ventilators). Equivalent area is a better measure of the airflow performance of a ventilator. Free area is simply the physical size of the aperture of the ventilator but may not accurately reflect the airflow performance which the ventilator will achieve. The more complicated and/or contorted the air flow passages in a ventilator, the less air will flow through it. So, two different ventilators with the same free area will not necessarily have the same airflow performance. A new European Standard. BS EN 13141-1:2004 (Clause 4). includes a method of measuring the equivalent area of background ventilator openings. As an approximation, the free area of a trickle ventilator is typically 25% greater than its equivalent area.

**0.25** As equivalent area cannot be verified with a ruler, it will be difficult to demonstrate to building control bodies that trickle ventilators and similar products have the correct equivalent area unless it is clearly marked on the product. For this reason, it is preferable to use ventilators which have the equivalent area (in mm2 at 1 Pa pressure difference), or equivalent area per metre (where the equivalent area of the product varies according to length) marked on the product in an easily visible location. Where it is not practical for the manufacturer to mark the ventilator because it can be used in conjunction with a range of other components, some form of temporary marking for the installed system should be acceptable to the building control body.

**0.26** Some manufactures will not have developed marking, or equivalent, systems for their products by 6 April 2006. Therefore, until 1 October 2006 it would be reasonable for building control bodies to adopt a flexible approach to assessing equivalent area where unmarked products are used.

## Ventilation effectiveness

0.27 Ventilation effectiveness is a measure of how well a ventilation system works in terms of delivering the supply air to the occupants of a building. If the supply air is mixed fully with the room air before it is breathed by the occupants, the ventilation effectiveness is 1. If the supply air is extracted from the room before it mixes with any room air, the ventilation effectiveness is 0. If the supply air reaches the occupant without mixing with any room air, the ventilation effectiveness tends towards infinity.

**0.28** This is important as a system with a higher ventilation effectiveness achieves acceptable pollutant levels at the occupant's breathing zone for a lower air supply rate, and offers potentially significant energy savings. However, it has been decided not to make an allowance for any reduction of fresh air supply rates based on ventilation effectiveness in Approved Document F at this time. This is because ventilation effectiveness is dependent on the ventilation system design, its installation and the way in which occupants use the space. Whilst it is possible to predict what the ventilation effectiveness of a system should be, there is currently insufficient knowledge of the actual ventilation effectiveness achieved in buildings to allow designers to guarantee performance and so avoid significant under-ventilation by reducing air supply rates. This is because ventilation effectiveness may be influenced by factors beyond the designer's control such as occupant usage (e.g. seating plan and use of computers within a space and whether the space is being heated or cooled by the ventilation air). In the designs shown in this Approved Document, it has been assumed that the ventilation effectiveness is 1.0. See CIBSE Guide A for further information on ventilation effectiveness.

## Source control

**0.29** A complementary strategy for achieving good indoor air quality is to reduce the release of water vapour and/ or air pollutants into the indoor air, i.e. source control. Source control is not considered within the main guidance of the Approved Document owing to limited knowledge about the emission of pollutants from construction and consumer products used in buildings and the lack of suitable labelling schemes for England and Wales. Some construction products such as glass, stone and ceramics are by their nature low emitters of air pollutants. Currently, some paints are labelled for their volatile organic compound (VOC) content, and some wood-based boards (class E1, BS EN 13986:2002) are available with low formaldehyde emission. This allows suitable products to be chosen when good indoor air quality is a priority, but at the present time it is not practical to make an allowance for use of these products in the ventilation requirements. Further information about control of emissions from construction products is available in BRE Digest 464.

**0.30** House dust mite allergens can trigger allergic reactions in susceptible individuals. Measures for source control are provided in BRE Report BR 417: *Building regulation health and safety.*

## Noisy locations

**0.31** In noisy areas it may be appropriate to use either sound-attenuating background ventilators or mechanical ventilation solutions, depending on the noise level and any planning conditions.

## Noise from ventilation systems

0.32 Noise generated by ventilation fans (which may propagate through ducts and ductwork) can disturb the occupants of the building and so discourage their use. Therefore, the designer should consider minimising noise by careful design and the specification of quieter products. Noise from the ventilation system may also disturb people outside the building, so externally emitted noise levels should also be considered.

## Historic buildings

**0.33** The inclusion of any particular ventilation measure in existing buildings should not introduce new or increased technical risk, or otherwise prejudice the use or character of the building. In particular, consideration should be given to the special needs of historic buildings. Such buildings include:

   **a.** listed buildings;

   **b.** buildings situated in a conservation area;

   **c.** buildings of local architectural and historical interest and which are referred to as a material consideration in a local authority's development plan;

   **d.** buildings within national parks, areas of outstanding natural beauty and world heritage sites.

**0.34** Advice on the factors determining the character of historic buildings is set out in PPG15: Planning and the historic environment. Specific guidance on meeting the requirements of Part F when undertaking work in historic buildings is given in Section 3 of this Approved Document.

## Modular and portable buildings

**0.35** Buildings constructed from sub-assemblies that are delivered newly made or selected from stock are no different from any other new building and must comply with all requirements in Schedule 1 of the Building Regulations 2000. In some applications, such as buildings that are constructed to be temporary (in the normal sense of the word), the provision of adequate ventilation may vary depending upon the circumstances in the particular case. For example, (a) a building created by dismantling, transporting and re-erecting the sub-assemblies on the same premises would normally be considered to meet the requirements and (b) a building constructed from sub-assemblies obtained from other premises or from stock manufactured before this Approved Document came into force would normally be considered to meet the requirement if it satisfies the relevant requirements of Part F that were applicable in 1995.

# Section 1: Dwellings

## Introduction to provisions

**1.1** This Approved Document shows three main ways of complying with the Requirement by:

**a**. providing the ventilation rates set out in paragraphs 1.4 to 1.7; or

**b.** following the system guidance set out:

- for dwellings without basements (paragraph 1.8); or

- for dwellings with basements (paragraphs 1.9 to 1.11); or

c. using other ventilation systems provided it can be demonstrated to the building control body that they satisfy the Requirement, e.g. by showing that they meet the moisture and air quality criteria set out in Appendix A.

**1.2**   There should be reasonable access for maintenance. This should include access for the purpose of changing fitters, replacing defective components and cleaning duct work.

**1.3**   Note that extract fans lower the pressure in a building, which can cause the spillage of combustion products from open-flued appliances. This can occur even if the appliance and the fan are in different rooms. Ceiling sweep fans produce air currents and hence local depressurisation which can also cause the spillage of flue gases from open-flued gas appliances or from solid fuel open fires. In buildings where it is intended to install open-flued combustion appliances and extract fans, the combustion appliance should be able to operate safely whether or not the fans are running. A way of showing compliance in these circumstances would be to follow the guidance given in Approved Document J on both the installation of the appliances and tests to show that combustion appliances operate safely whether or not fans are running.

## Ventilation rates

**1.4**   The performance will be achieved by providing the airflow rates set out in paragraphs 1.5 to 1.7. The airflow rates specified are for the performance of the complete installation. It is not intended that this should be measured on-site but the performance of the ventilation device (and associated components such as ducting for fans) should be tested according to the Standards listed under 'Performance requirements' in Table 1.6.

**1.5**   Extract ventilation to outside is required in each kitchen, utility room and bathroom and for sanitary accommodation. The extract can be either intermittent or continuously operating. The minimum extract airflow rates at the highest and lowest settings should be no Jess than specified in Table 1.1a.

**1.6**   Whole building ventilation rate for the supply of air to the habitable rooms in a dwelling should be no less than specified in Table 1.1b.

**1.7**   Purge ventilation provision is required in each habitable room (extract provisions are sufficient in other rooms, e.g. kitchens, bathrooms). It should be capable of extracting a minimum of four air changes per hour (ach) per room directly to outside.

| Table 1.1a **Extract ventilation rates** | | | |
|---|---|---|---|
| | | Continuous extract | |
| Room | Minimum intermittent extract rate | Minimum high rate | Minimum low rate |
| Kitchen | 30l/s (adjacent to hob); or 60l/8 (elsewhere) | 13l/s | Total extract rate must be at least the whole building ventilation rate in Table 1.1b |
| Utility room | 30l/s | 6l/s | |
| Bathroom | 15l/s | 8l/s | |
| Sanitary accommodation | 6l/s | | |

### Table 1.1b **Whole building ventilation rates**

|  | Number of bedrooms in dwelling | | | | |
|---|---|---|---|---|---|
|  | 1 | 2 | 3 | 4 | 5 |
| Whole building ventilation rate | 13 | 17 | 21 | 25 | 29 |

Notes:
a.  In addition, the minimum ventilation rate should be not less than 0.3l/s per m2 internal floor area (this includes each floor, e.g. for a two-storey building, add the ground and first floor areas).
b.  This is based on two occupants in the main bedroom and a single occupant in all other bedrooms. This should be used as the default value. If a greater level of occupancy is expected, then add 4l/s per occupant.

## Ventilation systems for dwellings without basements

**1.8**    The performance required for dwellings without basements could be achieved by following steps 1 to 5. Worked examples for each system are given in Appendix C.

**Step 1:** Select one of the following four ventilation systems (illustrated in Diagram 1).

> **System 1:** Background ventilators and intermittent extract fans. Guidance on minimum provisions for extract and whole building ventilation is set out in Table 1.2a. Note that it includes separate guidance for dwellings with only a single exposed facade. See Appendix E for installation guidance for intermittent extract fans.
>
> **System 2:** Passive stack ventilation. Guidance on minimum provisions for extract and whole building ventilation is set out in Table 1.2b. See Appendix D for design and installation guidance for PSV.
>
> **System 3:** Continuous mechanical extract. Guidance on minimum provisions for extract and whole building ventilation is set out in Table 1.2c.
>
> **System 4:** Continuous mechanical supply and extract with heat recovery. Guidance on minimum provisions for extract and whole building ventilation is set out in Table 1,2d.

**Step 2:** See Table 1.3 for guidance on minimum provision for purge ventilation.

**Step 3:** See Table 1.4 for guidance on suitable ventilator locations (and minimum background ventilator areas for each room).

**Step 4:** See Table 1.5 for guidance on appropriate ventilation controls. Step 5: See Table 1.6 for guidance on performance test methods.

## Diagram 1 **Ventilation systems**

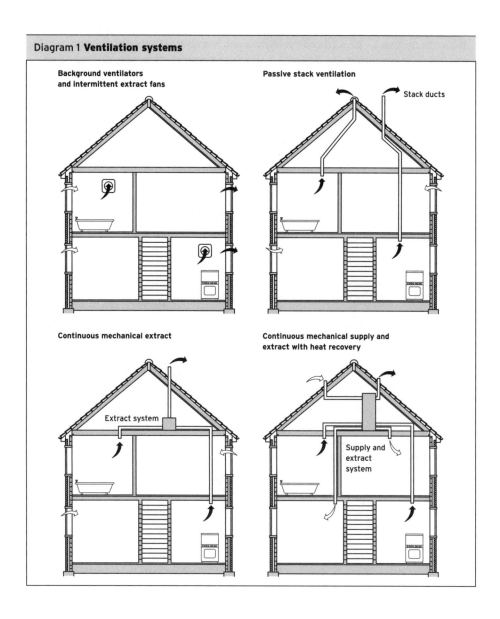

Background ventilators and intermittent extract fans

Passive stack ventilation

Stack ducts

Continuous mechanical extract

Extract system

Continuous mechanical supply and extract with heat recovery

Supply and extract system

## Table 1.2a System 1 - Background ventilators and intermittent extract fans (for additional information see Tables 1.3 to 1.6 and worked examples C1 and C5 in Appendix C)

**Intermittent extract**

• Intermittent extract rates are given in Table 1.1a. For sanitary accommodation only, as an alternative, the purge ventilation provisions (windows) given in Appendix B can be used where security is not an issue.

• Instead of a conventional intermittent fan, a continuously running single room heat recovery ventilator could be used in a wet room. It should use the minimum high rate in Table 1.1a and 50% of this value as the minimum low rate. No background ventilator is required in the same room as a single room heat recovery ventilator. Furthermore, the total equivalent background ventilator area described below can be reduced by 2500mm² for each room containing a single room heat recovery ventilator. Continuously running fans should be quiet so as not to discourage their use by the occupants.

**Background ventilators**

•• For dwellings with more than one exposed facade:

a. for multi-storey dwellings, and single-storey dwellings more than four storeys above ground level, the total equivalent area for the dwelling is given in the table below; or

b. for single-storey dwellings, up to tour storeys above ground level, take the total equivalent area for the dwelling from the table below and add 5000mm².

• For a dwelling with only a single exposed facade, cross ventilation is not possible using this type of ventilation system and an alternative is required. In this case, background ventilators should be located at both high and low positions in the facade to provide single-sided ventilation. The total equivalent area at a high position (typically 1.7m above floor level) for all dwelling types (i.e. all storey heights) is given in the main table. In addition, the same total equivalent ventilator area should be repeated and located at least 1m below the high ventilators. See Diagram 1b. Single-sided ventilation is most effective if the dwelling is designed so that the habitable rooms are on the exposed facade, and these rooms are no greater than 6m in depth.

**Equivalent ventilator area\* for dwellings (mm²)**

| Total floor area (m2) | Number of bedrooms[b] | | | | |
|---|---|---|---|---|---|
| | 1 | 2 | 3 | 4 | 5 |
| <50 | 25,000 | 35,000 | 45,000 | 45,000 | 55,000 |
| 51-60 | 25,000 | 30,000 | 40,000 | | |
| 61-70 | 30,000 | 30,000 | 30,000 | | |
| 71-80 | 35,000 | 35,000 | 35,000 | | |
| 81-90 | 40,000 | 40,000 | 40,000 | | |
| 91-100 | 45,000 | 45,000 | 45,000 | | |
| >100 | Add 5000mm2 for every additional 10m2 floor | | | | |

**Notes**

a. The equivalent area of a background ventilator should be determined at a 1 Pa pressure difference, using the appropriate test method given in Table 1.6.

b. This is based on two occupants in the main bedroom and a single occupant in all other bedrooms. For a greater level of occupancy, assume greater number of bedrooms (i.e. assume an extra bedroom per additional person). For more than five bedrooms, add an additional 10.000mm² per bedroom.

Diagram 1b **Single-sided ventilation**

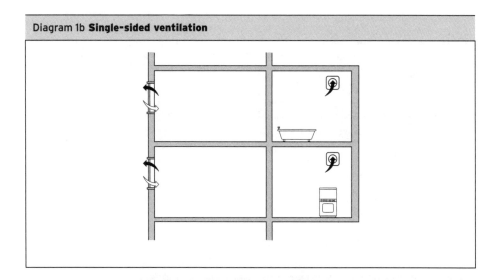

Table 1.2b **System 2 - Passive stack ventilation (for additional information see Tables 1.3 to 1.6 and worked examples C2 and C6 in Appendix C)**

**Passive stack ventilators\***

| Room | Internal duct diameter (mm) | Internal cross sectional area (mm²) |
|---|---|---|
| Kitchen | 125 | 12,000 |
| Utility room | 100 | 8000 |
| Bathroom | 100 | 8000 |
| Sanitary accommodation[b] | 80 | 5000 |

**Background ventilators[c]**

Calculate the total equivalent area of ventilators (mm²) required in the dwelling as follows:

Step 1: determine the equivalent ventilator area for the dwelling from Table 1.2a;

Step 2: make an allowance for the total airflow through all PSV units. As an approximation, assume that, under normal conditions, each PSV unit provides an equivalent ventilator area of 2500mm²;

Stop 3: equivalent area required = step 1 - step 2.

Note that the minimum equivalent area (step 3) must always be at least equal to the total maximum cross-sectional area of all the PSV ducts to ensure sufficient make-up air for the PSV to operate fully. For a dwelling with only a single exposed facade, the dwelling should be designed such that the habitable rooms are on the exposed facade so as to achieve cross ventilation.

**Notes:**

**a.** An open-flued appliance may provide sufficient extract ventilation for the room in which it is located when in operation, and can be arranged to provide sufficient ventilation when not firing. For instance, the provisions would be adequate if: (a) the solid fuel open-flued appliance is a primary source of heating, cooking or hot water production; or (b) the open-flued appliance has a flue of free area at least equivalent to a 125mm diameter duct and the appliance's combustion air inlet and dilution inlet are permanently open, i.e. there is path with no control dampers which could block the flow or the ventilation path can be left open when the appliance is not in use (see also paragraph 1.3).

**b**. For sanitary accommodation only, as an alternative, the purge ventilation provisions given in Appendix B can be used where security is not an issue.

**c.** In addition, use this procedure to calculate sizes of background ventilators if both PSV (or open-flued appliance as described in note a above) and intermittent extract fans are used in different rooms in the same dwelling. See also paragraph 1.3 if open-flued appliances are installed in the building.

---

### Table 1.2c **System 3 - Continuous mechanical extract (for additional information see Tables 1.3 to 1.6 and worked examples C3 and C7 in Appendix C)**

**Continuous extract**

Step 1: Determine the whole building ventilation rate from Table 1.1b.

(Note: no allowance is made for infiltration as the extract system lowers the pressure in the dwelling and limits the exit of air through the building fabric.)

Step 2. Calculate the whole dwelling air extract rate at maximum operation by summing the individual room rates for 'minimum high rate' from Table 1.1a.

(For sanitary accommodation only, as an alternative, the purge ventilation provisions given in Appendix B can be used where security is not an issue. In this case the 'minimum high extract rate' for the sanitary accommodation should be omitted from the step 2 calculation.)

Step 3: The required extract rates are as follows:

• the maximum rate (e.g. 'boost') should be at least the greater of step 1 and step 2. Note that the maximum individual room extract rates should be at least those given in Table 1.1a for minimum high rate;

• the minimum rate should be at least the whole building ventilation rate in step 1.

Note 1: this system could comprise either a central extract system or individual room fans (or a combination of both). In all cases, the fans should operate quietly at their minimum (i.e. normal) rate so as not to discourage their use (see paragraph 0.31). To ensure that the system provides the intended ventilation rate, measures should be taken to minimise likely wind effects when any extract terminal is located on the prevailing windward facade. Possible solutions include ducting to another facade, use of constant volume flow rate units or, for central extract systems, follow more detailed guidance which is being prepared by the Energy Saving Trust (EST) and the Building Research Establishment (BRE) in conjunction with The Electric Heating and Ventilation Association (TEHVA) and the Residential Ventilation Association (RVA) entitled 'Performance testing of products for residential ventilation' (to be published in February/March 2006 and will be made available on their websites).

Note 2: if a single room heat recovery ventilator (SRHRV) is used to ventilate a habitable room, with the rest of the dwelling provided with continuous mechanical extract, the airflow rates are determined as follows:

• determine the whole building ventilation rate from Table 1.1b;

• calculate the room supply rate required for the SRHRV from: (whole building ventilation rate x room volume) / (total volume of all habitable rooms).

Undertake steps 1 to 3 for sizing the continuous mechanical extract for the rest of the dwelling. However, when performing step 1, the supply rate specified for the SRHRV should be subtracted from the value given in Table 1.1b.

**Background ventilators**

The need for background ventilators will depend on the air permeability of the dwelling, and this is not normally known at the design stage. Therefore, as a precaution, it is recommended that controllable background ventilators having a minimum equivalent area of 2500mm² are fitted in each room, except wet rooms from which air is extracted. Where this approach causes difficulties (e.g. on a noisy site) seek expert advice.

---

Table 1.2d **System 4 - Continuous mechanical supply and extract with heat recovery (MVHR) (for additional information see Tables 1.3 to 1.6 and worked examples C4 and C8 in Appendix C)**

**Continuous supply and extract**

Step 1: Determine the whole building ventilation rate from Table 1.1b. Allow for infiltration by subtracting from this value:

• for multi-storey dwellings: 0.04 x gross internal volume of the dwelling heated space (m³);

• for single-storey dwellings: 0.06 x gross internal volume of the dwelling heated space (m³).

Step 2: Calculate the whole dwelling air extract rate at maximum operation by summing the individual room rates for 'minimum high rate from Table 1.1a.

(For sanitary accommodation only, as an alternative, the purge ventilation provisions given in Appendix B can be used where security is not an issue. In this case the 'minimum high extract rate' for the sanitary accommodation should be omitted from the step 2 calculation.)

Step 3: The required airflow rates are as follows:

• the maximum extract rate (e.g. 'boost') should be at least the greater of step 1 and step 2. Note that the maximum individual room extract rates should be at least those given in Table 1.1 a for minimum high rate;

• the minimum air supply rate should be at least the whole building ventilation rate in step 1..

---

Table 1.3 **Purge ventilation provisions for all four ventilation systems**

**Purge ventilation**

**For each habitable room with:**

• external walls, see Appendix B for window or external door (including patio door) sizing; '

• no external walls, see paragraphs 1.12 to 1.14.

There may be practical difficulties in achieving this (e.g. owing to excessive noise from outside). In such situations, seek expert advice.

For each wet room with:

• external walls, install an openable window (no minimum size);

• no external walls, the normal extract provisions will suffice, although it will take longer to purge the room (see Table 1.5 for intermittent extract use in System 1).

## Table 1.4 **Location of ventilation devices in rooms**

Mechanical (intermittent and continuous) extract or supply
• Cooker hoods should be 650 to 750mm above the hob surface (or follow manufacturer's instructions).
• Mechanical extract terminals and extract fans should be placed as high as practicable and preferably less than 400mm below the ceiling.
• Mechanical supply terminals should be located and directed to avoid draughts.
• Where ducts etc. are provided in a dwelling with a protected stairway, precautions may be necessary to avoid the possibility of the system allowing smoke or fire to spread into the stairway. See Approved Document B
• The fans or terminals should be located in the following rooms:
　　　**System 1:** extract should be from each wet room
　　　**System 3:** extract should be from each wet room.
　　　**System 4:** extract should be from each wet room. Air should normally be supplied to each habitable room. The total supply airflow should usually be distributed in proportion to the habitable room volumes. Recirculation by the system of moist air from the wet rooms to the habitable rooms should be avoided.

**Passive stack ventilation**

• PSV extract terminals should be located in the ceiling or on a wall less than 400mm below the ceiling. There should be no background ventilators within the same room as a PSV terminal. (For open-flued appliances, room air supply is necessary as given in Approved Document J.)

• Where PSV is provided in a dwelling with a protected stairway, precautions may be necessary to avoid the possibility of the system allowing smoke or fire to spread into the stairway. See Approved Document B.

**Background ventilators**

•They should be located in the following rooms:
**System 1:** located in all rooms. Minimum of 5000mm$^2$ equivalent area in all habitable rooms with an external wall. If a habitable room has no external walls, follow guidance in paragraphs 1.12 to 1.14. Minimum of 2500mm2 equivalent area in all wet rooms with an external wall. If a wet room has no external walls, follow the guidance for mechanical intermittent extract in Table 1.5. The total equivalent area should be at least that given in Table 1.2a. Where background ventilators and individual fans are fitted in the same room, they should be a minimum of 0.5m apart.

**System 2:** located in all rooms except within the same room as a passive stack ventilator. Minimum of 5000mm$^2$ in all habitable rooms with an external wall (with total at least that given in Table 1.2b). If a habitable room has no external walls, follow guidance in paragraphs 1.12 to 1.14.
**System 3:** located in each habitable room (see Table 1.2c).
**System 4:** no background ventilators required.
•In addition, background ventilators should be:

**All systems:** located so as to avoid draughts, e.g. typically 1.7m above floor level. For System 1, if dwelling has a single exposed facade, the low ventilators should be below this level (see Table 1.2a).
**Systems 1 and 2:** if the dwelling has more than one exposed facade, to maximise the airflow through the dwelling by encouraging cross ventilation, it is best to locate similar equivalent areas of background ventilators on opposite (or adjacent) sides of the dwelling.

Note that, for Systems 1 and 2, the background ventilators have been sized for the winter period. Additional ventilation may be required during warmer months as stack driving pressures are reduced. The provisions for purge ventilation (e.g. windows) could be used. Additional background ventilation provision or the use of Systems 3 or 4 may be more appropriate for dwellings designed to high air tightness standards. If uncertain, seek expert advice.

**Purge ventilation**

• Location not critical.

**Air transfer between rooms**

• To ensure good transfer of air throughout the dwelling, there should be an undercut of minimum area 7600mm² in all internal doom above the floor finish (equivalent to an undercut of 10mm for a standard 760mm width door).

## Table 1.5 Controls for ventilation devices

**Mechanical intermittent extract**

Intermittent extract can be operated manually and/or automatically by a sensor (e.g. humidity sensor, occupancy/usage sensor, detection of moisture/pollutant release). Humidity controls should not be used for sanitary accommodation as odour is the main pollutant.

In kitchens, any automatic control must provide sufficient flow during cooking with fossil fuels (e.g. gas) to avoid the build-up of combustion products.

Any automatic control must provide manual over-ride to allow the occupant to turn the extract on.

For a room with no openable window i.e. an internal room), the fan should have a 15 minute over-run. In rooms with no natural light, the fans could be controlled by the operation of the main room light switch

**Mechanical continuous supply or extract/passive stack ventilation**

Set up to operate without occupant intervention (may have manual control to select maximum 'boost' rate). May have automatic controls, (e.g. humidity sensor, occupancy/usage sensor, detection of moisture/pollutant release). Humidity controls should not be used for sanitary accommodation as odour is the main pollutant.

In kitchens, any automatic control must provide sufficient flow during cooking with fossil fuels (e.g. gas) to avoid the build-up of combustion products.

Ensure the system always provides the minimum whole building ventilation provision as specified in Table 1.1b.

**Background ventilators**

They can be either manually adjustable or automatically controlled (see paragraphs 0.17 to 0.19).

**Purge ventilation**
Manually operated.

**Accessible controls**

Where manual controls are provided, they should be within reasonable reach of occupants. It is recommended that they are located in accordance with the guidance for Requirement N3 Safe opening and closing of windows etc., which is given in Approved Document N. Where reasonable, the use of pull cords, operating rods or similar devices may help to achieve this. Although Requirement N3 only applies to work places, for the purposes of this Approved Document it should also apply to dwellings.

## Table 1.6 Performance test methods

The minimum performance requirements specified within Table 1.2 (a-d) for each ventilator, should be assessed using the test methods contained in relevant clauses of the following documents:

**i. Intermittent extract fan**

• BS EN 13141-4 Clause 4 'Performance testing of aerodynamic characteristics'. All sub-clauses are relevant.

**ii. Range hood**

• BS EN 13141-3 Clause 4 'Performance testing of aerodynamic characteristics'. All sub-clauses are relevant.

**iii. Background ventilator (non-RH controlled)**

• BS EN 13141-1 Clause 4 'Performance testing of aerodynamic characteristics'. Only the following sub-clauses are relevant:

  a. 4.1 'Flow rate/pressure'; and

  b. 4.2'Non-reverse flow ability'.

The performance requirement should normally be met for both airflow from outside to inside the dwelling and for inside to outside. To ensure the installed performance of background ventilators is similar to the results achieved when they are tested to this Standard, background ventilators and associated components should be installed according to manufacturers' instructions. This also applies to non-RH-controlled sound-attenuating background ventilators.

**iv. Passive stack ventilator**

• Follow Appendix D.

**v. Continuous mechanical extract ventilation (MEV) system**

• BS EN 13141 6 Clause 4 'Performance testing of aerodynamic characteristics'. Also see Note 2 below.

**vi. Continuous supply and the extract ventilation MVHR unit**

• BS EN 13141-7 Clause 6 Test methods'. Also see Note 2 below.

**vii. Single room heat recovery ventilator**

• prEN 13141-8 Clause 6 'Test methods'. Only the following sub-clauses are relevant:

  a. 6.1 'General'; and
  b. 6.2 'Performance testing of aerodynamic characteristics' sub-sub-clauses 6.2.1 'Leakages and mixing' and 6.2.2 'Airflow' only.

Note: for internal and external leakage and for mixing, the until should meet at least Class U4 given in Clause 3.2 'Classification'.

Note 1: for all ventilators discussed in this Table, the fitting of ducting, intake/exhaust terminals, filters, etc. will impose an additional resistance to the airflow through a ventilation device such as a fan, cooker hood or supply and extract ventilation unit. Where appropriate this should be allowed for when specifying ventilation system components because, for example a fan that meets the requirement in Table 1.2 when tested on its own many fail to meet the requirement when it is installed and fitted with ducting and intake/exhaust grilles. In such cases, the performance of the separate components should be assessed according to the relevant parts of BS EN 13141 and other relevant Standards, and the complete assembly, as installed, designed to meet the performance requirement by following good practice such as is given in the CIBSE Guides. Also see Appendix E for installation guidance for intermittent fans.

Note 2: Detailed guidance on the tests to be undertaken is being prepared by the Energy Saving Trust (EST) and the Building Research Establishment (BRE) in conjunction with The Electric Heating and Ventilation Association (TEHVA) and the Residential Ventilation Association (RVA) entitled 'Performance testing of products for residential ventilation' (to be published in February/ March 2006 and will be made available on their websites).

## VENTILATION SYSTEMS FOR BASEMENTS

**1.9**   For a dwelling which includes a basement that is connected to the rest of the dwelling above ground by a large permanent opening (e.g. an open stairway), the whole dwelling including the basement should be ventilated in accordance with paragraph 1.8 (for dwellings without basements) and treated as a multi-storey dwelling. If the basement has only a single exposed facade, while the rest of the dwelling above ground has more than one exposed facade, ventilation systems 3 and 4 are preferred, following the guidance in paragraph 1.8. If systems 1 or 2 are to be used, seek expert advice.

**1.10** For a dwelling which includes a basement that is not connected to the rest of the dwelling above ground by a large permanent opening:

**a.**   the part of the dwelling above ground should be considered separately and ventilated in accordance with paragraph 1.8. If the part of the dwelling above ground has no bedrooms, assume it has one bedroom for the purpose of determining ventilation provisions; and

**b.**   the basement should be treated separately as a single-storey dwelling above ground in accordance with paragraph 1.8. If the basement has no bedrooms, assume it has one bedroom for the purpose of determining ventilation provisions.

**1.11** For a dwelling which comprises only a basement it should be treated as a single-storey dwelling above ground in accordance with paragraph 1.8.

## VENTILATION OF HABITABLE ROOMS THROUGH ANOTHER ROOM OR A CONSERVATORY

**1.12** In a habitable room not containing openable windows (i.e. an internal room) the requirement will be met if the room is either ventilated through another habitable room (see paragraph 1.13) or through a conservatory (see paragraph 1.14).

**1.13** A habitable room not containing openable windows may be ventilated through another habitable room (see Diagram 2) if:

**a.**   there is, from the habitable rooms to outside, provision for both:

**i**. purge ventilation, one or more ventilation openings, with a total area given in Diagram 2 based on at least the combined floor area of the habitable rooms; and

**ii**. background ventilation of at least 8000mm2 equivalent area; and

**b.**   there is an area of permanent opening between the two rooms given in Diagram 2 based on at least the combined floor area of the habitable rooms.

**1.14** A habitable room not containing openable windows may be ventilated through a conservatory (see Diagram 3) if:

**a.**    there is, from the conservatory to outside, provisions for both:

**i**. purge ventilation, one or more ventilation openings, with a total area given in Diagram 3 based on at least the combined floor area of the habitable room and conservatory; and

**ii**. background ventilation, a ventilation opening (or openings) of at least 8000mm$^2$ equivalent area; and

**b.**    there are openings (which must be closable) between the habitable room and the conservatory for:

**i**. purge ventilation equivalent to 1.14a(i) above; and

**ii**. background ventilation equivalent to 1.14a(ii) above which should be located typically at least 1.7m above floor level and need not be within the door frame.

Diagram 2 **Two habitable rooms treated as a single room for ventilation purposes**

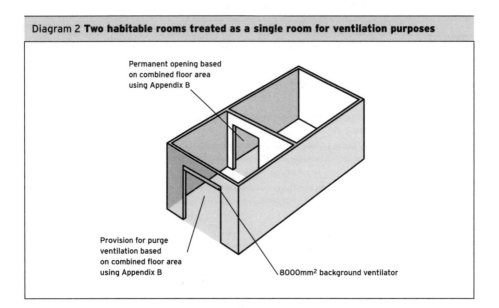

Permanent opening based
on combined floor area
using Appendix B

Provision for purge
ventilation based
on combined floor area
using Appendix B

8000mm² background ventilator

Diagram 3 **A habitable room ventilated through a conservatory**

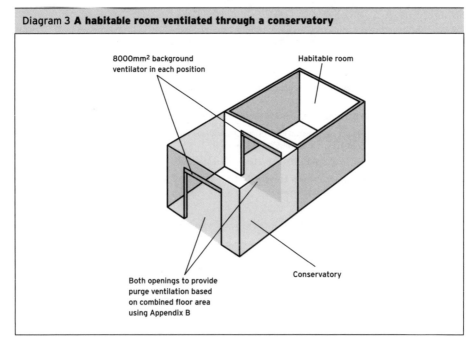

8000mm² background
ventilator in each position

Habitable room

Both openings to provide
purge ventilation based
on combined floor area
using Appendix B

Conservatory

# Section 2: Buildings other than dwellings

## General

**2.1**  This Approved Document sets out guidance for the following range of building types and uses:

**a.** offices - paragraphs 2.9 to 2.17;

**b.** car parks - paragraphs 2.19 to 2.22;

**c.** other building types - paragraph 2.18.

**2.2**  The ventilation provisions will not necessarily meet cooling needs. Guidance on the control of overheating is considered in Approved Document L2A *New buildings other than dwellings*.

**2.3**  Provision should be made to protect the fresh air supplies from contaminants injurious to health. Guidance on the siting of air inlets is provided in Appendix F.

**2.4**  Guidance on design measures to avoid *legionella* contamination, including design features not related to the ventilation of the building, is covered by HSE in *Legionnaires' disease:* the control of legionella bacteria in water systems. The relevant paragraphs are 79 to 144. Further guidance may be found in CIBSE TM13: *Minimising the risk of Legionnaires' disease.*

**2.5**  Guidance on recirculated air in air conditioning and mechanical ventilation systems is given by HSE in Workplace (Health, Safety and Welfare) Regulations 1992 *Approved Code of Practice and Guidance* L24, the relevant paragraph is 32.

## Access for maintenance

**2.6**  Reasonable provision would be to include:

    **a.** access for the purpose of replacing filters, fans and coils; and

    **b.** provision of access points for cleaning duct work.

**2.7**  In a central plant room adequate space should be provided as necessary for the maintenance of the plant. Where no special provision is required, the requirement could be satisfied if 600mm space is provided where access is required between plant and 1100mm where space for routine cleaning is required (see Diagram 4). These figures are the minimum necessary and additional space may be needed for opening of access doors, withdrawal of filters, etc. Further guidance for more complex situations can be found in Defence Works Functional Standard, Design & Maintenance Guide 08: *Space requirements for plant access* operation and maintenance. Further guidance for the cleaning of ducts is provided by CIBSE *Ventilation hygiene toolkit*.

### Diagram 4 **Spaces for access**

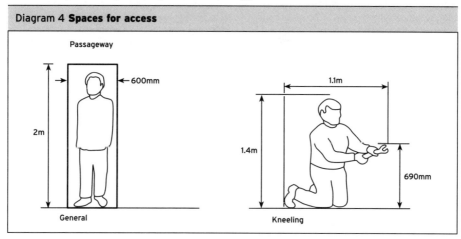

### Commissioning

**2.8**  See Approved Document L2A New buildings other than dwellings.

## OFFICES

### Introduction to provisions

**2.9**  This Approved Document shows four main ways of complying with the requirement by:

**a.** providing ventilation which meets the airflow rates set out in paragraphs 2.10 to 2.14; or

**b.** following the system guidance set out in paragraphs 2.15 to 2.17; or

**c.** using the alternative approaches set out in paragraph 2.18;

**d.** using other ventilation systems provided it can be demonstrated to the building control body that they satisfy the Requirement, e.g. by showing that they meet the moisture and air quality criteria set out in Appendix A.

### Ventilation rates

**2.10**  The performance will be achieved by ventilation which provides the airflow rates set out in paragraphs 2.11 to 2.14. The airflow rates specified are for the installed performance.

**2.11**  Extract to outside is required in all office sanitary accommodation, washrooms and in food and beverage preparation areas. In addition, printers and photocopiers in substantial use (greater than 30 minutes per hour) should be located in a separate room (to avoid any pollutants entering the occupied space) and extract provision installed. The extract flow rates should be no less than those specified in Table 2.1a.

**2.12**  The whole building ventilation rate for the supply of air to the offices should be no less than that specified in Table 2.1b.

**2.13**  Purge ventilation provision is required in each office. The total ventilation should be sufficient to reduce pollutants to an acceptable level before the space is occupied. The purged air should be taken directly to outside and should not be recirculated to any other part of the building.

**2.14**  The outdoor air supply rates in Table 2.1b for offices are based on controlling body odours with low levels of other pollutants. Where there are significant levels of other pollutants, adequate outdoor air supply can be achieved by following the calculation method provided in CIBSE GuideA.

### Natural ventilation of rooms

**2.15**  The airflow rates specified in Tables 2.1a and 2.1b can be provided by a mainly natural ventilation system by following the guidance in Tables 2.2a. 2.2b and 2.2c. A wide range of natural ventilation systems for providing whole building ventilation is given in CIBSE Application Manual AM 10: Natural ventilation in non-domestic buildings.

### Table 2.1a Extract ventilation rates

| Room | Extract rate |
|---|---|
| Rooms containing printers and photocopiers in substantial use (greater than 30 minutes per hour) | Air extract rate of 20l/s per machine during use. Note that, if the operators are in the room continuously, use the greater of the extract and whole building ventilation rates |
| Office sanitary accommodation and washrooms | Intermittent air extract rate of: 15l/s per shower/bath 6l/sperWC/urinal |
| Food and beverage preparation areas (not commercial kitchens) | Intermittent air extract rate of: 15l/s with microwave and beverages only 30l/8 adjacent to the hob vvtth cooker(s) 60l/s elsewhere w'rth cooker(s) All to operate while food and beverage preparation is in progress |
| Specialist buildings and spaces (e.g. commercial kitchens, sports centres) | See Table 2.3 |

### Table 2.1b Whole building ventilation rate for air supply to offices

| | Air supply rate |
|---|---|
| Total outdoor air supply rate for offices (no smoking and no significant pollutant sources) | 10l/s per person |

## Mechanical ventilation of rooms

**2.16** The requirement will be satisfied by following:

- the airflow rates set out in paragraphs 2.10 to 2.14 and
- the location guidance in Table 2.2b for extract ventilation; and
- the control guidance in Table 2.2c for extract ventilation.

## Alternative approaches

**2.17** As an alternative to paragraphs 2.10 to 2.14 the requirement will be satisfied by following the relevant recommendations of:

**a.** CIBSE Application Manual AM 13: 2000: Mixed mode Ventilation

**b.** CIBSE Guide A and CIBSE Guide B2.

## Table 2.2 **Ventilation for offices with natural air supply**

**a. Ventilation provisions**
**Extract**

Extract rates as per paragraph 2.11 (1,2)

**Whole building ventilation**

See CIBSE Application Manual AMIO:2005 Natural ventilation in non-domestic buildings.

**Purge ventilation**

See CIBSE Application Manual AMIO:2005 Natural ventilation in non-domestic buildings.

**Notes:**
1. PSV can be used as an alternative to a mechanical extract fan for office sanitary and washrooms and food preparation areas.

2. When an open-flued appliance is provided in a building with mechanical extract, the spillage of flue gases could occur. The open-flued appliance needs to operate safely whether or not the fan is running, and further guidance is provided in Approved Document J.

**b. Location of ventilators in rooms**

**Extract**
• Extract ventilators should be located as high as practicable and preferably less than 400mm below the ceiling. This will tend to remove pollutants from the breathing zone of the occupants as well as increase the effectiveness of extracting buoyant pollutants and water vapour.

• For PSV, extract terminals should be located in the ceiling of the room.

**Whole building ventilation**

• See CIBSE Application Manual AM10:2005 Natural ventilation in non-domestic buildings.

**Purge ventilation**

• See CIBSE Application Manual AM10:2005 Natural ventilation in non-domestic buildings.

**c. Controls for ventilators in rooms**

**Extract**

• For extract fans, they can be controlled either manually or automatically. For a room with no openable window (i.e. an internal room), the extract should have a 15 minute over-run.

• For PSV, either operated manually and/or automatically by a sensor or controller.

**Whole building ventilation**

• See CIBSE Application Manual AM10:2005 Natural ventilation in non-domestic buildings.

**Purge ventilation**

• See CIBSE Application Manual AM10:2005 Natural ventilation in non-domestic buildings.

**Accessible controls**

• • Readily accessible over-ride controls should be provided for the occupants.

# VENTILATION OF OTHER TYPES OF BUILDINGS

2.18 The requirement will be satisfied by following the appropriate design guidance for the other buildings given in Table 2.3. In addition to the guidance documents listed below, it should be noted that the Workplace (Health, Safety, Welfare) Regulations 1992 apply to most places where people work.

## Table 2.3 Ventilation of other buildings and spaces

| Building/space/activity | Regulations and guidance |
| --- | --- |
| Animal husbandry | The Welfare of Farm Animals (England) Regulations SI 2000 No.1870 London:The Stationery Office 2000.<br>The Welfare of Farm Animals (England) (Amendment) Regulations SI 2002 No.1646<br>The Welfare of Farm Animals (England) (Amendment) Regulations SI 2003 No. 299<br>BS 5502 Buildings and Structures for Agriculture<br>See also CIBSE Guide B2:2001, Section 3.24.1 |
| Assembly halls | CIBSE Guide B2:2001, Section 3.3 |
| Atria | CIBSE Guide B2:2001, Section 3.4 |
| Broadcasting studios | CIBSE Guide B2:2001, Section 3.5 |
| Building services plant rooms | Provision for emergency ventilation to control dispersal of contaminating gas releases (e.g. refrigerant leak)<br>is given in paragraphs 23-25 of HSE Guidance Note HSG 202 *General Ventilation in the Workplace -Guidance for Employers.* Other guidance in BS 4434:1989 *Specification for safety aspects in the design, construction and installation of refrigeration appliances and systems* |
| Call centres | CIBSE Guide B2:2001, Section 3.245 |
| Catering (inc. com kitchens) | HSE Catering Information Sheet No. 10,2000: Ventilation of kitchens in catering establishments<br><br>HSE Information Sheet No. 11.2000: The main health and safety law applicable to catering<br><br>See also CIBSE Guide B2:2001. Section 3.6 |
| Cleanrooms | CIBSE Guide B2:2001, Section 3.7 |
| Common spaces | These provisions apply to common spaces where large numbers of people are expected to gather, such as shopping malls and foyers. It does not apply to common spaces used solely or principally for circulation.<br><br>The provision will be satisfied if there is provision to spaces where large numbers of people are expected to gather for either<br>a. natural ventilation by appropriately located ventilation opening(s) with a total opening area of at least 1/50th of the floor area of the common space; or<br>b. mechanical ventilation installed to provide a supply of fresh air of 1l/s per m2 of floor area |
| Communal residential buildings | Energy Efficiency Best Practice in Housing, Good Practice Guide GPG 192: *Designing energy efficient multi-residential buildings*<br><br>See also CIBSE Guide B2:2001, Section 3.8 |
| Computer rooms | CIBSE B2:2001, Section 3.9 |
| Court rooms | Department for Constitutional Affairs Court standards and Design Guide, 2004 |
| Darkrooms (photographic) | CIBSE Guide B2:2001, Section 3.24.4 |

| Table 2.3 (continued) Ventilation of other buildings and spaces | |
|---|---|
| Dealing rooms | CIBSE Guide B2:2001, Section 3.24.5 |
| Factories and warehouses | Factories Act Health and Safety at Work etc. Act. |
| | See also CIBSE B2:2001, Section 3.11 |
| | Requirements are often exceeded by other criteria such as the ventilation requirements of the particular manufacturing process |
| High-rise (non-domestic buildings) | CIBSE Guide B2:2001, Section 3.12 |
| Horticulture | CIBSE Guide B2:2001. Section 2.42.6 |
| Hospitals and healthcare buildings | NHS Activity database |
| Hospital and healthcare building | NHS Activity database |
| | Health Technical Memorandum (HTM) 03 |
| | Health Building Notes (HBN) - various |
| | CIBSE B2:2001, Section 3.13 |
| Hotels | CIBSE Guide B2:2001, Section 3.14 |
| Industrial ventilation American Conference of | *Industrial Ventilation*, 24th Edition, *Manual of Recommended Practice*, Government Industrial Hygienists |
| | HS(G) 37 An introduction to local exhaust ventilation |
| | HS(G) 54 Maintenance, Examination and Testing of Local Exhaust Vantilation |
| | HS(G) 193 COSHH Essentials |
| Laboratories | CIBSE Guide B2:2001, Section 3.16 |
| Museums, libraries and art galleries | BS 5454:2000. |
| | CIBSE B2:2001. Section 3.17 |
| Plant rooms | CIBSE Guide B2: Section 3.18 |
| Prison cells NOMS Property, | Refer to National Offender Management Service (NOMS), Home Office, |
| | Technical Services, Room 401, Abell House, John Islip St., London SW1P 4LH |
| Schools and educational buildings | Ventilation provisions in schools can be made in accordance with the guidance in DfES Building Bulletin 101, Ventilation of School Buildings (see www.teachernet.gov.uk/iaq) and in the Education (School Premises) Regulations. Building Bulletin 101 can also be used as a guide to the ventilation required in other educational buildings such as further education establishments where the accommodation is similar to that found in schools, for e.g. sixth form accommodation.However, the standards may not be appropriate for particular areas where more hazardous activities take place than are normally found in schools, e.g. some practical and vocational activities requiring containment or fume extraction |
| | The Building Bulletin can also be used for childrens' centres and other early years settings, including day nurseries, playgroups, etc. |

| Shops and retail premises | CIBSE Guide B2:2001, Section 3.20 |
| --- | --- |
| Sports centres (inc. swimming pools) | CIBSE Guide B2:2001, Section 3.21 |
| Standards rooms | CIBSE Guide B2:2001, Section 3.24.7 |
| Sanitary accommodation | Same as for offices in Table 2.1 a |
| Transportation buildings and facilities | CIBSE Guide B2:2001. Section 3.23 |

## VENTILATION OF CAR PARKS

**2.19** The requirement will be satisfied for car parks below ground level, enclosed-type car parks and multi-storey car parks if the mean predicted pollutant levels are calculated and the ventilation rate designed and equipment installed to limit the concentration of carbon monoxide to not more than 30 parts per million averaged over an 8 hour period and peak concentrations, such as by ramps and exits, not more than 90 parts per million for periods not exceeding 15 minutes.

**2.20** Note that Approved Document B also includes provision for the ventilation of car parks for the purpose of fire risk management.

### Alternative approaches for ventilation of car parks

**2.21** As an alternative to paragraph 2.20, the following guidance would satisfy the requirement:

**a.** Naturally ventilated car parks. The provision of well distributed permanent natural ventilation, e.g. openings at each car parking level with an aggregate equivalent area equal to at least 1/20th of the floor area at that level, of which at least 25% should be on each of two opposing walls.

**b.** Mechanically ventilated car parks

Either:

**i.** the provision of both permanent natural ventilation openings of equivalent area not less than 1/40th of the floor area and a mechanical ventilation system capable of at least three air changes per hour (ach); or

**ii.** for basement car parks, the provision of a mechanical ventilation system capable of at least six air changes per hour (ach).

And:

For exits and ramps, where cars queue inside the building with engines running, provisions should be made to ensure a local ventilation rate of at least 10 air changes per hour (ach).

**2.22** Further guidance can be found in *Code of practice for ground floor, multi-storey and underground carparks* published by the Association for Petroleum and Explosives Administration (www.apea.org.uk); CIBSE Guide B2. Section 3.23.3; and Health and Safety Publication EH40: *Occupational exposure limits for limiting concentration of exhaust pollutants*. Fire safety issues are considered in Approved Document B.

# Section 3: Work on existing buildings

## General

**3.1**   When building work is carried out on an existing building the work should comply with the applicable requirements of Schedule 1 of the Building Regulations 2000 (as amended) and the rest of the building should not be made less satisfactory in relation to the requirements than before the work was carried out (see Building Regulations 3 and 4). Further, when a building undergoes a Material Change of Use, as defined in Regulations 5 and 6 of the Building Regulations 2000 (as amended), Part F applies to the building, or that part of the building, which has been subject to the change of use. Therefore, the guidance in other sections of this Approved Document may be applicable.

**3.2**  Until 1 October 2006, to comply with requirement F1, it will be sufficient if replacement windows comply with the guidance in Table 1 or Table 2 of Approved Document F 1995. Also, until this date, replacement windows need only have trickle ventilators (or an equivalent form of ventilation) where the original windows had them.

**3.3**  Windows are a controlled fitting (see Regulation 3(1) and 3(1A)) of the Building Regulations 2000 (as amended). This provision requires that, when windows in an existing building are replaced, the replacement work should comply with the requirements of Parts L and N. In addition, the building work once completed should not have a worse level of compliance with other applicable parts of Schedule 1 than before commencement of the work. Relevant parts of Schedule 1 may include Parts B, F and J.

**3.4**  To comply with Requirement F1, unless the room is ventilated adequately by other installed ventilation provisions, all replacement windows should include trickle ventilators, preferably with accessible controls as described in Table 1.5.

**3.5**  Alternatively, an equivalent background ventilation opening should be provided in the same room. A window with a night latch position is not normally recommended as an alternative because of the difficulty of measuring the equivalent area, the greater likelihood of draughts, and the potential increased security risk in some locations. Nevertheless a window with a night latch may be appropriate in exceptional situations where a trickle ventilator is an unsuitable solution. For example, where security considerations allow, for types of window that cannot reasonably accommodate trickle ventilators (e.g. some types of vertical sliding sash or very small windows).

**3.6**  In all cases, the ventilation opening should not be smaller than was originally provided, and it should be controllable. Where there was no ventilation opening, or where the size of the original ventilation opening is not known, the following minimum sizes should be adopted.

**a.** Dwellings:

• habitable rooms - 5000mm² equivalent area.

• kitchen, utility room and bathroom (with or without WC) - 2500mm² equivalent area.

**b.** Buildings other than dwellings:

• occupiable rooms: for floor areas up to 10m² - 2500mm² equivalent area; greater than 10m² at the rate of 250mm² equivalent area per m² of floor area;

• kitchens (domestic type) - 2500mm² equivalent area;

• bathrooms and shower rooms - 2500mm² equivalent area per bath or shower;

• sanitary accommodation (and/or washing facilities) - 2500mm² equivalent area per WC.

## Addition of a habitable room (not including a conservatory) to an existing building

**3.7**  The requirements will be met by following the guidance in paragraphs 3.8 to 3.10.

**3.8**  The general ventilation rate for the additional room and, if necessary, adjoining rooms could be achieved by one of the following options.

**a.** Background ventilators could be used as follows:

**i.** if the additional room is connected to an existing habitable room which now has no windows opening to outside, the guidance in paragraph 1.13 should be followed; or

**ii.** if the additional room is connected to an existing habitable room which still has windows opening to outside but with a total background ventilator equivalent area less than 5000mm², the guidance in paragraph 1.13 should be followed; or

**iii.** if the additional room is connected to an existing habitable room which still has windows opening to outside and with a total background ventilator equivalent area of at least 5000mm², there should be background ventilators of at least 8000mm² equivalent area between the two rooms and background ventilators of at least 8000mm² equivalent area between the additional room and outside.

**b.** A single room heat recovery ventilator could be used to ventilate the additional habitable room. The supply rate to that room should be determined as follows. First, determine the whole building ventilation rate from Table 1.1b. Second, calculate the room supply rate required from: (whole building ventilation rate x room volume) / (total volume of all habitable rooms).

**3.9**  For purge ventilation, follow the guidance in Table 1.3.

**3.10** Guidance on location, controls and performance standards is given in Tables 1.4 to 1.6 respectively.

### Addition of a wet room to an existing building

**3.11** The requirements for the additional wet room will be met by following the guidance in paragraphs 3.12 to 3.15.

**3.12** Whole building and extract ventilation can be provided by:

a. intermittent extract, as given in Table 1.2a, and a background ventilator of at least 2500mm2 equivalent area; or

**b.** single room heat recovery ventilator, as given in Table 1.2a; or

**c.** passive stack ventilator, as given in Table 1.2b; or

**d.** continuous extract fan, as given in Table 1.2c.

**3.13** In addition, there should be an undercut of minimum area 7600mm2 in any internal doors, between the wet room and the existing building (equivalent to an undercut of 10mm above the floor finish for a standard 760mm width door).

**3.14** For purge ventilation, follow the guidance in Table 1.3.

**3.15** Guidance on location, controls and performance standards is given in Tables 1.4 to 1.6 respectively.

### Addition of a conservatory to an existing building

**3.16** The guidance applies to conservatories with a floor area over 30m2.

**3.17** The requirements will be met by following the guidance in paragraphs 3.18 to 3.20.

**3.18** The general ventilation rate for the conservatory and, if necessary, adjoining rooms could be achieved by the use of background ventilators. Follow the guidance in paragraph 1.14 whatever the ventilation provisions in the existing room adjacent to the conservatory.

**3.19** For purge ventilation, follow the guidance in Table 1.3.

**3.20** Guidance on location, controls and performance standards is given in Tables 1.4 to 1.6 respectively.

### Historic buildings

3.21 Conserving the special characteristics of historic buildings needs to be recognised: see BS 7913. In such work, the aim should be to improve ventilation to the extent that is necessary, taking into account the need not to prejudice the character of the historic building nor to increase the risk of long-term deterioration to the building fabric or fittings. It may be that the fabric of the historic building is more leaky than a modern building, and this can be established by pressure testing. In arriving at a balance between historic building conservation and ventilation, it would be appropriate to take into account the advice of the local planning authority's conservation officer.

**3.22** Particular issues relating to work in historic buildings that warrant sympathetic treatment and where advice from others could therefore be beneficial include:

**a.** restoring the historic character of a building that had been subject to previous inappropriate alteration, e.g. replacement windows, doors and roof-lights;

**b.** rebuilding a former historic building (e.g. following a fire or filling in a gap site in a terrace);

**c.** making provisions enabling the fabric to 'breathe' to control moisture and potential long term decay problems: see SPAB Information Sheet No. 4, *The need for old buildings to breathe*, 1987.

# Section 4: Standards and publications

### Standards referred to

BS EN 378-3:2000

Refrigerating systems and heat pumps - safety and environmental requirements. Installation site and personal protection. AMD 14931 2004.

BSI PD CR 1752:1999

Ventilation for buildings - design criteria for the indoor environment.

BS 5502

Buildings and structures for agriculture. Various relevant parts including:

BS 550-33:1991 Guide to the control of odour pollution. AMD 10014 1998.

BS 550-52:1991 Code of practice for design of alarm systems, emergency ventilation and smoke ventilation for livestock housing. AMD 10014 1998.

**BS 5454:2000**
Recommendations for the storage and exhibition of archival documents.

**BS 5925:1991**
Code of practice for ventilation principles and designing for natural ventilation. AMD 8930 1995.

**BS 7913:1998**
Principles of the conservation of historic buildings.

**BS EN 13141-1:2004**
Ventilation for buildings. Performance testing of components/products for residential ventilation. Externally and internally mounted air transfer devices.

**BS EN 13141-3:2004**
Ventilation for buildings. Performance testing of components/products for residential ventilation. Range hoods for residential use.

**BS EN 13141-4:2004**
Ventilation for buildings. Performance testing of components/products for residential ventilation. Fans used in residential ventilation systems.

**BS EN 13141-6:2004**
Ventilation for buildings. Performance testing of components/products for residential ventilation. Exhaust ventilation system packages used in a single dwelling.

**BS EN 13141-7:2004**
Ventilation for buildings. Performance testing of components/products for residential ventilation. Performance testing of a mechanical supply and exhaust ventilation units (including heat recovery) for mechanical ventilation systems intended for single family dwellings.

**prEN 13141-8:2004**
Ventilation for buildings. Performance testing of components/products for residential ventilation. Performance testing of unducted mechanical supply and exhaust ventilation units [including heat recovery] for mechanical ventilation systems intended for a single room.

**BS EN 13986:2004**
Wood-based panels for use in construction. Characteristics, evaluation of conformity and marking.

## Other publications referred to

### American Conference of Government industrial hygienists (ACGIH)
Industrial ventilation 24th Edition, Manual of recommended practice. Available from www.acgih.org/store

### Building Research Establishment (BRE)
BRE Digest 464, Part 1: VOC emissions from building products. Sources, testing and emission data, 2002. ISBN 1 86081 546 4

BRE Digest 464, Part 2: VOC emissions from building products. Control, evaluation and labelling schemes, 2002. ISBN 1 86081 547 2

BRE Report BR 417: Building regulation health and safety, 2001. ISBN 1 86081 475 1

### Chartered Institution of Building Services Engineers (CIBSE)
Applications Manual AM10: Natural ventilation in non-domestic buildings, 2005. ISBN 1 80328 7561

Applications Manual AM13: Mixed mode ventilation, 2000. ISBN 1 90328 701 4

CIBSE Guide A: Environmental design, 1999. ISBN 0 90095 396 9

CIBSE Guide B2: Ventilation and air conditioning, 2001. ISBN 1 90327 816 2

TM13: Minimising the risk of Legionnaires' disease, 2002. ISBN 1 90328 723 5

Ventilation hygiene toolkit:

BSRIA Facilities Management Specification 1 Guidance to the standard specification for ventilation hygiene, 2002. ISBN 0 86022 454 6

CIBSE TM26 Hygienic maintenance of office ventilation ductwork, 2000. ISBN 1 90328 711 1

HSE HSG 202 General ventilation in the workplace. Guidance for employers, 2000. ISBN 0 71761 793 9

HVCA TR17 Guide to good practice cleanliness of ventilation systems, 2002. ISBN 0 90378 335 5 (Withdrawn and superseded by TR/19 Guide to good practice. Internal cleanliness of ventilation systems, 2005. ISBN 0 90378 335 5.)

### Defence Estates
Defence Works Functional Standard, Design and Maintenance Guide 08: Space requirements for plant access operation and maintenance, 1996. ISBN 0 11772 785 7. Available from www.defence-estates.mod.uk/publications/ dmg/dmg_08.pdf

### Department for Constitutional Affairs (DCA)
Court standards and design guide, 2004. CD available from the DCA

### .Department for Education and Skills (DfES)
Building Bulletin 101, Ventilation of school buildings, 2005. ISBN 0 11271 164 2. See www.teachernet.gov.uk/iaq

### Department of Health Estates and Facilities Division
HTM 03; Part 1 - Ventilation in healthcare premises: Design and validation, 2005.

HTM 03; Part 2 - Ventilation in healthcare premises: Verification and operational Management, 2005.

HBN (various).

### Energy Saving Trust
Good Practice Guide 192. Designing energy efficient multi-residential buildings, 1997. Available from www.est. org.uk/bestpractice/index.cfm.

### Health and Safety Executive (HSE)
HSE Catering Information Sheet No 10, Ventilation of kitchens in catering establishments, 2000. Available from www.hsebooks.com.

HSE Catering Information Sheet No 11, The main health and safety law applicable to catering, 2000. Available from www.hsebooks.com.

HSG 37. Introduction to local exhaust ventilation, 1993. ISBN 011882 134 2

HSG 54. Maintenance, examination and testing of local exhaust ventilation, 1998. ISBN 071761 485 9

HSG 193. COSHH Essentials. Accessed on www. coshh-essentials.org.uk.

HSG 202 General ventilation in the workplace - Guidance for employers, 2000. ISBN 0 71761 793 9

L8 Legionnaires Disease: The control of legionella bacteria in water systems. Approved code of practice and guidance. 2000. ISBN 0 71761 772 6

L24 Workplace (Health, Safety and Welfare) Regulations 1992. Approved code of practice and guidance, 1998. ISBN 0 71760 413 6

### Legislation
Factories Act 1961, Chapter 34.

Welfare of Farm Animals (England) Regulations 2000, Sl 2000/1870.

Welfare of Farm Animals (England) (Amendment) Regulations 2002, Sl 2002/1646.

Welfare of Farm Animals (England) (Amendment) Regulations 2003. Sl 2003/299.

Department of the Environment, Transport and the Regions (DETR)

Planning Policy Guidance (PPG) 15: Planning and the historic environment. Available from www. odpm.gov.uk

Society for the Protection of Ancient Buildings (SPAB)

Information Sheet No. 4, The need for old buildings to 'breathe', 1987.

# GLOSSARY

For the purposes of this Approved Document the following definitions apply.

**Air permeability:** the physical parameter used to quantify the *air tightness* of the building fabric. It measures the resistance of the building envelope to *infiltration*. It is defined as the average volume of air (in cubic metres per hour) that passes through 1 unit area of the building envelope (in square metres) when subject to an internal to external pressure difference of 50 Pascals. The envelope area of the building is defined as the total area of the floor, walls and roof separating the interior volume from the outside environment. It is measured with ventilators closed.

**Air tightness:** a general descriptive term for the resistance of the building envelope to *infiltration* with ventilators closed. The greater the air tightness at a given pressure difference across the envelope, the lower the *infiltration*.

**Automatic control:** where a ventilation device is opened and closed or switched on and off or its performance is adjusted by a mechanical or electronic controller which responds to a relevant stimulus. That stimulus is usually related to the humidity of the air in a room, pollutant levels (e.g. carbon dioxide concentration in a room), occupancy of the space (e.g. using a passive infra-red motion detector) or pressure difference across the device (e.g. due to the wind outside).

**Background ventilator:** a small ventilation opening designed to provide controllable *whole building ventilation*. See Diagram 5.

**Basement for dwellings:** a dwelling, or a usable part of a dwelling (i.e. a habitable room), that is situated partly or entirely below ground level. Note that a cellar is distinct from a basement in that it is used only for storage, heating plant or for purposes other than habitation.

**Bathroom:** a room containing a bath or shower and, in addition, can also include sanitary accommodation.

**Cellar:** see basement for dwellings.

**Closable:** a ventilation opening which may be opened and closed under either manual or automatic control.

**Common spaces:** those spaces where large numbers of people are expected to gather, such as shopping malls or cinema/theatre foyers. For the purposes of this Approved Document, spaces used solely or principally for circulation (e.g. corridors and lift lobbies in office buildings and blocks of flats) are not common spaces.

**Continuous operation:** a mechanical ventilation device that runs all the time, e.g. mechanical extract ventilation (MEV) and mechanical ventilation with heat recovery (MVHR). The airflow rate provided by the mechanical ventilation need not be constant but may be varied, under either manual or automatic control, in response to the demand for pollutant or water vapour removal.

## Diagram 5.

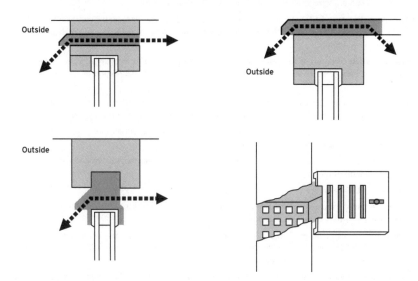

**Equivalent area:** a measure of the aerodynamic performance of a ventilator. It is the area of a sharp-edged orifice which air would pass at the same volume flow rate, under an identical applied pressure difference, as the opening under consideration.

**Extract ventilation:** the removal of air directly from a space or spaces to outside. Extract ventilation may be by natural means (e.g. by passive stack ventilation) or by mechanical means (e.g. by an extract fan or central system).

**Free area:** the geometric open area of a ventilator.

**Gross internal volume:** the total internal volume of the heated space, including the volume of all furniture, internal walls, internal floors, etc.

**Habitable room:** a room used for dwelling purposes but which is not solely a kitchen, utility room, bathroom, cellar or sanitary accommodation.

**Historic building:** these include: (a) listed buildings; (b) buildings situated in conservation areas; (c) buildings which are of architectural and historical interest and which are referred to as a material consideration in a local authority's development plan; (d) buildings of architectural and historical interest within national parks, areas of outstanding natural beauty and world heritage sites; and vernacular buildings of traditional form and construction.

**Infiltration:** the uncontrolled exchange of air between inside a building and outside through cracks, porosity and other unintentional openings in a building, caused by pressure difference effects of the wind and/or stack effect.

**Intermittent operation:** a mechanical ventilator that does not run all the time, usually only running when there is a particular need to remove pollutants or water vapour (e.g. during cooking or bathing). Intermittent operation may be under either manual control or automatic control.

**Manual control:** a ventilation device that is opened and closed or switched on and off or its performance is adjusted by the occupants of a room or building (c.f. automatic control).

**Occupiable room:** a room in a building other than a dwelling that is occupied by people, such as an office, workroom, classroom, hotel bedroom, but not a bathroom, sanitary accommodation, utility room or rooms or spaces used solely or principally for circulation, building services plant or storage purposes.

**Passive stack ventilation (PSV):** a ventilation device using ducts from terminals in the ceiling of rooms to terminals on the roof that extract air to outside by a combination of the natural stack effect and the pressure effects of wind passing over the roof of the building.

**Permanent:** a ventilation opening which is permanently fixed in the open position.

**Purge ventilation:** manually controlled ventilation of rooms or spaces at a relatively high rate to rapidly dilute pollutants and/or water vapour. Purge ventilation may be provided by natural means (e.g. an openable window) or by mechanical means (e.g. a fan).

**Purpose-provided ventilation:** that part of the ventilation of a building provided by ventilation devices designed into the building (e.g. via background ventilators, PSV, extract fans, mechanical ventilation or air conditioning systems).

**Sanitary accommodation:** a space containing one or more water closets or urinals. Sanitary accommodation containing one or more cubicles counts as a single space if there is free circulation of air throughout the space.

**Stack effect:** the pressure differential between inside and outside a building caused by differences in the density of the air due to an indoor/outdoor temperature difference.

**Utility room:** a room containing a sink or other feature or equipment which may reasonably be expected to produce water vapour in significant quantities.

**Ventilation:** the supply and removal of air

(by natural and/or mechanical means) to and from a space or spaces in a building. It normally comprises a combination of purpose-provided ventilation and infiltration.

**Ventilation opening:** any means of purpose- provided ventilation (whether it is permanent or closable) which opens directly to external air, such as the openable parts of a window, a louvre or a background ventilator. It also includes any door which opens directly to external air.

**Wet room:** a room used for domestic activities (such as cooking, clothes washing and bathing) which give rise to significant production of airborne moisture, e.g. a kitchen, utility room or bathroom. For the purposes of Part F, sanitary accommodation is also regarded as a wet room.

**Whole building ventilation (also called general ventilation):** nominally continuous ventilation of rooms or spaces at a relatively low rate to dilute and remove pollutants and water vapour not removed by operation of extract ventilation, purge ventilation or infiltration, as well as supplying outdoor air into the building.

# Appendix A: Performance-based ventilation

## Introduction

As specified in the section on Performance, this Approved Document recommends ventilation provisions to control both moisture and pollutants in buildings. In order to do this, acceptable levels of moisture and other pollutants need to be defined. This Appendix sets out the levels of moisture and other pollutants that the provisions in this Approved Document are designed to control.

Note that the guidance within this Approved Document may not be adequate to address pollutants from flueless combustion space heaters or from occasional, occupant-controlled events such as painting, smoking, cleaning or other high-polluting events. It does not address the airborne spread of infection nor contamination from outdoor sources. While many of these considerations could be important factors in achieving acceptable indoor air quality, solutions are not ready for inclusion in this guidance, and indeed they may be better controlled at source (e.g. avoidance, isolation or use of lower emitting products).

## Performance criteria for dwellings

The performance criterion for moisture is as follows:

• there should be no visible mould on external walls in a properly heated dwelling with typical moisture generation.

The principal performance criteria used for indoor air pollutants are as follows:

• nitrogen dioxide ($NO_2$) levels should not exceed:

- 288ug/m$^3$ (150ppb) - 1 hour average (DOH, 2004);

- 40ug/m$^3$ (20ppb) - long-term average (DOH, 2004);

• carbon monoxide should not exceed:

- 100mg/m³ (90ppm) - 15 minute averaging time (DOH, 2004);

- 60mg/m³ (50ppm) - 30 minute averaging time (DOH. 2004);

- 30mg/m³ (25ppm) - 1 hour averaging time (DOH. 2004);

- 10mg/m³ (10ppm) - 8 hours averaging time (DOH. 2004).

• Total volatile organic compound (TVOC) levels should not exceed 300ug/m³ averaged over 8 hours(ECA, 1992).

• Control of bio-effluents (body odours) for adapted individuals (reduction in perception due to being exposed to the environment for a period of time) will be achieved by an air supply rate of 3.5l/s/person (ASHRAE, 2003).

## Assumptions used in applying performance criteria for dwellings in Section 1

### General

• The dwelling has an air permeability of 3m3/h/m2 at 50Pa. This is approximately equivalent to an air leakage of 3ach at 50Pa for a multi-storey dwelling and an air leakage of 4ach at 50Pa for a single-storey dwelling.

• The infiltration rate is assumed to be 1/20th of the air leakage at 50Pa (using a common 'rule-of-thumb'). This is calculated at 0.15ach for a multi-storey dwelling and 0.20ach for a single-storey dwelling. This has been applied to the ventilation system types in Tables 1.2a, 1.2b and 1,2d. As discussed in Table 1,2c. infiltration is assumed to be negligible for mechanical extract ventilation systems.

• The ventilation effectiveness is 1.0.

• For the purposes of this Approved Document, the moisture criterion will be met if the relative humidity (RH) in a room does not exceed 70% for more than 2 hours in any 12 hour period, and does not exceed 90% for more than 1 hour in any 12 hour period during the heating season.

### Extract ventilation

• The principal pollutant to be removed by extract ventilation is moisture. The source rates were taken from BS 5250:2002 Table B.1.

• For intermittent extract:

- Historically, a ventilation rate of 60l/s has been specified in the kitchen for the removal of moisture and there is no strong justification to amend it. The ventilation rate removes moisture generated at a production rate of 2000g/h. A reduced ventilation rate of 30l/s is used for a cooker hood, owing to the greater ventilation effectiveness.

- Historically, a ventilation rate of 15l/s has been specified in the bathroom for the removal of moisture and there is no strong justification to amend it. The ventilation rate removes moisture generated at a production rate of 400g/h.

- In the utility room, it is assumed that the ventilation rate required is 50% of that in the kitchen.

- In WCs, the main pollutant is odour. Historically, a ventilation rate of 6l/s has been specified and there is no strong justification to amend it.

• For continuous extract:

- In the kitchen, several scenarios were considered. Effectively, they resulted in 1000g of water vapour being released into the kitchen air at a steady rate within a 1 hour period (after allowing for absorption and migration to other rooms, etc.). The ventilation rate was selected to prevent the 70% and 90% RH limits being exceeded in the kitchen.

- In the bathroom, several scenarios were considered. Effectively, they resulted in 650g of water vapour being released into the bathroom air at a steady rate within a 2 hour period (after allowing for absorption and migration to other rooms, etc.). The ventilation rate was selected to prevent the 70% and 90% RH limits being exceeded in the bathroom.

- In the utility room, it was assumed that the ventilation rate required is approximately 50% of that in the kitchen. For practicality. the ventilation rate required in the bathroom has been used.

- In WCs, the same value as intermittent extract has been applied.

- Combustion products can be generated from cooking, particularly from the use of gas. In particular, a BRE study of UK homes has shown that the levels of nitrogen dioxide can well exceed the performance criterion (Ross and Wilde, 1999). The data from this study were analysed to determine the maximum 1 hour nitrogen dioxide level for each home. The 90th percentile value of this sample was 1155mg/m3. Assuming a reasonable ventilation rate of 0.5ach in the kitchen during the study and an external nitrogen dioxide concentration of 20mg/m³ to meet the performance criterion of 288mg/m3 the extract ventilation rate in the kitchen would be required to be 2.2ach. For a kitchen of 20m³, this equates to approximately 121/s. Whilst this is less than required for moisture, it highlights that, if an alternative solution is determined for controlling moisture in the kitchen, 121/s is required to adequately control the level of nitrogen dioxide. Note that, at this ventilation rate, carbon monoxide from gas cooking should also be adequately controlled.

## Whole building ventilation

- The principal pollutant to be removed by whole building ventilation is moisture. The source rates were taken from BS 5250:2002 Table B.1.

- It was assumed that local extract removes 100% of the moisture generated in the bathroom and 50% of the moisture generated in the kitchen.

- An average ventilation rate was selected which removed all of the moisture produced in the dwelling over a 24 hour period (except for moisture removed by local extract). Further calculations, using typical occupant profiles (and moisture generation profiles), showed that the average relative humidity in the dwelling should not exceed 70% for more than 2 hours in any 12 hour period during winter and should not exceed 90% for more than 1 hour in any 12 hour period during winter.

- This results in the values in Table 1.1b.

- Note that these calculations are based on winter weather conditions. During warmer spring and autumn periods, the moisture removal capacity of the outdoor air will be less (i.e. the outdoor air on being heated to the internal temperature within the dwelling will have a higher relative humidity in the spring and autumn periods) and additional ventilation may be required. The provisions for purge ventilation (e.g. windows) may be used for this purpose.

- There are other pollutants which must also be adequately controlled. These are particularly important in homes of low occupant density where moisture production is low for the size of the property. Levels of volatile organic compounds were monitored in a recent BRE study of UK homes (Dimitroulopoulou et al, 2005). From these data, the total source production rate of volatile organic compounds was determined to be 300mg/h per m² of floor area. To meet the performance criterion of 300mg/m³, it requires a minimum whole building ventilation rate of 0.3 1/s per m² internal floor area.

## Purge ventilation

- A value of 4ach has been selected as:

  - it provides a purge ventilation rate an order of magnitude above whole building ventilation;

  - it is similar to the ventilation rate provided by windows in the 1995 edition of Approved Document F. The calculation assumes single-sided ventilation for a dwelling in an urban environment and an internal/external temperature difference of 3°C.

## Table 1.2 - whole building ventilation rates

- In determining the ventilation rates, the air supply rates in Table 1.1b have been used.

- The air supply rate has been reduced by 0.15ach (or 0.20ach for single-storey buildings) to allow for infiltration.

- To determine the equivalent areas, the standard airflow equation has been used as below:

$A = 1000. (Q/C^d).(p/.\Delta P)^{0.5}$

Where:

A = the background ventilator equivalent area (mm²)

Q = the air supply rate (l/s)

Cd = the discharge coefficient, taken as 0.61

p == the air density (kg/m³), taken as 1.2

$\Delta P$ = the pressure across the vent, which has been taken as 0.6Pa for single-storey dwellings and 1 .OPa for multi-storey dwellings.

Note that the total actual equivalent area required (Ar) is double that derived from the equation above. This only provides the equivalent area for air supplied to the dwelling. A similar equivalent **area** is required for air to exit the dwelling.

Note that in determining these pressure differences, a meteorological wind speed of 4m/s at 10m height was taken (based on BS 5925:1991) and an internal/external temperature difference of 15°C.

## Performance criteria for buildings other than dwellings

The main guidance within this document has focused on offices. For this, the main criteria have been:

• A supply rate, in the absence of tobacco smoking or other excessive pollutants, of 10l/s/person, based upon surveys which indicate that below this level the incidence of health effects becomes increasingly significant This will also satisfy the requirement of 8l/s/person needed to control bioeffluents for unadapted individuals.

• There should be no visible mould on external walls in a properly heated dwelling with typical moisture generation.

• Nitrogen dioxide (NO2) levels should not exceed:

- 288$\mu$g/m³ (150ppb) -1 hour average (Department of the Environment, 1996);

- 40$\mu$g/m³ (21ppb) - long-term average (WHO, 2003).

• Carbon monoxide for the general population should not exceed

- 100mg/m³ (90ppm) -15 minute averaging time (WHO. 2000);

- 60mg/m³ (50ppm) - 30 minute averaging time (WHO, 2000);

- 30mg/m³ (25ppm) -1 hour averaging time (WHO. 2000);

- 10mg/m³ (10ppm) - 8 hours averaging time (Department of the Environment, 1994a).

• Carbon monoxide for occupational exposure should not exceed:

- 35mg/m³ (30ppm) - 8 hours averaging time (HSE, 2003).

• Total volatile organic compound (TVOC) levels should not exceed 300$\mu$g/m3 averaged over 8 hours (ECA, 1992).

• Ozone levels should not exceed 100ug/m³ (Department of the Environment. 1994b).

Note that the guidance within this Approved Document may not be adequate to address pollutants from occasional, occupant-controlled events such as painting, smoking, cleaning or other high-polluting events. While these could be important factors in achieving acceptable indoor air quality, solutions are not ready for inclusion in this guidance, and indeed they may be better controlled at source (e.g. avoidance, isolation or use of lower emitting products).

Where the Health and Safety Executive gives guidance for specific situations, it should be followed in preference to the guidance given here.

## Assumptions used in applying performance criteria for offices in Section 2

### General
• The office has an air permeability of $3m^3/h/m^2$ at 50Pa.

• At this level of air permeability, in large buildings (low ratio of surface area to volume contained), infiltration can be assumed to be negligible compared with the purpose- provided ventilation.

• The ventilation effectiveness is 0.9 (for Table 2.1b).

• For the purposes of this Approved Document, the moisture criterion will be met if the relative humidity in a room does not exceed 70% for more than 2 hours in any 12 hour period, and does not exceed 90% for more than 1 hour in any 12 hour period, during the heating season.

### Extract ventilation
• Office equipment can emit pollutants including ozone and organic compounds. For example, a study by Black and Wortham (1999) suggests the following emission rates for laser printers and dry paper copiers assuming 30 minutes continual use in an hour:

- 25mg/h for TVOCs;

- 3mg/h for ozone.

To meet the performance criteria for these pollutants requires an extract rate of 20l/s per machine during use.

• For the sanitary accommodation, the extract rates used for dwellings have been applied.

• For food and beverage preparation areas, the extract rates used for dwellings have been applied.

### Whole building ventilation
• A number of studies have investigated ventilation and health in offices (principally sick building syndrome). Although there is no clear threshold ventilation rate below which health suddenly worsens, a number of sources have identified 10l/s/p as a significant level. This can probably be traced back to an analysis of experimental studies of office buildings by Mendell (1993). Hence the recommendation within the Approved Document for 10l/s/p for buildings with no smoking and no significant pollutant sources.

• Increasing the ventilation rate above 10l/s/p may improve health (results unclear), but there are diminishing returns (i.e. the improvement in health per 1/s/p increase in ventilation rate becomes smaller as the ventilation rate increases). It suggests that there is little advantage in increasing the whole building ventilation rate above 10l/s/p. Increased ventilation has a cost in economic and environmental terms. Having set a ventilation rate of 10l/s/p, if further improvements in indoor air quality are necessary, alternative approaches should be considered first, e.g. use of low-emission materials.

### Purge ventilation
• There are normally more options for the removal of high concentrations of pollutants from office spaces than for dwellings (e.g. leaving rooms unoccupied until acceptable pollutant levels are achieved). Hence, general guidance has been provided rather than specifying any ventilation rate(s).

### References
ASHRAE (2003). *Ventilation and acceptable indoor air quality In low-rise residential buildings*, ASHRAE Standard 62.2.

Black M S and Wortham A W (1999). *Emissions from office equipment*. Proceedings of the 8th International Conference on Indoor Air Quality and Climate, Indoor Air 99, Edinburgh 8-13 August 1999. Vol. 2. pp455-459.

BS 5250:2002 Code of practice for the control of condensation in buildings. BSI.

Department of the Environment (1994a). *Expert panel on air quality standards: Carbon monoxide.* London, HMSO. www.defra.gov.uk/environment/airquality/aqs

Department of the Environment (1994b). *Expert panel on air quality standards: Ozone.* London, HMSO. www.defra.gov.uk/environment/airquality/aqs

Department of the Environment (1996). *Expert panel on air quality standards: Nitrogen dioxide.* London, The Stationery Office, www.defra.gov. uk/environment/airquality/aqs

Department of Health (2004). Committee on the Medical Effects of Air Pollutants. Guidance on the effects on health of indoor air pollutants. http://www.advisorybodies.doh.gov.uk/comeap/ PDFS/guidanceindoorairqu alitydec04.pdf

Dimitroulopoulou C, Crump D, Coward S K D, Brown V, Squire R, Mann H, White M, Pierce B and Ross D (2005). *Ventilation, air tightness and indoor air quality in new homes.* Report BR 477. BRE bookshop.

ECA (1992). European Concerted Action on indoor air and its impact on man: Guidelines for ventilation requirements in buildings. Working Group Report No.11. EUR 14449 EN. Commission of the European Communities, Luxembourg.

HSE (2003). *Occupational exposure limits 2002, plus supplement 2003.* HSE Books.

Mendell M J (1993). *Non-specific symptoms in office workers: a review and summary of the epidemiologic literature.* Indoor air 3, 227-236.

Ross D I and Wilde D (1999). *Continuous monitoring of nitrogen dioxide and carbon monoxide levels in UK homes.* Proceedings of the 8th International Conference on Indoor Air Quality and Climate, Indoor Air 99, Edinburgh 8-13 August 1999, Vol. 3, pp147-152.

WHO (2000). *Guidelines for air quality.* World Health Organization, Geneva.

WHO (2003). *WHO working group meeting:Review of health aspects of air pollution with particulate matter, ozone and nitrogen dioxide,* Bonn, Germany. 13-15 January 2003.

# Appendix B: Purge ventilation

### Introduction
Adequate purge ventilation may be achieved by the use of openable windows and/or external doors. This Appendix provides details of necessary window and door sizes. It is a simplification of guidance in BS 5925:1991 Code of practice for ventilation principles and designing for natural ventilation. The diagrams below highlight the window dimensions of importance.

### Windows
• For a hinged or pivot window that opens 30°

or more, or for sliding sash windows, the height x width of the opening part should be at least 1/20 of the floor area of the room.

• For a hinged or pivot window that opens less than 30°, the height x width of the opening part should be at least 1/10 of the floor area of the room.

• If the room contains more than one openable window, the areas of all the opening parts may be added to achieve the required proportion of the floor area. The required proportion of the floor area is determined by the opening angle of the largest window in the room.

• Note that Approved Document B includes provisions for the size of escape windows. The larger of the provisions in Approved Document B or F should apply in all cases.

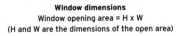

**Window dimensions**
Window opening area = H x W
(H and W are the dimensions of the open area)

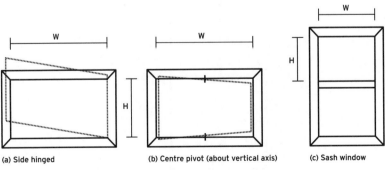

(a) Side hinged          (b) Centre pivot (about vertical axis)          (c) Sash window

**External doors (including patio doors)**

• For an external door, the height x width of the opening part should be at least 1/20 of the floor area of the room.

• If the room contains more than one external door, the areas of all the opening parts may be added to achieve at least 1/20 of the floor area of the room.

• If the room contains a combination of at least one external door and at least one openable window, the areas of

all the opening parts may be added to achieve at least 1/20 of the floor area of the room.

# Appendix C: Example calculations for ventilation sizing for dwellings

## Introduction

This appendix provides example calculations for each ventilation system set out in paragraph 1.8. A ground-floor flat and a semi-detached house have been considered for each system type. Thus there are eight examples as follows.

### Ground-floor flat:

• Example C1 - Background ventilators and intermittent extract fans

• Example C2 - Passive stack ventilation

• Example C3 - Continuous mechanical extract

• Example 04 - Continuous mechanical supply and extract

Semi-detached house:

• Example C5 Background ventilators and intermittent extract fans

• Example C6 - Passive stack ventilation

• Example C7 - Continuous mechanical extract

• Example C8 - Continuous mechanical supply and extract

---

**Diagram C1 Ground floor flat plan example**

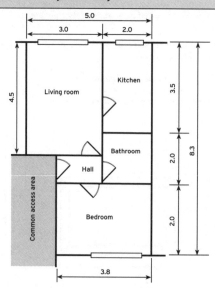

## Ground-floor flat

### Description

The flat contains the following rooms:

• kitchen;

• combined living/dining room;

• one double bedroom;

• internal bathroom containing WC; and in addition

• all rooms have an external wall except for the bathroom.

The floor plan is given in Diagram C1.

### Assumption:

• cooker hood adjacent to cooker hob;

• gross internal volume of the heated space of 83m³;

• total floor area of 36m²·

• two person occupancy; and

• side-hinged windows 1,0m high and openable to 60°.

### Example C1 Background ventilators and intermittent extract fans (this is based on Table 1.2a)

#### Intermittent extract

| Room | Intermittent extract rate |
|------|---------------------------|
| Kitchen | 30l/s (adjacent to hob) |
| Bathroom | 15l/s |

#### Background ventilator

• For a single-storey ground-floor dwelling of 36m² HOOT area, the dble shows that the equivalent background ventilator area is 30,000mm² (this includes the additional 5000mm² as we are considering a single-storey building).

• To maximise the airflow through the dwelling by encouraging cross ventilation, it is best to locate similar equivalent areas of background ventilators on opposite sides of the dwelling.

#### Purge ventilation

• Calculate the percentage window opening area (percentage of floor area) for each room having an external wafl.

• Using Appendix B with an opening angle of 60° gives: 1/20 of the floor area.

• Therefore, for a living room of 13.5m² floor area there should be a window opening area of at least 0.68m². This calculation should be carried out for all habitable rooms.

## Example C2 **Passive stack ventilation (this is based on Table 1 -2b)**

Choose appropriate Passive stack ventilation provision

| Room | Internal duct diameter (mm) | Internal cross-sectional area (mm²) | |
|---|---|---|---|
| Kitchen | 125 | 12,000 | |
| Bathroom | 100 | 8000 | |

**Background ventilator**

Calculate the total equivalent area of ventilators required for a dwelling as follows:

• Step 1: for a single-storey ground-floor dwelling of 36m² floor area, Table 1,2a shows that the equivalent background ventilator area is 30.000mm² (this includes the additional 5000mm² as we are considering a single-storey building).

• Step 2: for a PSV in both the kitchen and bathroom, an allowance of 5000mm² can be made.

• Step 3:30,000-5000= 25.000mm²·

• In addition, the equivalent area must be at least the total cross-sectional area of the ducts (20,000mm²), which it is. It should be distributed with similar areas on opposite sides of the dwelling (but not in the kitchen and bathroom).

**Purge ventilation**

• Calculate the percentage window opening area (percentage of floor area) for each room having an external wal.

• Using Appendix B with an opening angle of 60° gives: 1/20 of the floor area.

• Therefore, for a living room of 13.5m² floor area there should be a window opening area of at least 0.68m². Thte calculation should be carried out for all habitable rooms.

## Example C3 **Continuous mechanical extract (this is based on Table 1.2c)**

**Continuous extract**

Step 1: Whole builiding ventilation rate is 13l/s.

Step 2: Whoto dwelling extract rate is 21 l/s (assuming extract in kitchen and bathroom).

Step 3: Maximum rate (e.g. boost) is at least 21 l/s (with a minimum of 13l/s in the kitchen and 8l/3 in the bathroom). • The minimum rate is at least 13l/s (spread between the kitchen and bathroom).

**Background ventilators**

• Background ventilators of at least 2500mm² equivalent area should be located in the living room and bedroom.

**Purge ventilation**

• Calculate the percentage window opening area (percentage of floor area) for each room having an external wall.

• Using Appendix B with an opening angle of 60° gives: 1/20 of the floor area.

• Therefore, for a living room of 13.5m² floor area there should be a window opening area of at least 0.68m². This calculation should be carried out for all habitable rooms.

---

**Example C4 Continuous mechanical supply and extract with heat recovery (this is based on Table 1.2d)**

**Continuous supply and extract**

Step 1: Calculate the whole building ventilation supply rate:

i. from the table, the air supply rate = 131/s;

ii. allow for infiltration by subtracting 0.06 x gross internal volume of the dwelling (m3).
    Ventilation rate = 13 - 0.06 x 83 = 8»/s

Step 2: Calculate the whole dwelling air extract rate at maximum operation: whole dwelling extract rate for the dwelling is 21 l/s (assuming extract in kitchen and bathroom).

Step 3:
• Maximum rate (e.g. boost) is at toaat 211/8 (with 131/s extract in the kitchen and 81/s extract in the bathroom).
• The minimum rate is at least 81/s.

---

**Purge ventilation**

• Calculate the percentage window opening area (percentage of floor area) for each room having an external wall.

• Using Appendix B with an opening angle of 60° gives: 1/20 of the floor area.

• Therefore, for a living room of 13.5m² floor area there should be a window opening area of at least 0.08m². This calculation should be carried out for all habitable rooms.

---

## Semi-detached house
### Description
The semi-detached house contains the following rooms:

• entrance hall/stairway;
• kitchen;
• dining room;
• living room;
• three bedrooms;
• bathroom containing WC; and in addition
• all rooms have an external wall.

The floor plan is given in Diagrams C2 and C3.

### Assumptions:
• cooker hood adjacent to cooker hob;

- gross internal volume of the heated space of 210m³;
- total floor area of 84m²;
- four person occupancy; and
- side-hinged windows 1m high and openable to a fixed position of 15°.

**Diagram C2 Semi-detached house**

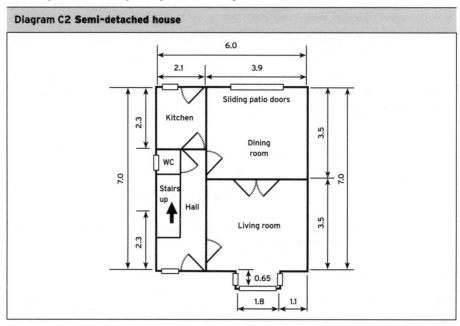

**Diagram C3 Semi-detached house first-floor plan example**

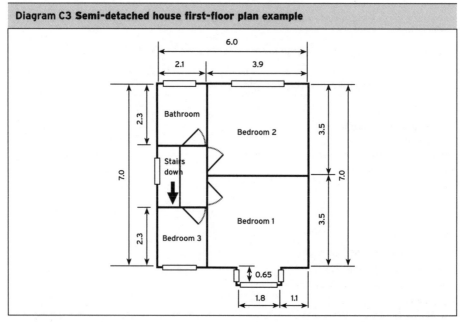

### Example C5 **Background ventilators and intermittent extract fans (this is based on Table 1.2a)**

**Intermittent extract**

| Room | Intermittent extract rate %. |
|------|------------------------------|
| Kitchen | 30l/8 (adjacent to hob) |
| Bathroom 1 | 5l/s |

**Background ventilators**

• For a two-storey semi-detached house of 84m² floor area, the table shows that the equivalent background ventilator area is 40,000mm².

• To maximise the airflow through the dwelling by encouraging cross ventilation, it is best to locate similar equivalent areas of background ventilators on opposite sides of the dwelling.

**Purge ventilation**

• Calculate the percentage window opening area (percentage of floor area) for each room having an external wall.

• Using Appendix B with an opening angle of 15° gives: 1/10 of the floor area.

• Therefore, for a living room of 14.8m² floor area there should be a window opening area of at least 1.48m². This calculation should be carried out for all habitable rooms.

### Example C6 **Passive stack ventilation (this is based on Table 1.2b)**

**Choose appropriate Passive stack ventilation provision**

| Room | Internal duct diameter (mm) | Internal cross sectional area (mm²) |
|------|------------------------------|--------------------------------------|
| Kitchen | 125 | 12,000 |
| Bathroom | 100 | 8000 |

**Background ventilators**

Calculate the total equivalent area of ventilators required for a dwelling as follows:

• Step 1: for a two-storey semi-detached house of 84m² floor area, Table 1.2a shows that the equivalent background ventilator area is 40,000mm².

• Step 2: for a PSV in both the kitchen and bathroom, an allowance of 5000mm² can be made.

• Step 3: 40,000-5000= 35,000mm².

• In addition, the equivalent area must be at least the total cross-sectional area of the ducts (20,000mm²), which it is. It should be distributed with similar areas on opposite sides of the dwelling (but not in the kitchen and bathroom).

**Purge ventilation**

• Calculate the percentage window opening area (percentage of floor area) for each room having an external wall.

• Using Appendix B with an opening angle of 15° gives: 1/10 of the floor area.

• Therefore, for a living room of 14.8m² floor area there should be a window opening area of at least 1.48m². This calculation should be carried out for all habitable rooms.

---

Example C7  **Continuous mechanical extract (this is based on Table 1.2c)**

---

**Continuous extract**

**Step1:**      • Whole building ventilation rate from the list in the table is 21 l/s.

• However, minimum air supply rate = 0.3 x floor area = 0.3 x 84 = 25l/s.

• Hence, whole house air supply rate is 25l/s.

**Step 2:**     Whole dwelling extract rate is 21 l/s (assuming extract in kitchen and bathroom).

**Step 3:**    • In this case the required whole house supply rate is greater than the whole house extract rate, and only a minimum extract rate of 25l/s is required (with at least 13l/s in the kitchen and 8l/s in the bathroom).

---

**Background ventilators •**

• Background ventilators of at least 2500mm² equivalent area should be located in the living room, dining room and each bedroom.

---

**Purge ventilation**

• Calculate the percentage window opening area (percentage of floor area) for each room having an external wall.

• Using Appendix B with an opening angle of 15° gives: 1/10 of the floor area.

• Therefore, for a living room of 14.8m² floor area there should be a window opening area of at least 1.48m² This calculation should be carried out for all habitable rooms.

---

Example C8  **Continuous mechanical supply and extract with heat recovery (this is based on Table 1.2d)**

---

**Continuous supply and extract**

**Step 1:** Calculate the whole dwelling air supply rate:

i. Whole building ventilation rate for the dwelling from the list in the table is 21l/8. However, minimum air supply rate = 0.3 x floor area = 0.3 x 84 = 25l/s. Hence, whole dwelling air supply rate is 25l/s.

ii. Allow for infiltration by subtracting 0.04 x gross internal volume of the dwelling (m³):

Ventilation rate = 25 - 0.04 x 210 = 17l/s.

**Step 2:** Calculate the whole dwelling air extract rate at maximum operation:

whole dwelling extract rate is 21 l/s (assuming extract in kitchen and bathroom).

**Step 3:** • Maximum rate (e.g. boost) is at least 21 l/s (with 13l/s extract in the kitchen and 8l/s extract in the bathroom).
• The minimum rate is at least 17l/s.

---

**Purge ventilation**

• Calculate the percentage window opening area (percentage of floor area) for each room having an external wan.

• Using Appendix B with an opening angle of 15° gives: 1/10 of the floor area.

• Therefore, for a living room of 14.8m² floor area there should be a window opening area of at least 1.48m². This calculation should be carried out for all habitable rooms.

---

# Appendix D: Passive stack ventilation system design and installation guidance

The design and installation of passive stack ventilation systems (PSV) can have a significant influence on their performance. However, if the following guidance is closely followed adequate performance may be assumed to have been achieved.

## DESIGN - SYSTEM LAYOUT

• The layouts shown in Diagram D1 are considered to be suitable for the majority of dwellings of up to four storeys. Placing the outlet terminal at the ridge of the roof (Diagram D1 (a)) is the preferred option for reducing the adverse effects of wind gusts and certain wind directions. A tile ventilator may be used to terminate a PSV system on the roof slope but the terminal must be positioned no more than 0.5m from the roof ridge. If the duct penetrates the roof more than 0.5m from the ridge, it must extend above the roof slope to at least ridge height to ensure that the duct terminal is in the negative pressure region above the roof (Diagram D1(b)).

• Separate ducts are taken from the ceilings of the kitchen, bathroom, utility room or WC to separate terminals on the roof. Do not use common outlet terminals or branched ducts.

• Ducts should ideally use no more than one offset (i.e. no more than two bends) and these should be of the 'swept' rather than 'sharp' type to minimise flow resistance. Offsets at an angle of no more than 45° to the vertical are preferred (Diagram D2).

• If a dwelling in which PSV is proposed is situated near a significantly taller building (i.e. more than 50% taller), it should be at least five times the difference in height away from the taller building (e.g. if the difference in height is 10m, PSV should not be installed in a dwelling within 50m of the taller building).

Diagram D1 **Suitable layouts for PSV systems**

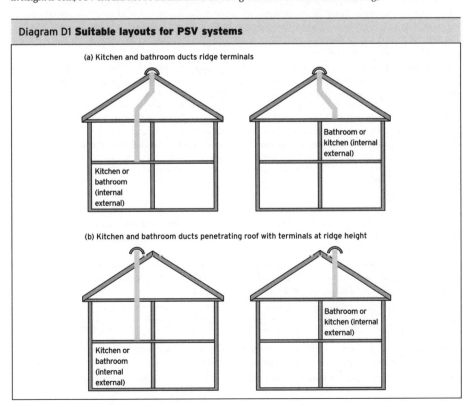

(a) Kitchen and bathroom ducts ridge terminals

Bathroom or kitchen (internal external)

Kitchen or bathroom (internal external)

(b) Kitchen and bathroom ducts penetrating roof with terminals at ridge height

Bathroom or kitchen (internal external)

Kitchen or bathroom (internal external)

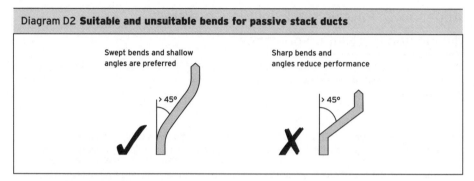

Diagram D2 **Suitable and unsuitable bends for passive stack ducts**

Swept bends and shallow angles are preferred

Sharp bends and angles reduce performance

> 45°

> 45°

## Design - component specifications

• Ceiling extract grilles should have a free area of not less than the duct cross-sectional area (when in the fully open position if adjustable).

• Both rigid ducting (e.g. PVCu pipes and fittings) and flexible ducting are suitable for PSV systems and have similar resistance to airflow at typical PSV system airflow rates.

• Ducts should be insulated in the roof space and other unheated areas with at least 25mm of a material having a thermal conductivity of 0.04W/m-K. Where a duct extends above roof level the section above the roof should be insulated or a condensation trap should be fitted just below roof level.

• The outlet terminal should have a free area of not less than the duct cross-sectional area. If a conversion fitting is required to connect the duct to the terminal then the duct cross-sectional area must be maintained (or exceeded) throughout the conversion fitting so as not to restrict the flow. The terminal should not allow ingress of large insects or birds and should be designed so that rain is not likely to enter the duct and run down into the dwelling. The terminal should also be designed such that any condensation forming inside it cannot run down into the dwelling but will run off onto the roof.

• Roof terminal design can be critical to PSV system performance. As a general guide, gas flue terminals tested to BS 715:1993 and having the required free areas are likely to perform well aerodynamically but may suffer from excessive water penetration in heavy or driving rain conditions. Specially made PSV roof outlet terminals should also perform well aerodynamically and are generally designed to resist water penetration to a greater extent than gas flue terminals. A draft European Standard for testing cowls and roof outlets is in preparation (prEN 13141-5) but at present there is insufficient information to recommend specific minimum or maximum values for performance parameters derived from that Standard. As interim guidance it is suggested that terminals, with any necessary conversion fitting, should have an overall static pressure loss (upstream duct static minus test room static) equivalent to no more than four times the mean duct velocity pressure when measured at a static pressure difference of 10 Pascal.

## Installation

• Carefully measure the length of duct to be used such that it is just sufficient to fit between the ceiling grille and the outlet terminal. Flexible ducting should be fully extended but not taut, allowing approximately 300mm extra to make smooth bends in an offset system.

• Ducting should be properly supported along its length to ensure that the duct can run straight without distortion or sagging and that there are no kinks at any bends or the connections to ceiling grilles and outlet terminals. Flexible ducting generally requires more support than rigid ducting.

• In the roof space it is recommended that the duct be secured to a wooden strut that is securely fixed at both ends. A flexible duct should be allowed to curve gently at each end of the strut to attach to the ceiling grille and roof outlet terminal.

• Use a rigid duct for that part of a PSV system which is outside, above the roof slope, to give it stability. It should project down into the roof space far enough to allow firm support.

• Ensure that the duct is securely fixed to the roof outlet terminal so that it cannot sag or become detached.

### Operation of PSV in hot weather

A PSV unit should extract sufficient air from the wet rooms during the heating season. However, during warmer weather, particularly the summer months, the temperature difference between the internal and external air will be significantly reduced. Consequently, the stack driving pressures will be reduced and, to ensure adequate ventilation during the warmer months, provision for purge ventilation should also be made in these wet rooms.

### Fire precautions

Where a dwelling extends to three or more storeys, and in blocks of flats, fire precautions may be required to ensure that escape routes are not prejudiced by the presence of PSV ducts. Guidance on such fire precautions may be found in Building Regulations: Approved Document B.

### Noise

In locations where external noise is likely to be intrusive (e.g. near busy roads and airports) some sound attenuation in the duct is desirable. In such situations it is suggested that fitting a proprietary sound attenuator duct section in the roof space just above the ceiling is likely to be effective.

# Appendix E: Good practice guide to the installation of fans for dwellings

### Introduction

The following is offered as general guidance, but accurate system design using manufacturers' performance data is recommended. In such designs, the resistance of the ducted system should be matched against the selected fan performance curve (available from the manufacturer) to achieve the installed performance for the room type referred to in the Approved Document.

With all installations it is important that simple good practice is followed to ensure that the fan installed is capable of meeting the relevant requirements. Different fan types should be used for the applications they are designed to meet. If the wrong fan type is used there is a risk of it not performing to the required airflow rate and also a chance of reducing its operational life.

This document covers four main fan types commonly used in domestic applications:

1. axial fans - wall or window and short ducts through the ceiling;

2. centrifugal - wall or window for exposed sites and longer ducts through the ceiling;

3. in-line axial fans for ducted applications;

4. in-line mixed flow fans.

If an application falls outside the limits described within this Appendix then alternative methods, such as those described elsewhere in this Approved Document, should be considered.

### Axial fans

The axial fan is the most common form of fan used for wall and window mounting applications. A short length of rigid round duct at least the same diameter as the fan outlet or equally sized flexible duct pulled taut is suitable to duct them through a wall up to 350mm thick.

Where necessary, the manufacturer may supply a window kit allowing the fan to be installed through a suitable glazing hole.

Bathroom applications using 100mm diameter fans can also utilise an axial fan for installations in the ceiling with up to 1.5m of flexible duct and two 90° bends. The duct must be pulled taut and the discharge terminal should have at least 85% free area of the duct diameter. Normally, any extension of the duct beyond this length will cause performance to drop. However, manufacturers' data should be referred to.

## Centrifugal fans

Centrifugal fans develop greater pressure allowing longer lengths of ducting to be used. They may also be used for wall or window applications in high rise (above three storeys) or exposed locations to overcome wind pressure.

Centrifugal fans are mostly designed with 100mm diameter outlets, which enable them to be connected to a wide variety of duct types. However, good practice still applies as detailed in the general notes section at the end of this Appendix.

In general:

• If using a wall/ceiling mounted centrifugal fan designed to achieve 60l/s for kitchens with 100mm diameter flexible duct or rectangular ducting it should not be ducted further than 3m with 1 x 90° bend.

• If using a wall/ceiling mounted centrifugal fan designed to achieve 15l/s for bathrooms with 100mm diameter flexible duct or rectangular dueling it should not be ducted further than 6m with 2 x 90° bends.

Note: Where this is not practical, a trade-off may be permitted such that the addition of one bend will equate to a reduction of 1m in duct length.

It should be noted that recirculating cooker hoods does not fulfil the ventilation requirements of Part F.

## In-line fans

The in-line fan type of installation has some advantages to offer over that of a typical window/wall fan installation, but there is a trade-off to be made. These systems are generally available for bathrooms (100mm diameter), utility rooms (125mm diameter) and kitchens (150mm diameter).

## In-line axial fan

An in-line axial fan should be installed with the shortest possible duct length to the discharge terminal. Refer to manufacturers' data.

## In-line mixed flow fans

An in-line mixed flow inline fan is a hybrid with the mixed characteristics of axial fans and centrifugal fans allowing them to be used on longer lengths of ducting. Refer to manufacturers' data.

## Terminals

For this situation only, the equivalent area may be assumed to be equal to the free area.

### 1. Room Terminal: Extract grille

Ensure that the equivalent area of the grille opening is a minimum of 85% of the equivalent area of the ducting being used.

### 2. Discharge Terminal

Ensure that the equivalent area of the grille opening is a minimum of 85% of the equivalent area of the ducting being used.

## GOOD PRACTICE GUIDE TO THE INSTALLATION OF FANS FOR DWELLINGS

## General notes

• Adequate replacement air must also be available, e.g. a 10mm gap under the door or equivalent.

• Fans and ducting placed in or passing through unheated voids or loft spaces should be insulated to reduce the possibility of condensation forming.

• Where a duct rises vertically it may be necessary to fit a condensation trap in order to prevent backflow of any moisture into the product.

• Horizontal ducting, including ducting in walls, should be arranged to slope slightly downwards away from the fan to prevent backflow of any moisture into the product.

• All duct runs should be straight, with as few bends and kinks as possible to minimise system resistance.

• Where ducting passes through a fire-stopping wall or fire compartment, the required measures to ensure compliance with Part B of the Building Regulations must be taken.

• All flexible ducting should be pulled taut to minimise system resistance.

• The inner radius of any bend should be greater or equal to the diameter of the ducting being used. If the radius is reduced, the resistance of the bend will increase and the volume of air being extracted will decrease (see Diagram E1).

• To reduce any incidence of draught it is desirable that a device (back-draught) be introduced into the system, this may be incorporated into the fan itself.

• Rectangular ducting is also available. Its use should fall within the limitations of the duct length guidelines given in this Appendix.

• Care should be taken when positioning the ducting to ensure that it cannot be damaged through occupier use of the space in which it is installed.

• Ensure flexible ducting is installed without peaks or troughs (see Diagram E1 a).

• Ensure that the circular profile of flexible duct is maintained throughout the full length of the duct run. Where the flexible ducting passes through a smaller gap and the flexible duct is deformed, the resistance will increase, leading to loss of extracted air volume (see Diagram E1 b).

## Diagram E1 **Correct installation**

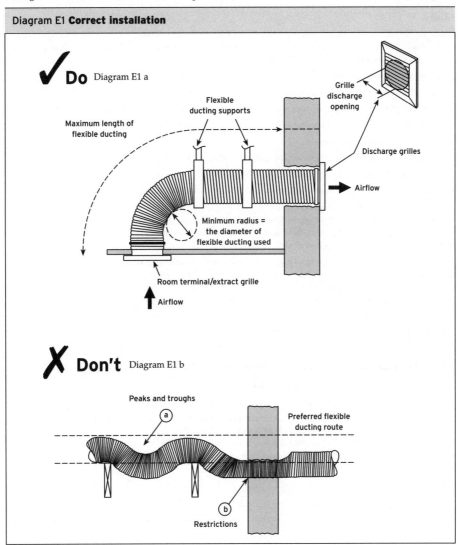

# Appendix F: Minimising ingress of external pollution into buildings in urban areas

Typical urban pollutants that need to be considered include those covered by the UK Air Quality Strategy (DETR(2000)). These are:

- carbon monoxide, CO;
- nitrogen dioxide, $NO_2$;
- sulphur dioxide, $SO_2$;
- ozone, $O_3$;
- particles ($PM_{10}$);
- benzene;
- 1,3-butadiene;
- lead

Although nitrogen oxide, NO, is not included in the UK Air Quality Strategy, it is a normal constituent of combustion discharges and in many cases (for example, from gas-fired plant) the largest polluting emitter; therefore, it also needs to be taken into account.

Typical pollution emission sources that need to be considered include:

- road traffic, including traffic junctions and underground car parks;
- combustion plant (such as heating appliances) running on conventional fuels, most commonly natural gas;
- other combustion processes (for example, waste incineration, thermal oxidation abatement systems);
- discharges from industrial processes;
- fugitive (i.e. adventitious/not effectively controlled) discharges from industrial processes and other sources;
- building ventilation system exhaust discharges;
- construction and demolition sites which are source of particles and vapourous discharges.

In urban areas, buildings are exposed simultaneously to a large number of individual pollution sources from varying upwind distances (long range, intermediate range and short range) and heights and also over different timescales. The relationship between these and their proportionate contribution under different circumstances governs pollutant concentrations over the building shell and also internally.

Internal contamination of buildings from outdoor pollution sources therefore depends upon the pollutant sources, the physical characteristics of the building and its relation to its surroundings, the ventilation strategy employed and the location of the air intake. Whatever type of ventilation system is used, it is important to ensure that the intake air is not contaminated. This is especially important in air quality management areas where, by definition, pollution levels of at least one pollutant are already close to the air quality standards.

Simplified guidance on ventilation intake placement for minimising ingress of pollutants may be summarised, as in Table F1.

**Table F1 Guidance on ventilation intake placement for minimising ingress of pollutants**

| Pollutant source | Recommendation |
|---|---|
| **Local static sources:** | Ventilation intakes need to be placed away from the direct impact of short-range pollution sources especially if the sources are within a few metres of the building.<br>Some guidance is given in CIBSE TM21. |
| • Parking areas<br>• Welding areas<br>• Loading bays<br>• Adjacent building exhausts<br>• Stack discharges | |

| Pollutant source | Recommendation |
|---|---|
| **Urban traffic** | |
| | Air intakes for buildings positioned directly adjacent to urban roads should be as high as possible and away from the direct influence of the source so as to minimise the ingress of traffic pollutants. There will be exceptions to this simple guide and these risks may need to be assessed by modelling. In such case it is recommended that expert advice is sought. |
| | For buildings located one or two streets away, the placement of intakes is less critical. |
| **Building Features/Layout:**<br>• Courtyards; | Intakes should not be located in these spaces where there are air pollutant discharges. This included emission discharges from building ventilation system exhausts. |
| • Street Canyons (i.e. a canyon formed in a street between two rows of tall buildings). | |
| | If air intakes are to be located in these spaces, they should be positioned as far as possible from the source in an open or well-ventilated area.<br>In addition, steps should be taken to reduce the polluted source, e.g. parking and loading should be avoided as pollutants can accumulate in enclosed regions such as courtyards. |
| **Multiple Sources** | Where there are large numbers of local sources, the combined effect of these around the facade of the building should be assessed. The facade experiencing the lowest concentration of the pollutants would be an obvious choice for locating ventilation intakes but this will require expert assistance such as numerical and wind tunnel modelling. In general, however, it is recommended that the air intakes be positioned as far from the source at a location where air is free to move around the intake. |
| **Weather Factors** | In areas where predominant wind comes from opposing directions (e.g. a valley location) the air intakes and outlets should point in opposite directions. |
| | In complex urban layouts, complex wind flows are likely to occur. In these cases, expert advice should be sought. |

## Control of ventilation intakes

For pollutant sources such as urban road traffic, whose concentration fluctuates with the time of day, reducing the flow of external air or closing ventilation intakes during peak periods of high external pollutant concentrations, for example during rush hours, for up to an hour may be an option.

Air intakes located on a less polluted side of the building may then be used for fresh air, or air may be fully re-circulated within the building. Alternatively, the building may be used as a 'fresh air' reservoir to supply air during these short periods. The use of atria as a source of 'fresh air' for this purpose may be an option.

However, care must be taken since, for example, reducing the inflow of external air will also reduce the outflow of internal air, resulting in a build-up of internally generated pollutants that need to be removed. Most modern buildings have low ceiling heights and therefore the concept of a substantial 'fresh air' reservoir available within the building may not apply. Further details of this principle with examples may be found in Liddament (2000).

## Location of exhaust outlets

The location of exhausts is as important as the location of air intakes. These should be located such that re-entry to a building, or ingestion into other nearby buildings, is minimised (for both natural and mechanical intakes) and such that there is no adverse effect to the surrounding area. Guidance on outlet placement may be summarised as follows.

• Exhausts should be located downstream of intakes where there is a prevailing wind direction.

• Exhausts should not discharge into courtyards, enclosures or architectural screens as pollutants tend to build up in such spaces and do not disperse very readily.

• It is recommended that stacks should discharge vertically upwards and at high level to clear surrounding buildings and so that downwash does not occur.

• Where possible, pollutants from stacks should be grouped together and discharged vertically upwards. The increased volume will provide greater momentum and increased plume height. This is common practice where there are a number of fume cupboard discharges; greater plume height dispersion can be achieved by adding the general ventilation exhaust.

## References
CIBSE (1999). CIBSE Technical Memorandum TM21. Minimising Pollution at Air Intakes. ISBN 0 90095 391 8

Liddament MW (2000) Chapter 13: Ventilation strategies. Indoor Air Quality Handbook. McGraw-Hill.

The Building Regulations 2000

# CONSERVATION OF FUEL AND POWER IN EXISTING DWELLINGS

**APPROVED DOCUMENT**

Came into effect April 2007

## MAIN CHANGES IN THE 2006 EDITIONS

**1.** This Approved Document L1 B comes into force on 06 April 2006 in support of the Building and Approved Inspectors (Amendment) Regulations 2006, Sl 2006/652. From that date the 2002 edition of Approved Document L1 will become obsolescent. The main changes in the legal requirements and the supporting technical guidance in this edition of Approved Document L1 B are as follows,

### Changes in the legal requirements

**2.** The main legal changes are reproduced at the front of this Approved Document and interleaved as well in the relevant text for ease of reference. In cases of doubt however refer to the Sl itself.

**3.** Part L of Schedule 1 has been consolidated into a single requirement L1, covering all types of building with no limits on application.

**4.** As well as changes to Part L, there are significant changes to the definitions of works and exempt works and a new definition of 'thermal element' is introduced to address more types of alteration and renovation work. New requirements apply when providing or renovating thermal elements and commissioning heating, ventilation and lighting systems.

**5.** The scope of the Competent Persons schemes in Schedule 2A has been widened and more scheme operators have been approved. Engaging an approved Competent Person is not obligatory but building control bodies are authorised to accept self-certification by such persons enabling reduced administrative burdens, delays and costs.

**6.** The list of works in Schedule 2B that need not be notified to building control bodies (but which must still comply) has been substantially increased to include minor works on heating, ventilation and lighting systems.

Changes in the technical guidance

**7.** Four Approved Documents are published reflecting the specialisation in the construction market. In the new Approved Documents regulatory requirements are shown on a green background and defined terms are highlighted. More use has been made of more comprehensive and detailed technical reference publications that therefore form part of the approved guidance. Commentary text has been added in places to explain, for instance, the aims of the guidance and how outcomes are calculated.

**8.** In this Approved Document the guidance is based on an elemental approach to compliance. The main technical changes comprise a general improvement in the performance standards that are considered reasonable for work on thermal elements, windows, doors heating, hot water, ventilation and lighting systems in existing dwellings. As an exception to this the standards for replacement windows, roof windows and rooflights are unchanged from those in ADL1 (2002),

**9.** More guidance is given enabling greater flexibility when building extensions including conservatories and other highly glazed designs. The exemption for conservatories remains unchanged.

**10.** A new section contains guidance on ways of complying with the new requirements for provision and renovation of thermal elements. A new Appendix A gives examples of what can be achieved cost-effectively.

# Contents:

# Use of guidance

## THE APPROVED DOCUMENTS

This document is one of a series that has been approved and issued by the Secretary of State for the purpose of providing practical guidance with respect to the technical requirements of the Building Regulations 2000 for England and Wales.

At the back of this document is a list of all the documents that have been approved and issued by the Secretary of State for this purpose.

Approved Documents are intended to provide guidance for some of the more common building situations. However, there may well be alternative ways of achieving compliance with the requirements. Thus there is no obligation to adopt any particular solution contained in an Approved Document if you prefer to meet the relevant requirement in some other way.

## OTHER REQUIREMENTS

The guidance contained in an Approved Document relates only to the particular requirements of the Regulations that the document addresses. The building work will also have to comply with the requirements of any other relevant paragraphs in Schedule 1 to the Regulations.

There are Approved Documents that give guidance on each of the Parts of Schedule 1 and on Regulation 7.

In accordance with Regulation 8, the requirements in Parts A to D, F to K and N (except for paragraphs H2 and J6) of Schedule 1 to the Building Regulations) do not require anything to be done except for the purpose of securing reasonable standards of health and safety for persons in or about buildings (and any others who may be affected by buildings or matters connected with buildings). This is one of the categories of purpose for which Building Regulations may be made.

Paragraphs H2 and J6 are excluded from Regulation 8 because they deal directly with prevention of the contamination of water. Parts E and M (which deal, respectively, with resistance to the passage of sound, and access to and use of buildings) are excluded from Regulation 8 because they address the welfare and convenience of building users. Part L is excluded from Regulation 8 because it addresses the conservation of fuel and power. All these matters are amongst the purposes, other than health and safety that may be addressed by Building Regulations.

Any building work which is subject to the requirements imposed by Schedule 1 to the Building Regulations should, in accordance with Regulation 7, be carried out with proper materials and in a workmanlike manner

You may show that you have complied with Regulation 7 in a number of ways. These include the appropriate use of a product bearing CE marking in accordance with the Construction Products Directive (89/106/EEC)[1], the Low Voltage Directive (73/23/EEC and amendment 93/68/EEC)[2] and the EMC Directive (89/336/ EEC)[3] as amended by the CE Marking Directive (93/68/EEC)[4] or a product complying with an appropriate technical specification (as defined in those Directives), a British Standard, or an alternative national technical specification of any state which is a contracting party to the European Economic Area which, in use, is equivalent, or a product covered by a national or European certificate issued by a European Technical Approval Issuing body, and the conditions of use are in accordance with the terms of the certificate. You will find further guidance in the Approved Document supporting Regulation 7 on materials and workmanship.

## INDEPENDENT CERIFICATION SCHEMES

There are many UK product certification schemes. Such schemes certify compliance with the requirements of a recognised document that is appropriate to the purpose for which the material is to be used. Materials which are not so certified may still conform to a relevant standard.

---

[1] As Implemented by the Construction Products Regulations 1991 (Sl 1991/1620).

[2] As implemented by the Electrical Equipment (Safety) Regulations 1994 (Sl 1994/3260).

[3] As implemented by the Electromagnetic Compatibility Regulations 1992 (Sl 1992/2372).

[4] As implemented by the Construction Products (Amendment) Regulations 1994 (Sl 1994/305. 1) and the Electromagnetic Compatibility (Amendment) Regulations 1994 (Sl 1994/3080).

Many certification bodies that approve such schemes are accredited by UKAS.

## TECHNICAL SPECIFICATIONS

Building Regulations are made for specific purposes: health and safety, energy conservation and the welfare and convenience of disabled people. Standards and technical approvals are relevant guidance to the extent that they relate to these considerations. However, they may also address other aspects of performance such as serviceability, or aspects which although they relate to health and safety are not covered by the Regulations.

When an Approved Document makes reference to a named standard, the relevant version of the standard is the one listed at the end of the publication. However, if this version has been revised or updated by the issuing standards body, the new version may be used as a source of guidance provided it continues to address the relevant requirements of the Regulations.

The appropriate use of a product that complies with a European Technical Approval as defined in the Construction Products Directive will meet the relevant requirements.

The Office intends to issue periodic amendments to its Approved Documents to reflect emerging harmonised European Standards. Where a national standard is to be replaced by a European harmonised standard, there will be a co-existence period during which either standard may be referred to. At the end of the coexistence period the national standard will be withdrawn

## THE WORKPLACE (HEALTH, SAFETY AND WELFARE) REGULATIONS 1992

The Workplace (Healthy Safety and Welfare) Regulations 1992 as amended by The Health and Safety (Miscellaneous Amendments) Regulations 2002 (SI 2002/2174) contain some requirements which affect building design. The main requirements are now covered by the Building Regulations, but for further information see: Workplace healthy safety and welfare: Workplace (Healthy Safety and Welfare) Regulations 1992, Approved Code of Practice, 124, HMSO, 1992 (ISBN 0 71760 413 6).

The Workplace (Health, Safety and Welfare) Regulations 1992 apply to the common parts of flats and similar buildings if people such as cleaners and caretakers are employed to work in these common parts. Where the requirements of the Building Regulations that are covered by this Part do not apply to dwellings, the provisions may still be required in the situations described above in order to satisfy the Workplace Regulations.

## MIXED USE DEVELOPMENT

In mixed use developments part of a building may be used as a dwelling while another part has a non-domestic use. In such cases, if the requirements of this Part of the Regulations for dwellings and non-domestic use differ, the requirements for non-domestic use should apply in any shared parts of the building.   The Requirement

This Approved Document, which takes effect on 6 April 2006, deals with the energy efficiency requirements in the Building Regulations 2000 (as amended by SI 2001/3335 and SI 2006/652). The energy efficiency requirements are conveyed in Part L of Schedule 1 to the Regulations and regulations 4A, 17C and 17D as described below.

# The Requirement

This Approved Document, which takes effect on 6 April 2006, deals with the energy efficiency requirements in the Building Regulations 2000 (as amended by SI 2001/3335 and SI 2006/652). The energy efficiency requirements are conveyed in Part L of Schedule 1 to the Regulations and regulations 4A, 17C and 17D as described below.

| Requirement | Limits on application |
|---|---|

**Part L Conservation of fuel and power**

LI. Reasonable provision shall be made for the conservation of fuel and power in buildings by:
a. limiting heat gains and losses:
i. through thermal elements and other parts of the building fabric; and
ii. from pipes, ducts and vessels used for space heating, space cooling and hot water services;
b, providing and commissioning energy efficient fixed building services with effective controls; and
c. providing to the owner sufficient information about the building, the fixed building services and their maintenance requirements so that the building can be operated in such a manner as to use no more fuel and power than is reasonable in the circumstances.

# Other changes to the Regulations

There are new Regulations that introduce new energy efficiency requirements and other relevant changes to the existing regulations. For ease of reference the principal elements of the regulations that bear on energy efficiency are repeated below and, where relevant, in the body of the guidance in the rest of this Approved Document. However it must be recognised that the Statutory Instrument takes precedence if there is any doubt over interpretation.

## Interpretation
Regulation 2(1) is amended to include the following new definitions.

'Change to a building's energy status' means any change which results in a building becoming a building to which the energy efficiency requirements of these Regulations apply, where previously it was not.

'Energy efficiency requirements' means the requirements of regulations 4A, 17C and 17D and Part L of Schedule 1,

'Fixed building services' means any part of, or any controls associated with:

a. fixed internal or external lighting systems, but does not include emergency escape lighting or specialist process lighting: or

b. fixed systems for heating, hot water service, air conditioning or mechanical ventilation.

'Renovation' in relation to a thermal element means the provision of a new layer in the thermal element or the replacement of an existing layer, but excludes decorative finishes, and 'renovate' shall be construed accordingly.

New paragraphs (2A) and (2B) are added to Regulation 2 as follows,

(2A) 'In these Thermal element' means a wall, floor or roof (but does not include windows, doors, roof windows or roof-lights) which separates a thermally conditioned part of the building ('the conditioned space') from:

a. the external environment (including the ground); or

b. in the case of floors and walls, another part of the building which is:

i. unconditioned;

ii.  an extension falling within class VII in Schedule 2; or

iii. where this paragraph applies, conditioned to a different temperature,

and includes all parts of the element between the surface bounding the conditioned space and the external environment or other part of the building as the case may be.

(2B) Paragraph (2A)(b)(iii) only applies to a building which is not a dwelling, where the other part of the building is used for a purpose which is not similar or identical to the purpose for which the conditioned space is used.

## Meaning of building work

Regulation 3 is amended as follows. 3.-(1) In these Regulations 'building work' means:

a. the erection or extension of a building;

b. the provision or extension of a controlled service or fitting in or in connection with a building;

c. the material alteration of a building, or a controlled service or fitting, as mentioned in paragraph (2);

d. work required by regulation 6 (requirements relating to material change of use);

e. the insertion of insulating material into the cavity wall of a building;

f. work involving the underpinning of a building;

g. work required by regulation 4A (requirements relating to thermal elements);

h. work required by regulation 4B (requirements relating to a change of energy status);

i. work required by regulation 17D (consequential improvements to energy performance).

(2) An alteration is material for the purposes of these Regulations if the work, or any part of it, would at any stage result:

a. in a building or controlled service or fitting not complying with a relevant requirement where previously it did; or

b. in a building or controlled service or fitting which before the work commenced did not comply with a relevant requirement, being more unsatisfactory in relation to such a requirement,

(3) In paragraph (2) 'relevant requirement' means any of the following applicable requirements of Schedule 1, namely:

Part A (structure)

paragraph B1 (means of warning

and escape)

paragraph B3 (internal fire spread -

structure)

paragraph B4 (external fire spread)

paragraph B5 (access and facilities for

the fire service)

Part M (access to and use of buildings).

## Requirements relating to building work

Regulation 4 is amended as follows

4.-(1) Subject to paragraph 1A building work shall be carried out so that:

a. it complies with the applicable requirements contained in Schedule 1; and

b. in complying with any such requirement there is no failure to comply with any other such requirement.

(1A) Where:

building work is of a kind described in

a. regulation 3(1)(g), (h) or (i); and

b. the carrying out of that work does not constitute a material alteration,

that work need only comply with the applicable requirements of Part L of Schedule 1,

(2) Building work shall be carried out so that, after it has been completed:

a. any building which is extended or to which a material alteration is made; or

b. any building in, or in connection with, which a controlled service or fitting is provided, extended or materially altered; or

c. any controlled service or fitting,

complies with the applicable requirements of Schedule 1 or, where it did not comply with any such requirement, is no more unsatisfactory in relation to that requirement than before the work was carried out.

## Requirements relating to thermal elements

A new regulation 4A is added as follows:

4A-(1) Where a person intends to renovate a thermal element, such work shall be carried out as is necessary to ensure that the whole thermal element complies with the requirements of paragraph L1(a)(i) of Schedule 1.

(2) Where a thermal element is replaced, the new thermal element shall comply with the requirements of paragraph L1 (a)(i) of Schedule 1.

## Requirements relating to a change to energy status

A new regulation 4B is added as follows:

4B.-(1) Where there is a change to a building's energy status, such work, if any, shall be carried out as is necessary to ensure that the building complies with the applicable requirements of Part L of Schedule 1.

(2) In this regulation 'building' means the building as a whole or parts of it that have been designed or altered to be used separately.

## Requirements relating to a material change of use

Regulation 6 is updated to take account of the changes to Part L

## Exempt buildings and work

Regulation 9 is substantially altered as follows.

9.-(1) Subject to paragraphs (2) and (3) these Regulations do not apply to:

a, the erection of any building or extension of a kind described in Schedule 2; or

b. the carrying out of any work to or in connection with such a building or extension, if after the carrying out of that work it is still a building or extension of a kind described in that Schedule.

(2) The requirements of Part P of Schedule 1 apply to:

a. any greenhouse;

b. any small detached building falling within class VI in Schedule 2; and

c. any extension of a building falling within class VII in Schedule 2,

which in any case receives its electricity from a source shared with or located inside a dwelling.

(3) The energy efficiency requirements of these Regulations apply to:

a. the erection of any building of a kind falling within this paragraph;

b. the extension of any such building, other than an extension falling within class VII in Schedule 2; and

c. the carrying out of any work to or in

connection with any such building or extension.

(4) A building falls within paragraph (3) if it:

a. is a roofed construction having walls;

b. uses energy to condition the indoor climate; and

c, does not fall within the categories listed in paragraph (5).

(5) The categories referred to in paragraph (4)(c) are:

a. buildings which are:

i. listed in accordance with section 1 of the Planning (Listed Buildings and Conservation Areas) Act 1990;

ii. in a conservation area designated in accordance with section 69 of that Act; or

iii. included in the schedule of monuments maintained under section 1 of the Ancient Monuments and Archaeological Areas Act 1979,

where compliance with the energy efficiency requirements would unacceptably alter their character or appearance;

b. buildings which are used primarily or solely as places of worship;

c. temporary buildings with a planned time of use of two years or less, industrial sites, workshops and non-residential agricultural buildings with low energy demand;

d. stand-alone buildings other than dwellings with a total useful floor area of less than 50m2.

(6) In this regulation:

a. 'building' means the building as a whole or parts of it that have been designed or altered to be used separately; and

b. the following terms have the same meaning as in European Parliament and Council Directive 2002/91/EC on the energy performance of buildings:

i. 'industrial sites';

ii. 'low energy demand';

iii. 'non-residential agricultural buildings';

iv. 'places of worship';

v. 'stand alone';

vi. 'total useful floor area';

vii. 'workshops'

## Giving of a building notice or deposit of plans

Regulation 12 is substantially amended as follows,

12.-(1) In this regulation 'relevant use' means a use as a workplace of a kind to which Part II of the Fire Precautions (Workplace) Regulations 1997 applies or a use designated under section 1 of the Fire Precautions Act 1971.

(2) This regulation applies to a person who intends to:

a. carry out building work;

b, replace or renovate a thermal element in a building to which the energy efficiency requirements apply;

c. make a change to a building's energy status; or d, make a material change of use.

(2A) Subject to the following provisions of this regulation, a person to whom this regulation applies shall:

a. give to the local authority a building notice in accordance with regulation 13; or

b, deposit full plans with the local authority in accordance with regulation 14.

(3) A person shall deposit full plans where he intends to carry out building work in relation to a building to which the Regulatory Reform (Fire Safety) Order 2005 applies, or will apply after the completion of the building work.

(4) A person shall deposit full plans where he intends to carry out work which includes the erection of a building fronting on to a private street.

(4A) A person shall deposit full plans where he intends to carry out building work in relation to which paragraph H4 of Schedule 1 imposes a requirement.

(5) A person who intends to carry out building work is not required to give a building notice or deposit full plans where the work consists only of work:

a. described in column 1 of the Table in Schedule 2A if the work is to be carried out by a person described in the corresponding entry in column 2 of that Table, and paragraphs 1 and 2 of that schedule have effect for the purposes of the descriptions in the Table; or

b. described in Schedule 2B.

(6) Where regulation 20 of the Building (Approved Inspectors etc.) Regulations 2000 (local authority powers in relation to partly completed work) applies, the owner shall comply with the requirements of that regulation

instead of with this regulation.

(7) Where:

a. a person proposes to carry out work which consists of emergency repairs to any fixed building services in respect of which Part L of Schedule 1 imposes a requirement;

b, it is not practicable to comply with paragraph (2A) before commencing the work; and

c. paragraph (5) does not apply,

he shall give a building notice to the local authority as soon as reasonably practicable after commencement of the work.

## Regulation 13 (particulars and plans where a building notice is given) and 14 (full plans)

These are amended to apply to renovation or replacement of a thermal element and a change to a building's energy status.

## Provisions applicable to self certification schemes

16A.-(1) This regulation applies to the extent that the building work consists only of work of a type described in column 1 of the Table in Schedule 2A and the work is carried out by a person who is described in the corresponding entry in column 2 of that Table in respect of that type of work.

(2) Where this regulation applies, the local authority is authorised to accept, as evidence that the requirements of regulations 4 and 7 have been satisfied, a certificate to that effect by the person carrying out the building work.

(3) Where this regulation applies, the person carrying out the work shall, not more than 30 days after the completion of the work -

(a)   give to the occupier a copy of the certificate referred to in paragraph (2); and

(b) give to the local authority - (i) notice to that effect, or

(ii) the certificate referred to in paragraph (2).

(4) Paragraph (3) of this regulation does not apply where a person carries out the building work described in Schedule 2B.

(3) Where this regulation applies, the person carrying out the work shall, not more than 30 days after the completion of the work -

(a)   give to the occupier a copy of the certificate referred to in paragraph (2); and

(b) give to the local authority - (i) notice to that effect, or

(ii) the certificate referred to in paragraph (2).

(4) Paragraph (3) of this regulation does not apply where a person carries out the building work described in Schedule 2B.

# NEW PART VA

### Energy Performance of Buildings
New Regulations are added as follows.

### Methodology of calculation of the energy performance of buildings
17A. The Secretary of State shall approve a methodology of calculation of the energy performance of buildings.

### Minimum energy performance requirements for buildings
17B. The Secretary of State shall approve minimum energy performance requirements for new buildings, in the form of target $CO_2$ emission rates, which shall be based upon the methodology approved pursuant to regulation 17A.

### New buildings
17C. Where a building is erected, it shall not exceed the target $CO_2$ emission rate for the building that has been approved pursuant to regulation 17B.

### Consequential improvements to energy performance
17D.–(1) Paragraph (2) applies to an existing building with a total useful floor area over 1000m2 where the proposed building work consists of or includes:

a. an extension;

b. the initial provision of any fixed building services; or

c. an increase to the installed capacity of any fixed building services.

(2) Subject to paragraph (3), where this regulation applies, such work, if any, shall be carried out as is necessary to ensure that the building complies with the requirements of Part L of Schedule 1.

(3) Nothing in paragraph (2) requires work to be carried out if it is not technically, functionally and economically feasible.

### Interpretation
17E. In this Part 'building' means the building as a whole or parts of it that have been designed or altered to be used separately.

# PART VI - MISCELLANEOUS

New Regulations are added as follows.

### Pressure testing
20B.–(1) This regulation applies to the erection of a building in relation to which paragraph L1(a)(i) of Schedule 1 imposes a requirement.

(2) Where this regulation applies, the person carrying out the work shall, for the purpose of ensuring compliance with regulation 17C and paragraph L1(a)(i) of Schedule 1:

a. ensure that:

i. pressure testing is carried out in such circumstances as are approved by the Secretary of State; and

ii. the testing is carried out in accordance with a procedure approved by the Secretary of State; and

b. subject to paragraph (5), give notice of the results of the testing to the local authority.

(3) The notice referred to in paragraph (2)(b) shall:

a. record the results and the data upon which they are based in a manner approved by the Secretary of State; and

b. be given to the local authority not later than seven days after the final test is carried out.

(4) A local authority is authorised to accept, as evidence that the requirements of paragraph (2)(a)(ii) have been

satisfied, a certificate to that effect by a person who is registered by the British Institute of Non-destructive Testing in respect of pressure testing for the air tightness of buildings.

(5) Where such a certificate contains the information required by paragraph (3)(a), paragraph (2)(b) does not apply.

## Commissioning

20C.-(1) This regulation applies to building work in relation to which paragraph L1 (b) of Schedule 1 imposes a requirement, but does not apply where the work consists only of work described in Schedule 2B.

(2) Where this regulation applies the person carrying out the work shall, for the purpose of ensuring compliance with paragraph L1(b) of Schedule 1, give to the local authority a notice confirming that the fixed building services have been commissioned in accordance with a procedure approved by the Secretary of State.

(3) The notice shall be given to the local authority:

a. not later than the date on which the notice required by regulation 15(4) is required to be given; or

b. where that regulation does not apply, not more than 30 days after completion of the work.

## $CO_2$ emission rate calculations

20D.-(1) Subject to paragraph (4), where regulation 17C applies the person carrying out the work shall provide to the local authority a notice which specifies:

a. the target $CO_2$ emission rate for the building; and

b. the calculated $CO_2$ emission rate for the building as constructed.

(2) The notice shall be given to the local authority not later than the date on which the notice required by regulation 20B is required to be given.

(3) A local authority is authorised to accept, as evidence that the requirements of regulation 17C would be satisfied if the building were constructed in accordance with an accompanying list of specifications, a certificate to that effect by a person who is registered by:

a. FAERO Limited; or b. BRE Certification Limited,

in respect of the calculation of $CO_2$ emission rates of buildings.

(4) Where such a certificate is given to the local authority:

a. paragraph (1) does not apply; and

b. the person carrying out the work shall provide to the local authority not later than the date on which the notice required by regulation 20B is required to be given a notice which:

i. states whether the building has been constructed in accordance with the list of specifications which accompanied the certificate; and

ii. if it has not, lists any changes to the specifications to which the building has been constructed.

# SCHEDULE 2A

Schedule 2A is amended as follows:

## Self-certification schemes and exemptions from requirement to give building notice or deposit full plans.

| Column 1 | Column 2 |
|---|---|
| *Type of work* | *Person carrying out work* |
| 1. Installation of a heat-producing gas appliance. | A person, or an employee of a person, who is a member of a class of persons approved In accordance with regulation 3 of the Gas Safety (Installation and Use) Regulations 1998. |
| 2. Installation of heating or hot water service system connected to a heat-producing gas appliance, or associated controls. | A person registered by CORGI Services Limited In respect of that type of work. |
| 3. Installation of:<br>**a.** an oil-fired combustion appliance which has a rated heat output of 100 kilowatts or less and which is Installed In a building with no more than 3 storeys (excluding any basement) or In a dwelling;<br>**b.** oil storage tanks and the pipes connecting them to combustion appliances; or<br>**c.** heating and hot water service systems connected to an oil-fired combustion appliance. | An Individual registered by Oil Firing Technical Association Limited, NAPIT Certification Limited or Building Engineering Services Competence Accreditation Limited in respect of that type of work. |
| 4. Installation of:<br>**a.** a solid fuel burning combustion appliance which has a rated heat output of 50 kilowatts or less which Is Installed in a building with no more than 3 storeys (excluding any basement); or<br>**b.** heating and hot water service systems connected to a solid fuel burning combustion appliance. | A person registered by HETAS Limited, NAPIT Certification Limited or Building Engineering Services Competence Accreditation Limited In respect of that type of work. |
| 5. Installation of a heating or hot water service system, or associated controls, in a dwelling. | A person registered by Building Engineering Services Competence Accreditation Limited in respect of that type of work. |
| 6. Installation of a heating, hot water service, mechanical ventilation or air conditioning system, or associated controls, in a building other than a dwelling. | A person registered by Building Engineering Services Competence Accreditation Limited in respect of that type of work. |
| 7. Installation of an air conditioning or ventilation system in an existing dwelling, which does not involve work on systems shared with other dwellings. | A person registered by CORGI Services Limited or NAPIT Certification Limited in respect of that type of work. |
| 8. Installation of a commercial kitchen ventilation system which does not involve work on systems shared with parts of the building occupied separately. | A person registered by CORGI Services Limited in respect of that type of work. |
| 9. Installation of a lighting system or electric heating system, or associated electrical controls. | A person registered by The Electrical Contractors Association Limited in respect of that type of work. |
| 10. Installation of fixed low or extra-low voltage electrical installations. | A person registered by BRE Certification Limited, British Standards Institution, ELECBA Limited. NICEIC Group Limited or NAPIT Certification Limited in respect of that type of work. |

| Column 1 *continued* | Column 2 |
|---|---|
| *Type of work* | *Person carrying out work* |
| 11. Installation of fixed low or extra-low voltage electrical installations as a necessary adjunct to or arising out of other work being carried out by the registered person. respect of that type of electrical work. | A person registered by CORGI Services Limited, ELECSA Limited, NAPIT Certification Limited, NICEIC Group Limited or Oil Firing Technical Association Limited in |
| 12. Installation, as a replacement, of a window, rooflight, roof window or door (being a door which together with Its frame has more than 50 per cent of its internal face area glazed) In an existing building. | A person registered under the Fenestratlon Self-Assessment Scheme by Fensa Ltd, or by CERTASS Limited or the British Standards Institution In respect of that type of work. |
| 13. Installation of a sanitary convenience, washing facility or bathroom In a dwelling, which does not Involve work on shared or underground drainage. | A person registered by CORGI Services Limited or NAPIT Certification Limited In respect of that type of work. |
| 14.-**(1)** Subject to paragrap **(2)**, any building work, other than the provision of a masonry chimney, which Is necessary to ensure that any appliance, service or fitting which Is Installed and which is described In the preceding entries In column 1 above, complies with the applicable requirements contained In Schedule 1.(2) Paragraph (1) does not apply to: c, building work which Is necessary to ensure that a heat-producing gas appliance complies with the applicable requirements contained in Schedule 1 unless the appliance: i. has a rated heat output of 100 kilowatts or less; and ii. Is installed in a building with no more than 3 storeys (excluding any basement), or In a dwelling; or d. the provision of a masonry chimney. | The person who Installs the appliance, service or fitting to which the building work relates and who Is described In the corresponding entry In column 2 above. |

# SCHEDULE 2B Schedule 2B is amended as follows:

Descriptions of work where no building notice or deposit of full plans required.

**1 Work consisting of:**

a. replacing any fixed electrical equipment which does not include the provision of

    i. any new fixed cabling;

    ii. a new consumer unit; and

b. replacing a damaged cable for a single circuit only;

c. re-fixing or replacing enclosures of existing installation components, where the circuit protective measures are unaffected;

d. providing mechanical protection to an existing fixed installation, where the circuit protective measures and current carrying capacity of conductors are unaffected by the increased thermal insulation.

e. installing or upgrading main or supplementary equipotential bonding;

f. in heating or cooling systems:

    i. replacing control devices that utilise existing fixed control wiring or pneumatic pipes;

    ii. replacing a distribution system output device;

    iii. providing a valve or a pump;

    iv. providing a damper or fan;

g. in hot water service systems, providing a valve or pump

h. replacing an external door (where the door together with its frame has not more than 50% of its internal face area glazed);

i. in existing buildings other than dwellings, providing fixed internal lighting where no more than 100m² of the floor area of the building is to be served by the lighting

**2 Work which:**

a. is not in a kitchen, or a special location,

b. does not involve work on a special installation, and

c. consists of:

    i. adding light fittings and switches to an existing circuit; or

    ii. adding socket outlets and fused spurs to an existing ring or radial circuit;

**3 Work on:**

a. telephone wiring or extra-low voltage wiring for the purposes of communications, information technology, signalling, control and similar purposes, where the wiring is not in a special location;

b. equipment associated with the wiring referred to in sub-paragraph (a).

c. pro-fabricated equipment sets and associated flexible leads with integral plug and socket connections.

**4 For the purposes of this Schedule:**

'kitchen' means a room or part of a room which contains a sink and food preparation facilities;

'special installation' means an electric floor or ceiling heating system, an outdoor lighting or electric power installation, an electricity generator, or an extra-low voltage lighting system which is not a pro-assembled lighting set bearing the CE marking referred to in regulation 9 of the Electrical Equipment (Safety) Regulations 1994; and

'special location' means a location within the limits of the relevant zones specified for a bath, a shower, a swimming or paddling pool or a hot air sauna in the Wiring Regulations, sixteenth edition, published by the Institution of Electrical Engineers and the British Standards Institution as BS 7671: 2001 and incorporating amendments 1 and 2.

# SECTION 0: GENERAL GUIDANCE

## CONVENTIONS USED IN THIS DOCUMENT

**1** In this document the following conventions have been adopted to assist understanding and interpretation:

a. Texts shown against a grey background are extracts from the Building Regulations as amended and convey the legal requirements that bear on compliance with Part L. It should be remembered however that building works must comply with all the other relevant provisions. Similar provisions are conveyed by the Building (Approved Inspectors) Regulations as amended.

b. Key terms are printed **in bold italic** text and defined for the purposes of this Approved Document in Section 5 of this document.

c. References given as footnotes and repeated as end notes are given as ways of meeting the requirements or as sources of more general information as indicated in the particular case. The Approved document will be amended from time to time to include new references and to refer to revised editions where this aids compliance.

d. Additional *commentary in italic text* appears after some numbered paragraphs. The commentary is intended to assist understanding of the immediately preceding paragraph or sub-paragraph, but is not part of the approved guidance.

## TYPES OF WORK COVERED BY THIS APPROVED DOCUMENT

**2** This Approved Document gives guidance on what, in ordinary circumstances, will meet the requirements of Regulation 4A and Part L when carrying out different classes of building work on existing *dwellings.*

**3** In particular guidance is given on the following activities:

a. extensions (see paragraphs 14 to 24)

b. when creating a new *dwelling* or part of a dwelling through a material change of use (paragraphs 25 to 28)

c. material alterations to existing *dwellings* (paragraphs 29 to 30)

d. the provision of a controlled fitting (paragraphs 32 to 34)

e. the provision of extension of a controlled service (paragraphs 35 to 48)

f. the provision or *renovation* of a *thermal element* (paragraphs 49 to 57).

**4** Where the activities include building work in a *dwelling* that is part of a mixed use building, account should also be taken of the guidance in Approved Document L2B in relation to those parts of the building that are not *dwellings*, including any common areas,

*It should be noted that dwellings refer to self- contained units. Rooms for residential purposes are not dwellings, and so Approved Document L2B applies to them.*

**5** The **energy efficiency requirements,** *apart from those in regulation 17C and 17D,* apply to work in existing dwellings. In most instances, this will require the **BCB** to be notified of the intended work before the work commences, either in the form of a deposit of full plans or by a building notice. In certain situations however other procedures apply. These include:

a. Where the work is being carried out under the terms of an approved Competent Persons self-certification (CP) scheme. In these cases, in accordance with Regulation 16A and Schedule 2A no advance notification to the building control body is needed. At the completion of the work, the registered CP provides the building owner with a certificate confirming that the installation has been carried out in accordance with the requirements of the relevant requirements, and the scheme operator notifies the local authority to that effect.

b. Where the work involves an emergency repair, e.g. a failed boiler or a leaking hot water cylinder In these cases, in accordance with Regulation 12 (7), there is no need to delay making the repair in order to make an advance notification to the building control body. However, in such cases it will still be necessary for the work to comply with the requirements and to give a notice to the **BCB** at the earliest opportunity, unless an installer registered under an appropriate CP scheme carries out the work. A completion certificate can then be issued in the normal way.

c. Where the work is of a minor nature as described in Schedule 2B of the Building Regulations. Again, the work must comply with the relevant requirements, but need not be notified to building control.

## TECHNICAL RISK

**6** Building work must satisfy all the technical requirements set out in Regulations 4A and Schedule 1 of the Building Regulations. Part B (Fire safety), Part E (Resistance to the passage of sound), Part F (Ventilation), Part C (Site preparation and resistance to moisture), Part J (Combustion appliances and fuel storage systems) and Part P (Electrical safety) are particularly relevant when considering the incorporation of energy efficiency measures.

**7** The inclusion of any particular energy efficiency measure should not involve excessive technical risk. BR 262 provides general guidance on avoiding risks in the application of thermal insulation.

## HISTORIC BUILDINGS

**8** Special considerations apply if the building on which the work is to be carried out has special historic or architectural value and compliance with the **energy efficiency requirements** would unacceptably alter the character or appearance9.

**9** When undertaking work on or in connection with buildings with special historic or architectural value, the aim should be to improve energy efficiency where and to the extent that it is practically possible. This is provided that the work does not prejudice the character of the host building or increase the risk of long-term deterioration to the building fabric or fittings. The guidance given in the English Heritage publication10 should be taken into account in determining appropriate energy performance standards for such building works. Particular issues relating to work in historic buildings that warrant sympathetic treatment and where advice from others could therefore be beneficial include:

a. restoring the historic character of a building that has been subject to previous inappropriate alteration, e.g. replacement windows, doors and rooflights;

b. rebuilding a former building (e.g. following a fire or filling a gap site in a terrace);

c. making provisions enabling the fabric of historic buildings to 'breathe' to control moisture and potential long-term decay problems.

**10** In arriving at a balance between historic building conservation and energy efficiency improvements, it would be appropriate to take into account the advice of the local authority's conservation officer.

## CALCULATION OF U-VALUES

**11** U-values must be calculated using the methods and conventions set out in BR 44311, 'Conventions for U-value calculations'.

**12** The U-values for roof windows and rooflights given in this Approved Document are based on the U-value having been assessed with the roof window or rooflight in the vertical position. If a particular unit has been assessed in a plane other than the vertical, the standards given in this Approved Document should be modified by making a U-value adjustment following the guidance given in BR 443.

*For example: the standard for a replacement rooflight in Table 2 is $2.0W/m^2.K$. This is for the unit assessed in the vertical plane. The performance of a double glazed rooflight in the horizontalplane, based on the guidance given in BR 443, would be adjusted by $0.5W/m^2.K$ to $2.0 + 0.5 = 2.5W/m^2.K$.*

## BUILDINGS THAT ARE EXEMPT FROM THE REQUIREMENTS IN PART L

**13** The provisions for exempting buildings and building work from the Building Regulations requirements have changed and the new provisions are given in regulation 9.

# SECTION 1: GUIDANCE RELATING TO BUILDING WORK

## THE EXTENSION OF A DWELLING

### Fabric standards

**14** Reasonable provision would be for the proposed extension to achieve the following performance standards:

a. Controlled fittings that meet the standards set out in paragraphs 32 to 34 of this Approved Document.

b. Newly constructed **thermal elements** that meet the standards set out in paragraphs 49 to 53 of this Approved Document.

c. When working on existing fabric elements that are to become thermal elements a way of complying would be to follow the guidance in paragraphs 54 and 57.

### Area of windows, roof windows and doors

**15** In most circumstances reasonable provision would be to limit the area of windows, roof windows and doors in extensions so that it does not exceed the sum of:

a. 25% of the floor area of the extension; plus

b. the area of any windows or doors which, as a result of the extension works, no longer exist or are no longer exposed.

**16** In some cases different approaches may be adopted by agreement with the **BCB** in order to achieve a satisfactory level of daylighting. BS 820612 gives guidance on this.

### Heating and lighting in the extension

**17** Where a fixed building service is provided or extended as part of constructing the extension, reasonable provision would be to follow the guidance in paragraphs 35 to 48.

### Optional approaches with more design flexibility

**18** More flexibility in the selection of U-values and opening areas than is available by following the guidance in paragraphs 14 and 15 can be obtained by compensation elsewhere in the design. A way of complying would be to show that:

a. the area-weighted U-value of all the elements in the extension is no greater than that of an extension of the same size and shape that complies with the U-value standards referred to in paragraph 14 and the opening area in paragraph 15; and

*The area-weighted U-value is give by the following expression:*

$$\{(U_1 \times A_1) + (U_2 \times A_2) + (U_3 \times A_3) + ...)\} \div \{(A_1 + A_2 + A_3...)\}$$

b. the area-weighted U-value for each element type is no worse than the value given in column (a) of Table 1; and

c. the U-value of any individual element is no worse than the relevant value in column (b) of Table 1.

*To minimise condensation risk in localised parts of the envelope. Individual elements are defined as those areas of the given element type that have the same construction details.*

**19** In the case of windows, doors and rooflights, the assessment should be based on the whole unit (i.e. in the case of a window, the combined performance of the glazing and frame).

## Table 1 Limiting U-value standards (W/m². K)

| Element | (a) Area-weighted average U-value | (b) Limiting U-value |
|---|---|---|
| Wall | 0.35 | 0.70 |
| Floor | 0.25 | 0.70 |
| Roof | 0.25 | 0.35 |
| Windows, roof windows, rooflights[1] and doors | 2.2 | 3.3 |

Notes: [1] BS 8206-2:1092 Lighting for buildings. Code of practice for daylighting.

**20** Where even greater design flexibility is required, reasonable provision would be to use SAP 2005[13] to show that the calculated CO2 emission rate from the *dwelling* with its proposed extension is no greater than for the *dwelling* plus a notional extension built to the standards of paragraphs 14 to 17, In these cases the area-weighted average U-value of each element type should be no worse than the standards set out in column (a) of Table 1, and the U-value of any individual element should be no worse than the values in column (b) of Table 1. The data in SAP 2005 Appendix S can be used to estimate the performance of the elements of the existing building where these are unknown.

**21** If, as part of achieving the standard set out in paragraph 20, improvements are proposed to the existing *dwelling*, such improvements should be implemented to a standard that is no worse than set out in the relevant guidance contained in this Approved Document The relevant standards for improving retained thermal elements are as set out in column (b) of Table 5.

*Where it is proposed to upgrade, then the standards set out in this Approved Document are cost effective and should be implemented in full. It will be worthwhile implementing them even if the improvement is more than necessary to achieve compliance. In some cases therefore, the standard of the extended house may be better than that required by paragraph 20 alone. Paragraph 21 ensures that no cost-effective improvement opportunities are traded away.*

## CONSERVATORIES AND SUBSTANTIALLY GLAZED EXTENSIONS

**22** Where the extension is a conservatory that is not exempt by Regulation 9(3)14, then reasonable provision would be to provide:

a. Effective thermal separation from the heated area in the existing *dwelling.* The walls, doors and windows between the *dwelling* and the extension should be insulated and draught- stripped to at least the same extent as in the existing *dwelling.*

*If a highly glazed extension is not thermally separated from the dwelling, then it should be regarded as a conventional extensions Compliance in such cases could be demonstrated using the approach set out in paragraphs 14 to 27\**

b. Independent temperature and on/off controls to any heating system. Any heating appliance should also conform to the standards set out in paragraph 35.

c. Glazed elements should comply with the standards given in column (b) of Table 2 and any thermal elements should have U- values that are no worse than the standards given in column (b) of Table 4.

**23** Conservatories built at ground level and with a floor area no greater than 30m² are exempt from the Building Regulations (other than having to satisfy the requirements of Part N).

**24** If a substantially glazed extension fails to qualify as a *conservatory* because it has less than the minimum qualifying amounts of translucent material, but otherwise satisfies paragraph 22, reasonable provision would be to demonstrate that the performance is no worse than a conservatory of the same size and shape. A way of doing so would be to show the area-weighted U-value of the elements in the proposed extension is no greater than that of a conservatory that complies with the standards set out in paragraph 22.

Notes: [13] The Government's Standard Assessment Procedure for Energy Rating of Dwellings, 2005 edition, SAP 2005. Defra.

## MATERIAL CHANGE OF USE

25 Material changes of use involving dwellings are defined in Regulation 5 as follows:

For the purposes of paragraph 8(1)(e) of Schedule 1 to the Act and for the purposes of these Regulations, there is a material change of use where there is a change in the purposes for which or the circumstances in which a building is used, so that after that change:

a. the building is used as a dwelling, where previously it was not;

b. the building contains a flat, where  previously it did not;

c. the building  is used as an hotel or a boarding house, where previously it was not;

d . the building is used as an Institution, where previously it was not;

e. the building is used as a public building, where previously it was not;

f. the building is not a building described in Classes I to VI in Schedule 2, where previously it was;

g. the building, which contains at least one dwelling, contains a greater or lesser number of dwellings than it did previously;

h. the building contains a room for residential purposes, where previously it did not;

i. the building, which contains at least one room for residential purposes, contains a greater or lesser number of such rooms than it did previously; or

j. the building is used as s hop where previously it was not

26 When carrying out a material change of use, the Reasonable provision would be:

a.    when carrying out a material change of use; or b. when a building changes it's energy status to follow the guidance in paragraph 27.

27 In normal circumstances, reasonable provision would be:

a.    Where controlled services or fittings are being provided or extended, to meet the standards set out in paragraphs 31 to 48 of this Approved Document.

b.    Where the work involves the provision of a **thermal element,** to meet the standards set out in paragraphs 49 to 53 of this Approved Document.

*For the purposes of Building Regulations, provision means both new and replacement elements.*

c.    Where the work involves the **renovation** of **thermal elements**, to meet the guidance in paragraphs 54 to 55 of this Approved Document.

d.    Any **thermal element** that is being retained should be upgraded following the guidance given in paragraphs 56 and 57 of this Approved Document.

e.    Any existing window (including roof window or roof light) or door which separates a conditioned space from an unconditioned space or the external environment and which has a U-value that is worse than $3.3W/m^2.K$, should be replaced following the guidance in paragraphs 32 to 34.

14   See the copy of Regulation 9 on page 7.

### Option providing more design flexibility

28 To provide more design flexibility SAP 2005 can be used to demonstrate that the total $CO_2$ emissions from all the **dwellings** in the building as it will become are no greater than if each **dwelling** had been improved following the guidance set out in paragraph 27. In these cases the U-values of any individual element should be no worse that the values in column (b) of Table 1.

## MATERIAL ALTERATION

**29** Material alterations are defined in Regulation 3(2) as follows,

3(2) An alteration is material for the purposes of these Regulations if the work, or any part of it, would at any stage result:

a. in a building or controlled service or fitting not complying with a relevant requirement where previously it did; or

b. in a building or controlled service or fitting which before the work commenced did not comply with a relevant requirement, being more unsatisfactory in relation to such a requirement.

3(3) In paragraph (2) 'relevant requirement' means any of the following applicable requirements of Schedule 1, namely:

a. Part A (structure)

b. Paragraph B1 (means of warning and escape)

c. Paragraph B3 (internal fire spread – structure)

d. Paragraph B4 (external fire spread)

e. Paragraph B5 (access and facilities for the fire service)

f. Part M (access to and use of buildings).

**30** When carrying out a material alteration, reasonable provision would be

a.  when the work involves the provision of a **thermal element**, to follow the guidance in paragraphs 50 to 53 of this Approved Document.

*For the purposes of Building Regulations, provision means both new and replacement elements.*

b.  when the work involves the renovation of a **thermal element**, to follow the guidance in paragraphs 54 and 55 of this Approved Document.

c.  where an existing element becomes part of the thermal envelope of the building where previously it was not, to follow the guidance in paragraphs 56 and 57 of this Approved Document.

d.  when providing controlled fittings, to limit glazing area to reasonable provision and to follow the guidance on controlled fittings given in paragraphs 32 to 34 of this Approved Document.

*Reasonable provision for glazing area depends on the circumstances in the particular case, A way of showing compliance would be to follow the approaches given in paragraphs 15 and 76.*

e.  when providing or extending a controlled service, to follow the guidance on controlled services given in paragraphs 35 to 48 of this Approved Document.

## WORK ON CONTROLLED FITTINGS AND SERVICES

**31** Controlled services or fittings are defined in Regulation 2 as follows:

**Controlled service or fitting** means a service or fitting in relation to which Part G, H, J L or P of Schedule 1 imposes a requirement;

### Controlled fittings

**32** Where windows, roof windows, roof lights or doors are to be provided, reasonable provision Would be the provision of draught-proofed units whose area-weighted average performance is no worse than given in Table 2» Column (a) applies to fittings provided as part of constructing an extension, column (b) to replacement fittings or new fittings installed in the existing **dwelling.**

**33** The U-value or Window Energy Rating of a window, roof window or rooflight fittings can be taken as the value for either:

a.  the standard configuration as set out in BR 443; or

b.  the particular size and configuration of the actual fitting.

**34** SAP 2005 Table 6e gives values for different window configurations that can be used in the absence of test data or calculated values.

### Table 2 Reasonable provision when working on controlled fittings

| Fitting | (a) Standard for new fittings in extensions | (b) Standard for replacement fittings in an existing dwelling |
|---|---|---|
| Window, roof window and roof light | | |
| | U-value 1.8W/m².K or | U-value = 2.0W/m².K or |
| | Window energy rating[15] = Band D; or | Window energy rating = Band E; or |
| | Centre-pane U-value = 1.2W/m².K | Centre-pane U-value = 1.2W/m².K |
| Doors with more than 50% of their internal face area glazed | 2.2W/m².K or centre-pane U-value =1.2W/m².K | 2.2W/m².K or centre-pane U-value: 1.2W/m².k |
| Other doors | 3.0W/m2.k | 3.0W/m2.k |

## Controlled services

### Heating and hot systems

**35** Where the work involves the provision or extension of a heating or hot water system or part thereof, reasonable provision would be:

a.    the installation of an appliance with an efficiency:

i. not less than that recommended for its type in the Domestic Heating Compliance Guide[16]; and

ii. where the appliance is the primary heating service, an efficiency which is not worse than two percentage points lower than that of the appliance being replaced. If the new appliance uses a different fuel, then the efficiency of the new appliance should be multiplied by the ratio of the $CO_2$ emission factor of the fuel used in the appliance being replaced to that of the fuel used in the new appliance before making this check. The $CO_2$ emission factors should be taken from Table 12 of SAP 2005, In the absence of specific information, the efficiency of the appliance being replaced may be taken from Table 4a or 4b of SAP 2005.

*The aim is to discourage an existing appliance being replaced by a significantly less carbon efficient one. When fuel switchingf if an old oil fired boiler with an efficiency of 72% is to be replaced by a dual solid fuel boiler with an efficiency of 65%, the equivalent efficiency of the dual solid fuel boiler would be 65% x (0.265/0.187) = 92.1% and so the test in paragraph 35a)ii) would be satisfied. 0.265 and 0.187 kgCO-1 pt/kWh are the emission factors for oil and dual fuel appliances respectively given in ADL1A.*

b.    the provision of controls that meet the minimum control requirements as given in the Domestic Heating Compliance Guide for the particular type of appliance and heat distribution system.

**36** The heating and hot water system(s) should be commissioned so that at completion, the system(s) and their controls are left in working order and can operate efficiently for the purposes of the conservation of fuel and power* In order to demonstrate that the heating and hot water systems have been adequately commissioned, Regulation 20C states that:

---

[15]   CE66 Windows -for new and existing houses, EST, 2006.

[16]   Domestic Heating Compliance Guide,  NBS, 2006.

20C.–(1) This regulation applies to building work in relation to which paragraph L1(b) of Schedule 1 imposes a requirement, but does not apply where the work consists only of work described in Schedule 2B.

(2) Where this regulation applies the person carrying out the work shall, for the purpose of ensuring compliance with paragraph L1(b) of Schedule 1, give to the local authority a notice confirming that the fixed building services have been commissioned in accordance with a procedure approved by the Secretary of State.

3. The notice shall be given to the local authority:

(a) not later than the date on which the notice required by regulation 15(4) is required to be given; or

(b) Where that regulation does not apply, not more than 30 days after completion of the work.

**37** The procedure approved by the Secretary of State is set out in the Domestic Heating Compliance Guide.

**38** The notice should include a declaration signed by someone suitably qualified to do so that the manufacturer's commissioning procedures have been completed satisfactorily.

*One option would be to engage a member of an approved Competent Persons scheme.*

## Insulation of pipes and ducts

**39** As part of the provision or extension of a heating or hot water service, reasonable provision would be demonstrated by insulating pipes ducts and vessels to standards that are not worse than those set out in the Domestic Heating Compliance Guide.

*The TIMSA Guide[17] explains the derivation of the performance standards and how they can be interpreted in practice.*

## Mechanical ventilation

**40** Where the work involves the provision of a mechanical ventilation system or part thereof, reasonable provision would be to install systems no worse than those described in GPG 268[18] which also have specific fan powers and heat recovery efficiency not worse than those in Table 3.

### Table 3 Limits on design flexibility for mechanical ventilation systems

| System type | Performance |
| --- | --- |
| Specific Fan Power (SFP) for continuous supply only and continuous extract only | 0.8 litre/s.W |
| SFP for balanced systems | 2.0 lltre/s.W |
| Heat recover efficiency | 66% |

**41** Mechanical ventilation systems must satisfy the requirements in Part F.

## Mechanical cooling

**42** Where the work involves the provision of a fixed household air conditioner; reasonable provision would be to provide a unit having an energy efficiency classification equal to or better than class C in Schedule 3 of the labelling scheme adopted under The Energy Information (Household Air Conditioners) (No. 2) Regulations 2005[19].

## Fixed internal lighting

Reasonable provision should be made for dwelling occupiers to obtain the benefits of efficient electric lighting whenever

a. a **dwelling** is extended; or

b. a new **dwelling** is created from a material change of use; or

c. an existing lighting system is being replaced as part of re-wiring works.

*The re-wiring works must comply with Part R*

**44** A way of showing compliance would be to provide lighting fittings (including lamp, control gear and an appropriate housing, reflector, shade or diffuser or other device for controlling the output light) that only take lamps having a luminous efficacy greater than 40 lumens per circuit-Watt, Circuit-Watts means the power consumed in lighting circuits by lamps and their associated control gear and power factor correction equipment.

*Fluorescent and compact fluorescent lighting fittings would meet this standard. Lighting fittings for GLS tungsten lamps with bayonet cap or Edison screw bases, or tungsten halogen lamps would not.*

45 Reasonable provision would be to provide in the areas affected by the building work, fixed energy efficient light fittings that number not less than the greater of:

a.    one per 25m² of **dwelling** floor area (excluding garages) or part thereof; or

b.    one per four fixed lighting fittings.

*This assessment should be based on the extension, the newly created **dwelling** or the area served by the lighting system as appropriate to the particular case.*

*Installing mains frequency fluorescent lighting in garages may cause dangers through stroboscopic interaction with vehicle engine parts or machine toolSt Fluorescent lamps with high frequency electronic ballasts substantially reduce this risk.*

**46** A light fitting may contain one or more lamps.

**47** Lighting fittings in less used areas like cupboards and other storage areas would not count towards the total. GIL 20[20] gives guidance on identifying suitable locations for energy efficient luminaires, In some cases, it may be more appropriate to install the energy efficient light fitting in a location that is not part of the building worky e.g. to replace the fitting on the landing when creating a new bedroom through a loft conversion.

## Fixed external lighting

*Fixed external lighting means lighting fixed to an external surface of the **dwelling** supplied from the occupier's electrical system. It excludes the lighting in common areas in blocks of flats and other access-way lighting provided communally.*

**48** When providing fixed external lighting, reasonable provision should be made to enable effective control and / or the use of efficient lamps such that:

a.    EITHER: Lamp capacity does not exceed 150 Watts per light fitting and the lighting automatically switches off:

i. When there is enough daylight; and

ii. When it is not required at night; or

b.    the lighting fittings have sockets that can only be used with lamps having an efficacy greater than 40 lumens per circuit-Watt.

*Compact fluorescent lamp types would meet the standard in (b), but GLS tungsten lamps with bayonet cap or Edison screw bases, or tungsten halogen lamps would not.*

---

17    HVAC Guidance for Achieving Compliance with Part L of the Building Regulations, TIMSA, 2006.

18    GPG268 Energy efficient ventilation in dwellings – a guide for specifiers EST, 2C306.

19    Statutory Instrument 81 2005/1726, the Energy Information (Household Air Conditioners) (No. 2) Regulations 2005.

20 GIL20, Low energy domestic lighting, EST, 2006.

# Section 2: Guidance on thermal elements

49 New **thermal elements** must comply with requirement L1 (a)(i). Work on existing elements is covered by regulation 4A which states:

4A.-(1) Where a person intends to renovate a thermal element, such work shall be carried out as is necessary to ensure that the whole thermal element complies with the requirements of paragraph L1(a)(i) of Schedule 1. (2) Where a thermal element is replaced, the new thermal element shall comply with the requirements of paragraph L1(a)(i) of Schedule 1.

## THE PROVISION OF THERMAL ELEMENTS

### U-values

50 Reasonable provision for newly constructed **thermal elements** such as those constructed as part of an extension would be to meet the standards set out in column (a) of Table 4. In addition, no individual element should have a U-value worse than those set out in column (b) of Table 1.

51 Reasonable provision for those **thermal elements** constructed as replacements for existing elements would be to meet the standards set out in column (b) of Table 4. In addition, no part of a **thermal element** should have a U-value worse than those set out in column (b) of Table 1.

### Continuity of insulation and airtightness

52 The building fabric should be constructed so that there are no reasonably avoidable thermal bridges in the insulation layers caused by gaps within the various elements, at the joints between elements and at the edges of elements such as those around window and door openings. Reasonable provision should also be made to reduce unwanted air leakage through the new envelope parts.

53 A suitable approach to showing the requirement has been achieved would be to submit a report signed by a suitably qualified person confirming that appropriate design details and building techniques have been specified, and that the work has been carried out in ways that can be expected to achieve reasonable conformity with the specifications. Reasonable provision would be to:

a.   adopt design details such as those set out in the TSO Robust Details catalogue[21]; or
     A list of additional approved details may be provided in due course.
b.   to demonstrate that the specified details deliver an equivalent level of performance using the guidance in
     BRE IP 1/06[22].

### Table 4 Standards for thermal elements W/m².K

| Element[1] | (a) Standard for new thermal elements in an extension | (b) Standard for replacement thermal elements in an existing dwelling |
|---|---|---|
| Wall | 0.30 | 0.35 [2] |
| Pitched roof - insulation at ceiling level | 0.16 | 0.16 |
| Pitched roof - insulation at rafter level | 0.20 | 0.20 |
| Flat roof or roof with integral insulation | 0.20 | 025 |
| Floors | 0.22 [3] | 0.25 [3] |

**Notes:**

1. Roof includes the roof parts of dormer windows and wall refers to the wall parts (cheeks) of dormer windows.

2. A lesser provision may be appropriate where meeting such a standard would result in a reduction of more than 5% in the internal floor area of the room bounded by the wall.

3. A lesser provision may be appropriate where meeting such a standard would create significant problems in relation to adjoining floor levels. The U-value of the floor of an extension can be calculated using the exposed perimeter and floor area of the whole enlarged dwelling.

21   Limiting thermal bridging and air leakage: Robust construction details for dwellings and similar buildings, Amendment 1, TSO, 2002. See www.est.org.uk.

22   IP 1/06 Assessing the effects of thermal bridging at junctions and around opening in the external elements of buildings, BRE 2006.

# RENOVATION OF THERMAL ELEMENTS

54 Where a **thermal element** is being renovated reasonable provision in most cases would be to achieve the standard set out in column (b) of Table 5. Where the works apply to less than 25% of the surface area however reasonable provision could be to do nothing to improve energy performance.

55 If such an upgrade is not technically or functionally feasible or would not achieve a **simple payback** of 15 years or less, the element should be upgraded to the best standard that is technically and functionally feasible and which can be achieved within a **simple payback** of no greater than 15 years. Guidance on this approach is given in Appendix A.

# RETAINED THERMAL ELEMENTS

56 Part L applies to retained **thermal elements** in the following circumstances:

a.    where an existing thermal element is part of a building subject to a material change of use;

b.    where an existing element is to become part of the thermal envelope and is to be upgraded.

57 Reasonable provision would be to upgrade those **thermal elements** whose U-value is worse than the threshold value in column (a) of Table 5 to achieve the U-value given in column (b) of Table 5 provided this is technically, functionally and economically feasible. A reasonable test of economic feasibility is to achieve a **simple payback** of 15 years or less. Where the standard given in column (b) is not technically, functionally or economically feasible, then the element should be upgraded to the best standard that is technically and functionally feasible and delivers a simple payback period of 15 years or less.

*Examples of where lesser provision than column (b) might apply are where the thickness of the additional insulation might reduce usable floor area by more than 5% or create difficulties with adjoining floor levels, or where the weight of the additional insulation might not be supported by the existing structural frame.*

## Table 5 Upgrading retained thermal elements

| Element | (a) Threshold value W/m².K | (b) Improved value W/m².K |
|---|---|---|
| Cavity wall* | 0.70 | 0.55 |
| Other wall type | 0.70 | 038 |
| Floor | 0.70 | 0.25 |
| Pitched roof - insulation at ceiling level | 0.35 | 0.16 |
| Pitched roof - insulation between rafters | 0.35 | 020 |
| Flat roof or roof with integral insulation | 0.35 | 0.25 |

* This only applies In the case of a wall suitable for the installation of cavity insulation. Where this is not the case it should be treated as for 'other wall type.'

# SECTION 3: PROVIDING INFORMATION

**58** On completion of the work, in accordance with requirement L1(c), the owner of the *dwelling*, should be provided with sufficient information about the building, the fixed building services and their maintenance requirements so that the building can be operated in such a manner as to use no more fuel and power than is reasonable in the circumstances.

**59** A way of complying would be to provide a suitable set of operating and maintenance instructions aimed at achieving economy in the use of fuel in terms that householders can understand in a durable format that can be kept and referred to over the service life of the system(s). The instructions should be directly related to the particular system(s) installed as part of the work that has been carried out.

*The aim is that this information could eventually form part of the Home Information Pack.*

**60** Without prejudice to the need to comply with health and safety requirements, the instructions should explain to the occupier of the *dwelling* how to operate the system(s) efficiently. This should include

a.   the making of adjustments to the timing and temperature control settings and

b    what routine maintenance is needed to enable operating efficiency to be maintained at a reasonable level through the service live(s) of the system(s).

**61** Where a new *dwelling* is created by a material change of use (see paragraphs 25 to 28), an energy rating shall be prepared and fixed in a conspicuous place in the dwelling as required by Regulation 16, which states that:

16.–(1) This regulation applies where a new dwelling is created by building work or by a material change of use in connection with which building work is carried out.

(2) Where this regulation applies, the person carrying out the building work shall calculate the energy rating of the dwelling by means of a procedure approved by the Secretary of State and give notice of that rating to the local authority.

(3) The notice referred to in paragraph (2) shall be given not later than the date on which the notice required by paragraph (4) of regulation 15 is given, and where a new dwellingis created by the erection of a building, it shall be given at least five days before occupation of the dwelling.

(4) Where this regulation applies, subject to paragraphs (6) and (7), the person carrying out the building work shall affix, as soon as practicable, in a conspicuous place in the dwelling, a notice stating the energy rating of the dwelling.

(5) The notice referred to in paragraph (4) shall be affixed not later than the date on which the notice required by paragraph (4) of regulation 15 is given, and, where a new dwelling is created by the erection of a building, it shall be affixed not later than five days before occupation of the dwelling.

(6) Subject to paragraph (7), if, on the date the dwelling is first occupied as a residence, no notice has been affixed in the dwelling in accordance with paragraph (4), the person carrying out the building work shall, not later than the date on which the notice required by paragraph (4) of regulation 15 is given, give to the occupier of the dwelling a notice stating the energy rating of the dwelling calculated in accordance with paragraph (2).

(7) Paragraphs (4) and (6) shall not apply in a case where the person carrying out the work intends to occupy, or occupies, the dwelling as a residence.

**62** The approved calculation procedure is SAP 2005 as announced in ODPM Circular 03/2006.

**63** Guidance on the preparation of the notices is given in DTLR Circular 3/2001.

# SECTION 4: DEFINITIONS

**64** For the purpose of this Approved Document, the following definitions apply.

**65** *BCB* means Building Control Body: a local authority or an approved inspector

**66** A *conservatory* is an extension to a building which:

a.   has not less than three quarters of its roof area and not less than one half of its external wall area made from translucent material and.

b.   is thermally separated from the dwelling by walls, windows and doors with the same U-value and draught-stripping provisions as provided elsewhere in the *dwelling*.

**67** *Dwelling* means a self-contained unit designed to be used separately to accommodate a single household.

**68** *Energy efficiency* requirements means the requirements of Regulations 4A, 17C and 17D and Part L of Schedule 1.

**69** *Fixed building services* means any part of, or any controls associated with:
a. fixed internal or external lighting systems but does not include emergency escape lighting and specialist process lighting; or
b. fixed systems for heating, hot water service systems, air conditioning or mechanical ventilation.

**70** *Renovation* in relation to a thermal element means the provision of a new layer in the thermal element or the replacement of an existing layer, but excludes decorative finishes and 'renovate' shall be constructed accordingly.

**71** *Room for residential purposes* means a room, or a suite of rooms, which is not a dwelling-house or a flat and which is used by one or more persons to live and sleep and includes a room in a hostel, a hotel, a boarding house, a hall of residence or a residential home, whether or not the room is separated from or arranged in a cluster group with other rooms, but does not include a room in a hospital, or other similar establishment, used for patient accommodation and, for the purposes of this definition, a 'cluster' is a group of rooms for residential purposes which is:
a.   separated from the rest of the building in which it is situated by a door which is designed to be locked; and
b.   not designed to be occupied by a single household

**72** *Simple payback* means the amount of time it will take to recover the initial investment through energy savings, and is calculated by dividing the marginal additional cost of implementing an energy efficiency measure by the value of the annual energy savings achieved by that measure taking no account of VAT.

a.   The marginal additional cost is the additional cost (materials and labour) of incorporating (e.g.) *additional* insulation, not the whole cost of the work.

b.   the cost of implementing the measure should be based on prices current at the date the proposals are made known to the BCB and be confirmed in a report signed by a suitably qualified person.

c.   the annual energy savings should be estimated using SAP 2005 or SBEM[23].

d   for the purposes of this Approved Document, the following energy prices that were current in 2005 should be used when evaluating the value of the annual energy savings:

    i. Mains gas - 1.63 p/kWh ii. Electricity - 3.65 p/kWh

*This is a weighted combination at peak and off peak tariffs*

    iii. Heating oil - 2.17 p/kWh iv. LPG—3.71 p/kWh

*For example if the cost of implementing a measure was £430 and the value of the annual energy savings was £38/year, the simple payback would be (430/38) =11.3 years.*

*Energy prices are increasing significantly so dwelling owners may wish to use higher values such as those prevailing when they apply for Building Regulations approval*

---

[23] Simplified Building Energy Model (SBEM) user manual and Calculation Tool, available at www.odpm.gov.uk.

**73** Thermal *element* is defined in Regulation 2A as follows.

(2A) In these Regulations 'thermal element' means a wall, floor or roof (but does not include windows, doors, roof windows or roof-lights) which separates a thermally conditioned part of the building ('the conditioned space') from:

a. the external environment (including the ground); or

b. in the case of floors and walls, another part of the building which is:

i. unconditioned;

ii. an extension falling within class VII of Schedule 2; or

iii. where this paragraph applies, conditioned to a different temperature,

and includes all parts of the element between the surface bounding the conditioned space and the external environment or other part of the building as case may be.

(2B) Paragraph (2A)(b)(iii) only applies to a building which is not a dwelling, where the other part of the building is used for a purpose which is not similar or identical to the purpose for which the conditioned space is used.

# APPENDIX A: WORK TO THERMAL ELEMENTS

1 Where the work involves the **renovation** of a **thermal element,** an opportunity exists for cost- effective insulation improvements to be undertaken at marginal additional cost. This appendix provides guidance on the cost effectiveness of insulation measures when undertaking various types of work on a **thermal element.**

2 Table A1 sets out the circumstances and the level of performance that would be considered reasonable provision in ordinary circumstances. When dealing with existing **dwellings** some flexibility in the application of standards is necessary to ensure that the context of each scheme can be taken into account while securing, as far as possible, the reasonable improvement. The final column in Table A1 provides guidance on a number of specific issues that may need to be considered in determining an appropriate course of action. As part of this flexible approach, it will be necessary to take into account technical risk and practicality in relation to the **dwelling** under consideration and the possible impacts on any adjoining building. In general the proposed works should take account of:

a.    the other parts of Schedule 1; and

b.    the general guidance on technical risk relating to insulation improvements contained in BR 262; and

c.    if the existing building has historic value, the guidance produced by English Heritage.

Where, it is not reasonable in the context of the scheme to achieve the performance set out in Table A1 the level of performance achieved should be as close to this as practically possible.

3 Table A1 incorporates, in outline form, examples of construction that would achieve the proposed performance, but designers are free to use any appropriate construction that satisfies the energy performance standard, so long as they do not compromise performance with respect to any other part of the regulations.

## GENERAL GUIDANCE

4 This section lists general guidance documents that provide advice on the **renovation** options available and their application. The listing of any guide, British Standard or other document does not indicate that the guidance contained is approved or applicable to any particular scheme. It is for the applicant and his or her advisors to assess the applicability of the guidance in the context of a particular application. Responsibility for the guidance contained in the documents listed rests with the authors and authoring organisations concerned.

5 In a number of documents (particularly those produced by the Energy Saving Trust's Energy Efficiency Best Practice in Housing programme) a recommended thermal performance is stated in

the form of a U value for different elements and forms of construction. The inclusion of such a performance value in any guidance document in this Appendix does not constitute a performance limit or target for the purposes of this Approved Document. In all cases the relevant target U values are those contained in Table A1.

### General guidance

Stirling, C. (2002) Thermal insulation: Avoiding Risks, Building Research Establishment report BR 262, Watford, Construction Research Communications Ltd.

EST (2004) Energy efficient refurbishment of existing housing, Good Practice guide 15, Energy Efficiency Best Practice in Housing, London, Energy Saving Trust.

EST (2005) Advanced Insulation in housing Refurbishment, CE 97, Energy Efficiency Best Practice in Housing, London, Energy Saving Trust

EST (2004) Refurbishing Cavity Walled Dwellings, CE 57, Energy Efficiency Best Practice in Housing, London, Energy Saving Trust.

EST (2004) Refurbishing Dwellings with Solid Walls, CE 58, Energy Efficiency Best Practice in Housing, London, Energy Saving Trust.

EST (2004) Refurbishing Timber-Framed Dwellings, CE 59, Energy Efficiency Best Practice in Housing, London, Energy Saving Trust.

### Roofs

EST (2002) Refurbishment Site Guidance for Solid-Walled Houses - Roofs, GPG 296, Energy Efficiency Best Practice in Housing, London, Energy Saving Trust.

Stirling (2000) Insulating roofs at rafter level:

sarking insulation, Good Building Guide 37, Watford, Building Research Establishment.

Code of practice for loft insulation: National Insulation Association.

## Walls

EST (2000) External Insulation Systems for Walls of Dwellings, GPG 293, Energy Efficiency Best Practice in Housing, London, Energy Saving Trust.

EST (2003) Internal Wall insulation in Existing housing, GPG 13 8, Energy Efficiency Best Practice in Housing, London, Energy Saving Trust.

EST (2000) Refurbishment Site Guidance for SolJd-Walled Houses-Walls, GPG 297, Energy Efficiency Best Practice in Housing, London, Energy Saving Trust.

## Floors

EST (2002) Refurbishment Site Guidance for Solid-Walled Houses - Ground Floors, GPG 294, Energy Efficiency Best Practice in Housing, London, Energy Saving Trust.

## International, European and British Standards

BS 5250:2002 Code of practice for the control of condensation in buildings.

BS EN ISO 13788:2001 Hygrothermal performance of building components and building elements. Internal surface temperature to avoid critical surface humidity and interstitial condensation. Calculation methods.

BS 6229:2003, Flat roofs with continuously supported coverings - Code of practice.

BS 5803-5:1985, Thermal insulation for use in pitched roof spaces in dwellings. Specification for installation of man-made mineral fibre and cellulose fibre insulation. Amended 1999 incorporating amendment no.1 1994.

### Table A1 Cost-effective U-value targets when undertaking renovation works to thermal elements

| Proposed works | Target U-value (W/m².K) | Typical construction | Comments (reasonableness, practicability and cost-effectiveness) |
|---|---|---|---|
| **Pitched roof constructions** | | | |
| Renewal of roof covering - N living accommodation in the roof void - existing insulation (if any) at ceiling level. No existing insulation. existing insulation less than 50mm, in poor condition, and/or likely to be significantly disturbed or removed as part of the planned work | 0.16 | Provide loft insulation - 250mm mineral fibre or cellulose fibre as quilt laid between and across ceiling joists or loose fill or equivalent. This may be inappropriate if the loft is already boarded out and the boarding is not to be removed as part of the work | Assess condensation risk in roof space and make appropriate provision in accordance with the requirements of Part C relating to the control of condensation. Additional provision may be required to provide access to and insulation of services in the roof void |
| Renewal of roof covering - Existing insulation in good condition and wil not be significantly disturbed by proposed works. Existing insulation thickness 50mm or more but less than 100mm | 0.20 | Top-up loft insulation to at least 200mm mineral fibre or cellulose fibre as quilt laid between and across ceiling joists or loose fill or equivalent | Assess condensation risk in roof space and make appropriate provision in line with the requirements of Part C relating to the control of condensation Additional provision may be required to provide insulation and access to services the roof void Where the loft is already boarded out and the boarding is not to be removed as part of the work, the practicality of insulation works would need to be considered |

## Table A1 Cost-effective U-value targets when undertaking renovation works to thermal elements

| Proposed works | Target U-value (W/m².K) | Typical construction | Comments (reasonableness, practicability and cost-effectiveness) |
|---|---|---|---|
| Renewal of the ceiling to cold loft space. Existing insulation at ceiling evel removed as part of the works | 0.16 | Provide loft insulation - 250mm mineral fibre or cellulose fibre as quilt laid between and across ceiling joists or loose fiii or equivalent | Assess condensation risk in roof space and make appropriate provision in line with the requirements of Part C relating to the control of condensation Additional provision may be required to provide insulation and access to services considered Where the loft is already boarded out and the boarding is not to be removed as part of the work, insulation can be installed from the underside but the target U-value may not be achievable |
| Renewal of roof covering - living accommodation in roof space room-in-the-roof type arrangement), with or without dormer windows | 0.20 | Cold structure - insulation (thickness dependent on material) placed below rafters Warm structure - insulation placed between and above rafters | Assess condensation risk (particularly interstitial condensation), and make appropriate provision in accordance with the requirements of Part C relating to the control of condensation (Clause 8.4 of BS 5250:2002 and BS EN ISO, 13788:2001) Practical considerations with respect to an increase in structural thickness (particularly in terraced dwellings) may necessitate a lower performance target |
| **Dormer window constructions** | | | |
| Renewal of cladding to side walls | 0.35 | Insulation (thickness dependent on material) placed between and/or fixed to outside of wall studs. Or fully external to existing structure depending on construction | Assess condensation risk and make appropriate provision in accordance with the requirements of Part C |
| Renewal of roof covering | - | Follow guidance on improvement to pitched or flat roofs asappropriate | Assess condensation risk and make appropriate provision in accordance with the requirements of Part C |
| **Flat roof constructions** | | | |
| Renewal of roof covering - Existing Insulation, if any, less than 100mm, mineral fibre (or equivalent resistance), or in poor condition and likely to be significantly disturbed or removed as part of the planned work | 0.25 | Insulation placed between and over joists as required to achieve the target U-value - Warm structure | Assess condensation risk and make appropriate provision in accordance with the requirements of Part C. Also see BS 6229:2003 for design guidance |
| Renewal of the ceiling to flat roof Area. Existing insulation removed as part of the works | 0.25 | Insulation placed between and to underside of joists to achieve target U-value | Assess condensation risk and make appropriate provision in accordance with the requirements of Part C. Also see BS 6229:2003 for design guidance Where ceiling height would be adversely affected, a lower performance target may be appropriate |

## Table A1 Cost-effective U-value targets when undertaking renovation works to thermal elements

| Proposed works | Target U-value (W/m².K) | Typical construction | Comments (reasonableness, practicability and cost-effectiveness) |
|---|---|---|---|
| **Solid wall constructions** | | | |
| Renewal of internal finish to external wall or applying a finish for the first time | 0.35 | Dry-lining to inner face of wall - Insulation between studs fixed to wall to achieve target U-value - thickness dependent on insulation and stud material used Insulated wall board fixed to internal wall surface to achieve the required U-value - thickness dependent on material used | Assess the Impact on Internal floor area. In general It would be reasonable to accept a reduction of no more than 5% of the area of a room. However, the use of the room and the space requirements for movement and arrangements of fixtures, fittings and furniture should be assessed |
| | | | In situations where acoustic attenuation issues are particularly important (e.g. where Insulation Is returned at party walls) a less demanding U-value may be more appropriate. In such cases, the U-value target may have to be increased to 0.35 or above depending on the circumstances |
| | | | Assess condensation and other moisture risks and make appropriate provision In accordance with the requirements of Part C. This will usually require the provision of a vapour control and damp protection to components. Guidance on the risks Involved Is provided in Sterling (2002) and, on the technical options, in EST (2003) |
| Renewal of finish or cladding to external wall area or elevation (render or other cladding) or applying a finish or cladding for the first time | 0.35 | External insulation system with rendered finish or cladding to give required U-value | Assess technical risk and Impact of Increased wall thickness on adjoining buildings |
| **Cavity wall constructions** | | | |
| Replace wall ties to at least one elevation | 0.55 | Include cavity wall Insulation | Assess suitability of cavity for full fill insulation in accordance with requirements of Part C |
| **Ground floor constructions** | | | |
| Renovation of a solid or suspended floor involving the replacement of screed or a timber floor deck | See comment | Solid floor - replace screed with an Insulated floor deck to maintain existing floor level Suspended timber floor - fit Insulation between floor joists prior to replacement of floor deck | The cost-effectiveness of floor insulation is complicated by the Impact of the size and shape of the floor (Perimeter/Area ratio). In many cases existing uninsulated floor U-values are already relatively low when compared with wall and roof U-values. Where the existing floor U-value is greater than 0.70W/m2.K, then the addition of Insulation is likely to be cost-effective. Analysis shows that the cost-benefit curve for the thickness of added insulation is very flat, and so a target U-value of 0.25W/m2.K Is appropriate subject to other technical constraints (adjoining floor levels, etc.) |

# DOCUMENTS REFERRED TO

**BRE**

www.bre.co.uk

BR 262 *Thermal insulation: avoiding risks*, 2001. ISBN1 86081 5154

BRE Report BR 443 *Conventions for U-value calculations*, 2006. (Available at www.bre.co.uk/uvalues.)

Information Paper IP1/06 *Assessing the effects of thermal bridging at functions and around openings in the external elements of buildings*, 2006. ISBN1 86081 9044

Simplified Building Energy Model (SBEM) user manual and Calculation Tool. (Available from www.odpm.gov.uk)

**Department of the Environment, Food and Rural Affairs (Defra) www.defra.gov.uk**

The Government's Standard Assessment Procedure for energy rating of dwellings, SAP 2005. (Available at www,bre,co.uk/sap2005,)

**Department of Transport, Local Government and the Regions (DTLR)**

*Limiting thermal bridging and air leakage: Robust construction details for dwellings and similar buildings*, Amendment 1. Published by TSO, 2002. ISBN 011753 631 8

(or download from Energy Saving Trust (EST) website on http://portalest.org.uk/ housingbuildings/calculators/robustdetails/)

**Energy Saving Trust (EST) www.est.org.uk**

CE66 *Windows for new and existing housing*, 2006.

GPG268 *Energy efficient ventilation in dwellings - a guide for specifiers*, 2006.

GIL20 *Low energy domestic lighting*, 2006.

**English Heritage www.english-heritage.org.uk**

*Building Regulations and Historic Buildings*, 2002 (revised 2004).

**Health and Safety Executive (HSE) www.hse.gov.uk**

L24 *Workplace Healthy Safety and Welfare: Workplace (Health, Safety and Welfare) Regulations 1992, Approved Code of Practice and Guidance, The Health and Safety Commission*, 1992. ISBN 071760 413 6

**NBS (on behalf of ODPM) www.thebuildingregs.com**

*Domestic Heating Compliance Guide*, 2006. ISBN 1 85946 225 1

**Thermal Insulation Manufacturers and Suppliers Association (TIMSA) www.timsa.org.uk**

*HVAC Guidance for Achieving Compliance with Part L of the Building Regulations*, 2006,

**Legislation**

SI 1991/1620 Construction Products Regulations 1991.

SI 1992/2372 Electromagnetic Compatibility Regulations 1992.

SI 1994/3051 Construction Products (Amendment) Regulations 1994.

SI 1994/3080 Electromagnetic Compatibility (Amendment) Regulations 1994.

SI 1994/3260 Electrical Equipment (Safety) Regulations 1994.

SI 2001/3335 Building (Amendment) Regulations 2001.

SI 2005/1726 Energy Information (Household Air Conditioners) (No. 2) Regulations 2005.

SI 2006/652 Building And Approved Inspectors (Amendment) Regulations 2006.

## STANDARDS REFERRED TO

BS 8206-2:1992 Lighting for buildings. Code of practice for daylighting.

## APPROVED DOCUMENTS

The following documents have been approved and issued by the First Secretary of State for the purpose of providing practical guidance with respect to the requirements of the Building Regulations 2000 (as amended).

**Approved Document A: Structure**

2004 edition incorporating 2004 amendments

**Approved Document B: Fire safety**

2000 edition incorporating 2000 and 2002 amendments

**Approved Document C: Site preparation and resistance to contaminants and moisture**

2004 edition

**Approved Document D:Toxic substances**

1992 edition incorporating 2002 amendments

**Approved Document E: Resistance to the passage of sound**

2003 edition incorporating 2004 amendments

**Approved Document F: Ventilation**

2006 edition

**Approved Document G: Hygiene**

1992 edition incorporating 1992 and 2000 amendments

**Approved Document H: Drainage and waste disposal**

2002 edition

**Approved Document J: Combustion appliances and fuel storage systems**

2002 edition

**Approved Document J: 2002 Edition:**

**Guidance and Supplementary Information on the UK Implementation of European Standards for Chimneys and Flues**

2002 edition

**Approved Document K: Protection from falling collision and impact**

1998 edition incorporating 2000 amendments

**Approved Document L1A: Conservation of fuel and power**

New dwellings 2006 edition

**Approved Document L1B: Conservation of fuel and power**

Existing dwellings 2006 edition

**Approved Document L2A: Conservation of fuel and power**

New buildings other than dwellings 2006 edition

**Approved Document L2B: Conservation of fuel and power**

Existing buildings other than dwellings 2006 edition

**Approved Document M: Access to and use of buildings**

2004 edition

**Approved Document N: Glazing - safety in relation to impact, opening and cleaning**

1998 edition incorporating 2000 amendments

**Approved Document P: Electrical safety - Dwellings 2006 edition**

**Approved Document to support regulation 7:**

**Materials and workmanship**

1992 edition incorporating 2000 amendments

The Building Regulations 2000

# ELECTRICAL SAFETY-DWELLINGS
## APPROVED DOCUMENT

### DESIGN AND INSTALLATION OF ELECTRICAL INSTALLATIONS

Came into effect April 2007

# Contents

# Use of guidance

## THE APPROVED DOCUMENTS

This document is one of a series that has been approved and issued by the Secretary of State for the purpose of providing practical guidance with respect to the requirements of Schedule 1 to and regulation 7 of the Building Regulations 2000 (Sl 2000/2531) for England and Wales. Sl 2000/2531 has been amended by the Building (Amendment) Regulations 2001 (Sl 2001/3335), the Building (Amendment) Regulations 2002 (Sl 2002/440), the Building (Amendment Regulations 2002 (Sl 2002/2871), the Building (Amendment) Regulations 2003 (Sl 2003/2692), the Building amendment) Regulations 2004 (Sl 2004/1465) and the Building amendment) (No 3) Regulations 2004 (Si 2004/3210) and the Building and Approved Inspectors (Amendment) Regulations 2006 (Sl 2006/652).

**At the back of this document is a list of all the documents that have been approved and issued by the Secretary of State for this purpose.**

Approved Documents are intended to provide guidance for some of the more common building situations. However, there may well be alternative ways of achieving compliance with the requirements. **Thus there is no obligation to adopt any particular solution contained in an Approved Document if you prefer to meet the relevant requirement in some other way.**

### Supplementary guidance

The Office of the Deputy Prime Minister occasionally issues additional material to aid interpretation of the guidance contained in Approved Documents. This material may be conveyed in official letters to Chief Executives of Local Authorities and Approved Inspectors and/ or posted on the websites accessed through:

http://www.odpm.gov.uk/building-regulations.

## OTHER REQUIREMENTS

The guidance contained in an Approved Document relates only to the particular requirements of the Regulations which the document addresses* The building work will also have to comply with any other relevant requirements in Schedule 1 to the Regulations.

There are Approved Documents which give guidance on each of the Parts of Schedule 1 and on Regulation 7.

## LIMITATION ON REQUIREMENTS

In accordance with regulation 8, the requirements in Parts A to D, F to K, N and P (except for paragraphs H2 and J6) of Schedule 1 to the Building Regulations do not require anything to be done the purpose of securing reasonable standards of health and safety for persons in or about buildings (and any others who may be affected by buildings or matters connected with buildings). This is one of the categories of purpose for which Building Regulations may be made.

Paragraphs H2 and J6 are excluded from regulation 8 because they deal directly with prevention of the contamination of water Parts E and M (which deal, respectively, with resistance to the passage of sound, and access to and use of buildings) are excluded from regulation 8 because they address the welfare and convenience of building users. Part L is excluded from regulation 8 because it addresses the conservation of fuel and power. All these matters are amongst the purposes, other than health and safety, that may be addressed by Building Regulations.

## MATERIALS AND WORKMANSHIP

Any building work which is subject to the requirements imposed by Schedule 1 to the Building Regulations should, in accordance with regulation 7, be carried out with proper materials and in a workmanlike manner.

You may show that you have complied with regulation 7 in a number of ways. These include the appropriate use of a product bearing CE marking in accordance with the Construction Products Directive (89/106/EEC)[1], the Low Voltage Directive (73/23/EEC and amendment 93/68/EEC)[2] and the EMC Directive (89/336/ EEC)[3], as amended by the CE marking Directive (93/68/EEC)[4], or a product complying with an appropriate technical specification (as defined in those Directives), a British Standard, or an alternative national technical specification of any state which is a contracting party to the European Economic area which, in use, is equivalent  or a product covered by a national or European certificate issued by a European Technical Approval issuing body, and the conditions of use are in accordance with the terms of the certificate. You will find further guidance in the Approved Document supporting regulation 7 on materials and workmanship.

### Independent certification schemes

There are many UK product certification schemes. Such schemes certify compliance with the requirements of a recognised document which is appropriate to the purpose for which the material is to be used. Materials which are not so certified may still conform to a relevant standard,

Many certification bodies which approve such schemes are accredited by UKAS.

### Technical specifications

Under section 1 (1) of the Building Act 1984, Building Regulations may be made for various purposes including health, safety, welfare, convenience, conservation of fuel and power and prevention of waste or contamination of water, furthering the protection or enhancement of the environment, facilitating sustainable development or the prevention and detection of crime. Standards and technical approvals are relevant guidance to the extent that they relate to these considerations, However, they may also address other aspects of performance such as serviceability, or aspects which, although they relate to the purposes listed above, are not covered by the current Regulations.

When an Approved Document makes reference to a named standard, the relevant version of the standard is the one listed at the end of the publication. However, if this version has been revised or updated by the issuing standards body, the new version may be used as a source of guidance provided it continues to address the relevant requirements of the Regulations.

The appropriate use of a product which complies with a European Technical Approval as defined in the Construction Products Directive will meet the relevant requirements.

The Office intends to issue periodic amendments to its Approved Documents to reflect emerging harmonised European Standards, Where a national standard is to be replaced by a European harmonised standard, there will be a co-existence period during which either standard may be referred to. At the end of the co-existence period the national standard will be withdrawn.

## MIXED USE DEVELOPMENT

In mixed use developments part of a building may be used as a dwelling while another part has a non-domestic use. In such cases, if the requirements of the Regulations for dwellings and non-domestic use differ, the requirements for non-domestic use should apply in any shared parts of the building.

---

[1] As implemented by the Construction Products Regulations 1991 (SI 1620/1991).

[2] As implemented by the Electrical Equipment (Safety) Regulations 1994 (SI 3260/1994).

[3] As implemented by the Electromagnetic Compatibility Regulations 1992 (SI 2372/1992).

[4] As implemented by the Construction Products (Amendment) Regulations 1994 (Sl 3051/1994) and the Electromagnetic Compatibility Amendment) Regulations 1994 (Sl 3080/1994).

## THE WORKPLACE (HEALTH, SAFETY AND WELFARE) REGULATIONS 1992

The Workplace (Health, Safety and Welfare) Regulations 1992 as amended contain some requirements which affect building design. The main requirements are now covered by the Building Regulations, but for further information see: *Workplace health, safety and welfare: Workplace (Health, Safety and Welfare) Regulations 1992, Approved Code of Practice, L24, HMSO, 1992 (ISBN 07176 0413 6)*.

The Workplace (Health, Safety and Welfare) Regulations 1992 apply to the common parts of flats and similar buildings if people such as cleaners and caretakers are employed to work in these common parts. Where the requirements of the Building Regulations that are covered by this Part do not apply to buildings other than dwellings, the provisions may still be required in the situations described above in order to satisfy the Workplace Regulations.

# THE REQUIREMENTS

This Approved Document, which takes effect on 6 April 2006, deals with the requirements of Part P of Schedule 1 to the Building Regulations 2000 (as amended by Sl 2004/3210 and Sl 2006/652).

| Requirement | Limits on application |
|---|---|
| **PART P ELECTRICAL SAFETY** | |
| Design and installation | The requirements of this part apply only to electrical installations that are intended to operate at low or extra-low voltage and are: |
| P1. Reasonable provision shall be made in the design and installation of electrical installations in order to protect persons operating, maintaining or altering the installations from fire or injury. | (a) in or attached to a dwelling; |
| | (b) in the common parts of a building serving one or more dwellings, but excluding power supplies to lifts; |
| | (c) in a building that receives its electricity from a source located within or shared with a dwelling; and |
| | (d) in a garden or in or on land associated with a building where the electricity is from a source located within or shared with a dwelling. |

## NOTES

### Examples of application of Part P

Part P applies to electrical installations in or attached to buildings or parts of buildings comprising:

• dwelling houses and flats;

• dwellings and business premises that have a common supply – for example shops and public houses with a flat above;

• common access areas in blocks of flats such as corridors and staircases;

• shared amenities of blocks of flats such as laundries and gymnasiums.

Part P applies also to parts of the above electrical installations:

• in or on land associated with the buildings – for example Part P applies to fixed lighting and pond pumps in gardens;

• in outbuildings such as sheds, detached garages and greenhouses.

### Interaction with other Parts of the Building Regulations

Other Parts of Schedule 1 to the Building Regulations contain requirements affecting electrical installations. Examples include, but are not limited to:

• Part A (Structure): depth of chases in walls, and size of holes and notches in floor and roof joists;

• Part B (Fire safety): fire safety of certain electrical installations; provision of fire alarm and fire detection systems; fire resistance of penetrations through floors and walls;

• Part C (Site preparation and resistance to moisture): moisture resistance of cable penetrations through external walls;

• Part E (Resistance to the passage of sound): penetrations through floors and walls;

• Part L (Conservation of fuel and power): energy efficient lighting; reduced current- carrying capacity of cables in insulation;

• Part M (Access to and use of buildings): height of socket outlets, switches and consumer units.

Further guidance is available in:

• the Electrician's guide to the Building Regulations, published by the IEE (Institution of Electrical Engineers), available from www.iee.org

• the Electrical Installers' Guide to the Building Regulations published by the NICEIC Group Limited and the EGA (Electrical Contractors' Association), available from wwwniceic.org.uk orwww.eca.co.uk.

Regulation 4(2) states that, on completion of electrical installation work, the building (and parts of the electrical installations in the building that were not the subject of work) should be no worse in terms of the level of compliance with the other applicable Parts of Schedule 1 to the Building Regulations than before the work was undertaken.

For example, one or more perforations of a ceiling lining beneath a floor – made to accommodate recessed lighting or similar fittings - may have an adverse effect on that floor's performance in terms of its resistance to fire and sound penetration. Due regard should therefore be paid to the guidance in Approved Documents B and E on the performance of compartment floors.

Regulation 4(2) also means that, when extending or altering an installation, only the new work must meet current requirements and there is no obligation to upgrade the existing installation unless the new work would adversely affect the safety of the existing installation, or the state of the existing installation was such that work could not be operated safely, Or where there is a requirement to upgrade imposed by the energy efficiency requirements of the Building Regulations.

# Section 0: General guidance

## Performance

**0.1** In the Secretary of State's view, the requirements will be met by adherence to the 'Fundamental Principles' for achieving safety given in BS 7671:2001 Chapter 13. To achieve these requirements electrical installations must be:

a.   designed and installed to afford appropriate protection against mechanical and thermal damage, and so that they do not present electric shock and fire hazards to people;

b.   suitably inspected and tested to verify that they meet the relevant equipment and installation standards.

## General

**0.2** A way of satisfying the fundamental principles would be to follow:

a.   the technical rules described in the body of BS 7671:2001 as amended or in an equivalent standard approved by a member of the EEA; and

b.   guidance given in installation manuals that are consistent with BS 7671:2001, such as:

    i. the IEE (Institution of Electrical Engineers) On-Site Guide;

    ii. the series of IEE Publications, Guidance Notes Nos 1 to 7.

**0.3** The diagrams in Appendix A give an indication of the sorts of electrical services encountered in dwellings, some of the ways they can be connected and the complexity of the wiring and protective systems necessary to supply them. They are not an indication of the scope of Part P and must not be used for installation purposes.

## Definitions

**0.4** The following meanings apply throughout this document:

**Electrical installation** is defined in the Building Regulations as fixed electrical cables or fixed electrical equipment located on the consumer's side of the electricity supply meter.

**Extra-low voltage** is defined in the Building Regulations as voltage not exceeding 50 volts between conductors and earth for alternating current or 120 volts between conductors for direct current.

**Low voltage** which normally exceeds extra-low voltage is defined in the Building Regulations as not exceeding 1000 volts between conductors or 600 volts between conductors and earth for alternating current; or 1500 volts between conductors or 900 volts between conductors and earth for direct current.

**Kitchen** is defined in the Building Regulations as 'a room or part of a room which contains a sink and food preparation facilities'.

*As a guide only, in open plan areas the zone of a kitchen may be considered to extend from the edge of the sink to a distance of 3m or to a nearer dividing wall.*

## Other Regulations

**0.5** Electrical work is also affected by the Electricity at Work Regulations 1989 as amended and the Electricity Safety, Quality and Continuity Regulations 2002 as amended, as described in paragraphs 3.1 to 3.13.

### Notification of work

**When necessary to involve building control bodies**

**0.6** Except in the circumstances outlined in paragraph 0.7 below, notification of proposals to carry out electrical installation work must be given to a building control body (the local authority or an approved inspector before work begins.

**When not necessary to involve building control bodies**

**0.7** It is not necessary to give prior notification of proposals to carry out electrical installation work to building control bodies in the following circumstances:

a. The proposed installation work is undertaken by a person registered with an electrical self- certification scheme prescribed in regulations (see schedule 2A of the Regulations). In these cases the person is responsible for ensuring compliance with BS 7671:2001 or an equivalent standard and all relevant building regulations requirements. A full list of schemes with contact details is given in Appendix E.

OR

b. The proposed electrical installation work is non-notifiable work of the type described in Table 1 and does not include the provision of a new circuit (see schedule 2B of the Regulations).

## Table 1 Work that need not be notified to building control bodies

**Work consisting of:**

Replacing any fixed electrical equipment (for example, socket-outlets, control switches and ceiling roses) which does not include the provision of any new fixed cabling

Replacing the cable for a single circuit only, where damaged, for example, by fire, rodent or impact [a]

Re-fixing or replacing the enclosures of existing installation components [b]

Providing mechanical protection to existing fixed installations [c]

Installing or upgrading main or supplementary equipotential bonding [d]

**Work that is not in a kitchen or special location and does not involve a special installation [e] and consists of:**

Adding lighting points (light fittings and switches) to an existing circuit [f]

Adding socket-outlets and fused spurs to an existing ring or radial circuit [f]

**Work not in a special location, on:**

Telephone or extra-low voltage wiring and equipment for the purposes of communications, information technology, signalling, control and similar purposes

Prefabricated equipment sets and associated flexible leads with integral plug and socket connections

**Notes:**

(a) On condition that the replacement cable has the same current-carrying capacity and follows the same route.

(b) If the circuit's protective measures are unaffected.

(c) If the circuit's protective measures and current-carrying capacity of conductors are unaffected by increased thermal insulation.

(d) Such work will need to comply with other applicable legislation, such as the Gas Safety (installation and Use) Regulations.

(e) Special locations and installations are listed in Table 2.

(f) Only if the existing circuit protective device is suitable and provides protection for the modified circuit, and other relevant safety provisions are satisfactory.

---

### Table 2 Special locations and installations(a)

**Special locations**
Locations containing a bath tub or shower basin Swimming pools or paddling pools
Hot air saunas
**Special installations**
Electric floor or ceiling heating systems Garden lighting or power installations Solar photovoltaic (PV) power supply systems Small scale generators such as microCHP units Extra-low voltage lighting installations, other than pre-assembled, CE-marked lighting sets

Note:
(a) See IEE Guidance Note 7 which gives more guidance on achieving safe installations where risks to people are greater.

---

## Additional notes

Tables 1 and 2 above give the general rules for determining whether or not electrical installation work is notifiable. The rules are based on the risk of fire and injury and what is practicable. The following notes provide additional guidance and specific examples:

a.   Notifiable jobs include new circuits back to the consumer unit, and extensions to circuits in kitchens and special locations (bathrooms, etc) and associated with special installations (garden lighting and power installations, etc).

b.   Replacement, repair and maintenance jobs are generally not notifiable, even if carried out in a kitchen or special location or associated with a special installation.

c.   Consumer unit replacements are, however, notifiable.

d.   In large bathrooms, the location containing a bath or shower is defined by the walls of the bathroom.

e.   Conservatories and attached garages are not special locations. Work in them is therefore not notifiable unless it involves the installation of a new circuit or the extension of a circuit in a kitchen or special location or associated with a special installation.

f.   Detached garages and sheds are not special locations. Work within them is notifiable only if it involves new outdoor wiring.

g.   Outdoor lighting and power installations are special installations. Any new work in, for example, the garden or that involves crossing the garden is notifiable.

h.   The installation of fixed equipment is within the scope of Part P, even where the final connection is by a 13A plug and socket. However, work is notifiable only if it involves fixed wiring and the installation of a new circuit or the extension of a circuit in a kitchen or special location or associated with a special installation.

i.   The installation of equipment attached to the outside wall of a house (for example security lighting, air conditioning equipment and radon fans) is not notifiable provided that there are no exposed outdoor connections and the work does not involve the installation of a new circuit or the extension of a circuit in a kitchen or special location or associated with a special installation.

j.   The installation of a socket outlet on an external wall is notifiable, since the socket- outlet is an outdoor connector that could be connected to cables that cross the garden and requires RCD protection.

k.   The installation of prefabricated, "modular" systems (for example kitchen lighting systems and armoured garden cabling) linked by plug and socket connectors is not notifiable, provided that products are CE-marked and that any final connections in kitchens and special locations are made to existing connection units or points (possibly a 13A socket outlet).

l.   Work to connect an electric gate or garage door to an existing Isolator is not notifiable, but installation of the circuit up to the isolator is notifiable.

m.   The fitting and replacement of cookers and electric showers is not notifiable unless a new circuit is needed.

n.   New central heating control wiring installations are notifiable even where work in kitchens and bathrooms is avoided.

# Section 1: Design, installation, inspection and testing, and provision of information

## General

**1.1**  Where electrical installation work is to be carried out professionally, compliance is necessary with the Electricity at Work Regulations 1989 as amended.

**1.2**  In accordance with the Electricity Safety, Quality and Continuity Regulations 2002 and the contract for a mains supply, proposals for new installations of a mains supply or significant alterations to an existing mains supply must be agreed with the electricity distributor.

## Design and installation

### General

**1.3**  Electrical installations should be designed and constructed, suitably enclosed and separated by appropriate distances to provide mechanical and thermal protection, so that they afford appropriate protection for persons against the risks of electric shock, burn or fire injuries.

**1.4**  A way of complying is to follow the technical rules in BS 7671:2001 as amended or an equivalent standard.

### Protection against flooding

**1.5**  The Electricity Safety Quality and Continuity Regulations 2002 require the electricity distributor to install the cut-out and meter in a safe location where they are mechanically protected and can be safely maintained. In compliance with this requirement, the electricity distributor and installer may be required to take into account the risk of flooding. Some guidance is given in the ODPM publication Preparing for flooding, available from www.odpm.gov.uk.

### Accessibility

**1.6**  Wall-mounted socket-outlets, switches and consumer units should be located so that they are easily reachable where this is necessary to comply with Part M of the Building Regulations. Approved Document M shows ways of complying. Accessible consumer units should comply with BS EN 60439-3.

## Inspection and testing before taking into service

### General

**1.7**  Electrical installations should be inspected and tested as necessary and appropriate during and at the end of installation, before they are taken into service, to verify that they are safe to use, maintain and alter and comply with Part P of the Building Regulations and with any other relevant Parts of the Building Regulations.

### BS 7671 installation certificates

**1.8**  In general, compliance with Part P can be demonstrated by the issue of the appropriate BS 7671 electrical installation certificate.

**1.9**  Inspection and testing should be carried out to follow procedures in Chapters 71 and 74 of BS 7671:2001, and a copy of the appropriate installation certificate should be supplied to the person ordering the work. The electrical installation certificate must be made out and signed only by someone "qualified" to do so. Where this is the case, a safety certificate should be issued for all but the simplest of like-for-like replacements.

**1.10**  "Qualified" in this context means having the appropriate qualifications, knowledge and experience to carry out the inspection and testing procedures and complete the relevant electrical installation certificate.

*1.11* The certificate should show that the electrical installation work has been:

a.  Inspected appropriately during erection as well as on completion to verify that the components are:

i. made in compliance with appropriate British Standards or harmonised European Standards;

ii. selected and installed in accordance with BS 7671:2001 (including consideration of external influences such as the presence of moisture);

iii. not visibly damaged or defective so as to be unsafe.

b.  Tested appropriately to check satisfactory performance in relation to continuity of conductors, insulation resistance, separation of circuits, polarity, earthing and bonding arrangements, earth fault loop impedance and functionality of all protective devices including residual current devices. It is not necessary to carry out all these tests for each and every installation, only those which are needed to establish whether the installation is safe.

**1.12** Appendix 6 of BS 7671 and Appendix B of this Approved Document contain models of the various BS 7671 certificates. Qualified installers should use the one appropriate to the work they have carried out.

1.13 BS 7671 does not insist on a Minor Works Certificate being issued for the replacement of equipment such as accessories or luminaires, but advises that this should be done where appropriate inspection and testing has been carried out, irrespective of the extent of the work undertaken. The Minor Works Certificate is not appropriate for the replacement of consumer units or similar items, for which the full Electrical Installation Certificate should be used.

**1.14** Section 712 of BS 7671:2001 provides a list of all the inspections that may be necessary although in particular cases only some elements will be relevant. A schedule of inspections forms part of the Electrical Installation Certificate in Appendix 6 of BS 7671 and in this Approved Document at Appendix B.

**1.15** Section 713 of BS 7671:2001 provides a list of all the tests that may be necessary although, again, in particular cases only some elements may be relevant. A blank schedule for recording test results also forms part of the Electrical Installation Certificate. Tests should be carried out using appropriate and accurate instruments under the conditions given in BS 7671, and the results compared with the relevant performance criteria to confirm compliance.

1.16 The Minor Works Certificate lists six essential tests for additions and alterations that do not include the provision of a new circuit. Appropriate tests should be carried out depending on the nature of the work.

### *Building Regulations compliance certificates/notices for notifiable work*

**1.17** A Building Regulations compliance certificate (issued by Part P competent person scheme installers), completion certificates (issued by local authorities) and final notices (issued by approved inspectors) are evidence that compliance with the Building Regulations has been achieved, and are issued on completion of notifiable works only. They are different documents than a BS 7671 installation certificate and attest compliance with all relevant requirements of the Building Regulations, not just Part R

## Certification of notifiable work

**a.   Where the installer is registered with a Part P competent person self-certification scheme**

**1.18** Installers registered with a Part P competent person self-certification scheme are qualified to complete BS 7671 installation certificates and should do so in respect of every job they undertake. A copy of the certificate should always be given to the person ordering the electrical installation work.

**1.19** Where Installers registered with Part P competent person self-certification scheme, a Building Regulations compliance certificate must be issued to the occupant either by the installer or the installer's registration body within 30 days of the work being completed. The relevant building control body should also receive a copy of the information on the certificate within 30 days.

**1.20** The Regulations call for the Building Regulations compliance certificate to be issued to the occupier However, in the case of rented properties, the certificate may be sent to the person ordering the work with a copy sent also to the occupant.

**b.   Where the installer is not registered with a Part P competent person self-certification scheme but qualified to complete BS 7671 installation certificates**

**1.21** Where notifiable electrical installer work is carried out by a person not registered with a Part P competent person self-certification the work should be notified to a building control body (the local authority or an approved inspector) before work starts. Where the work is necessary because of an emergency the building control body should be notified as soon as possible. The building control body becomes responsible for making sure the work is safe and complies with all relevant requirements of the Building Regulations.

**1.22** Where installers are qualified to carry out inspection and testing and completing the appropriate BS 7671 installation certificate, they should do so. A copy of the certificate should then be given to the building control body. The building control body will take this certificate into account in deciding what further action (if any) needs to be taken to make sure that the work is safe and complies fully with all relevant requirements. Building control bodies may ask for evidence that installers are qualified in this case.

**1.23** Where the building control body decides that the work is safe and meets all building regulations it will issue a building regulation completion certificate (the local authority) on request or a final certificate (an approved inspector).

*c. Where installers are not qualified to complete BS 7671 completion certificates*

**1.24** Where such installers (who may be contractors or DIYers) carry out notifiable electrical work, the building control body must be notified before the work starts. Where the work is necessary because of an emergency the building control body should be notified as soon as possible. The building control body then becomes responsible for making sure that the work is safe and complies with all relevant requirements in the Building Regulations.

**1.25** The amount of inspection and testing needed is for the building control body to decide, based on the nature and extent of the electrical work. For relatively simple notifiable jobs, such as adding a Socket-outlet to a kitchen circuit, the Inspection and testing requirements will be minimal. For a house re-wire, a full set of inspections and tests may need to be carried out.

**1.26** The building control body may choose to carry out the inspection and testing itself, or to contract out some or all of the work to a specialist body which will then carry out the work on its behalf. Building control bodies will carry out the necessary inspection and testing at their expense, not at the householders' expense.

**1.27** A building control body will not issue a BS 7671 installation certificate (as these can be issued only by those carrying out the work), but only a Building Regulations completion certificate (the local authority) or a final certificate (an approved inspector).

### Third party certification

**1.28** Unregistered installers should not themselves arrange for a third party to carry out final inspection and testing. The third party - not having supervised the work from the outset - would not be in a position to verify that the installation work complied fully with BS 7671:2001 requirements. An electrical installation certificate can be issued only by the installer responsible for the installation work.

**1.29** A third party could only sign a BS 7671:2001 Periodic Inspection Report or similar. The Report would indicate that electrical safety tests had been carried out on the installation which met BS 7671:2001 criteria, but it could not verify that the installation complied fully with BS 7671:2001 requirements - for example with regard to routing of hidden cables.

## Inspection and testing of non-notifiable work

**1.30** Non-notifiable electrical installation work must also be carried out in accordance with the requirements of BS 7671:2001 or an equivalent standard. However, it is not necessary for the work to be checked by a building control body or alternatively carried out by an installer registered with a Part P competent person self-certification scheme.

**1.31** Local authorities, however, can take enforcement action if non-notifiable work – for example electrical work which is part of a wider project - is found to be unsafe and non-compliant.

**1.32** Those qualified to complete BS 7671 installation certificates who carry out non- notifiable work should issue the appropriate electrical installation certificate for all but the simplest of like-for-like replacements. DIYers may wish to employ a qualified third party to carry out inspection and testing of non-notifiable work to make sure it is safe. The qualified person need not necessarily be registered with a Part P competent person scheme self-certification scheme but, as required by BS 7671, must be qualified in respect of the inspection and testing of an installation.

## Provision of information

**1.33** Sufficient information should be left with the occupant to ensure that persons wishing to operate, maintain or alter an electrical installation can do so with reasonable safety.

**1.34** The information should comprise items called for by BS 7671:2001 or an equivalent standard and other appropriate information including:

a.    electrical installation certificates describing the installation and giving details of work carried out;
b.    permanent labels, for example, on earth connections and bonds, and on items of electrical equipment such as consumer units and RCDs;
c.    operating instructions and log books;
d.    for unusually large or complex installations only, detailed plans.

# SECTION 2: EXTENSIONS, MATERIAL ALTERATIONS AND MATERIAL CHANGES OF USE

**2.1** Where any electrical installation work is classified as an extension, a material alteration or a material change of use, the addition and alteration work must include:

a.    such works on the existing fixed electrical installation in the building as are necessary to enable the additions and alterations, the circuits which feed them, the protective measures and the relevant earthing and bonding systems to meet the requirements; and

b.    establishing that the mains supply equipment is suitable.

**2.2** A way of complying would be to follow for the new work the guidance given above in Section 1 in relation to design, construction and inspection and testing and to show that for the altered circumstances:

a.    the rating and the condition of the existing equipment belonging to both the consumer and to the electricity distributor:
i. can carry the additional loads being allowed for, or
ii. are improved so that they can carry the additional loads being allowed for; and

b.    the correct protective measures are used; and

c.    the earthing and equipotential bonding arrangements are satisfactory.

**2.3** In accordance with Regulation 4(2), the whole of the existing installation does not need to be upgraded to current standards, but only to the extent necessary for the new work to meet current standards except where upgrading is required by the energy efficiency requirements of the Building Regulations.

**2.4** Appendix C offers guidance on some of the types of older installations that might be encountered in alteration work.

2.5  Appendix D offers guidance on applying the harmonised European cable identification system when making additions and alterations to existing installations.

# SECTION 3: INFORMATION ABOUT OTHER LEGISLATION

## Electricity at Work Regulations 1989

**3.1** All electrical installations must be accommodated in ways that meet the requirements of the Building Regulations. However electrical installations carried out by persons on whom duties are imposed by the Electricity at Work Regulations 1989 must meet the requirements of those Regulations.

**3.2** The advice given below reflects the present state of the Electricity at Work Regulations 1989 following amendments by Statutory Instruments 1996/192,1997/1993 and 1999/2Q24,

**3.3** Regulation 3 imposes duties on employers, employees and the self-employed. Regulation 3(2)(b) places duties on employees equivalent to those placed on employers and self-employed persons where there are matters within their control.

**3.4** The text of the Electricity at Work Regulations and guidance on how to comply with them are contained in the Health and Safety guidance document 'Memorandum of Guidance on the Electricity at Work Regulations 1989 - HSR25'. Important elements of the Regulations include:

a.    The Electricity at Work Regulations require that electrical work is only carried out by persons that are competent to prevent danger and injury while doing it, or who are appropriately supervised (Regulation 16).

b.    The Electricity at Work Regulations set general requirements for the design, construction and suitability of equipment for its intended use (Regulations 4(1), 5, 6, 7, 8, 9, 10, 11, 12).

## Electricity Safety, Quality and Continuity Regulations 2002

**3.5**  The Electricity Safety, Quality and Continuity Regulations 2002 (SI 2002/2665) came into force on 31 January 2003. These Regulations replaced the Electricity Supply Regulations 1988 (as amended).

**3.6**  The Regulations specify safety standards which are aimed at protecting the general public from danger. In addition, the Regulations specify power quality and supply continuity requirements to ensure an efficient and economic electricity supply service for consumers .The Regulations were introduced to improve standards in public safety and to align requirements to modern electricity markets.

**3.7**  The duty holders are generators, distributors, suppliers, meter operators, consumers and specified persons. Most of the duties apply to distributors who own or operate networks used to supply consumers' installations, street furniture or other networks.

**3.8**  Amongst other duties, distributors are required to provide an earthing facility for new connections (unless this would be inappropriate for safety reasons), to maintain the supply within defined tolerance limits and to provide certain technical and safety information to consumers to enable them to design their installations.

**3.9**  Distributors and meter operators must ensure that their equipment on consumers' premises is suitable for its purpose and safe in its particular environment and that the polarity of conductors is clearly indicated.

**3.10** The Regulations allow the Secretary of State to issue safety enforcement notices to consumers in circumstances where consumers' installations outside buildings present a danger to the public.

**3.11** In relation to 'embedded' generation[5], the Regulations require persons operating 'switched alternative' sources of energy in their installations to prevent a parallel connection occurring with the distributor's network and to comply with BS 7671. Sources of energy that operate in parallel with the distributor's network must meet certain additional safety standards: for example the equipment must not be a source of danger or cause interference with the distributor's network. Persons installing domestic combined heat and power equipment must advise the local distributor of their intentions before or at the time of commissioning the source.

**3.12** Distributors are prevented by the Regulations from connecting installations to their networks which do not comply with BS 7671. Other persons may connect installations to distributors' networks provided they obtain the prior consent of the distributor, who may require evidence that the installation complies with BS 7671 and that the connection itself will meet safety and operational requirements. Distributors may disconnect consumers' installations which are a source of danger or cause interference with their networks or other installations.

**3.13** Detailed Guidance on the Regulations is available at www.dti.gov.uk/electricity-regulations.

## Functionality requirements

**3.14** Part P of the Building Regulations makes requirements covering the safety of fixed electrical installations, but does hot cover system functionality. The functionality of electrically powered systems such as fire alarm systems, fans and pumps is covered in other Parts of the Building Regulations and other legislation.

---

[5]  'Embedded' generators are those connected to the distribution networks of public electricity suppliers rather than directly to the National Grid. Most CHP and renewable generating stations are embedded.

# APPENDIX A: EXAMPLES OF ELECTRICAL INSTALLATION DIAGRAMS

## Notes

1.   The diagrams do not give all the information needed to achieve compliance with BS 7671, nor do they cover all the electrical services found in dwellings, some of which (e.g. swimming pools and saunas) are subject to special requirements specified in Part 6 of BS 7671:2001. The diagrams must not be used for installation purposes.

2.   The diagrams are simplified examples of what  may be encountered. They are not a substitute for the proper consideration of for instance:

**a**. Cross-sectional areas (csa) of the phase and neutral conductors of circuits. The minimum csa required by BS 7671 depends on a number of variables, including: type of cable, number of cores, type and nominal current of overcurrent protective device, grouping with other circuits, ambient temperature, contact with thermally insulating materials and circuit length.

**b**. Cross-sectional areas of protective conductors. BS 7671 contains different rules, involving a number of variables, for determining the minimum csa for each type of protective conductor, including the earthing conductor, circuit protective conductors, main equipotential bonding conductors and supplementary bonding conductors.

c. Types and nominal current ratings of fuses or circuit breakers. These particulars depend on the circuit design current and load characteristics, and need to be co-ordinated with the circuit conductors and with the earth fault loop impedance of the circuit.

d. Types of wiring or wiring system. While PVC insulated and sheathed cables are likely to be sheathed for much of the wiring in a typical dwelling other types of cable may also be necessary. For example, heat-resisting flexible cables are required for the final connections to certain equipment; the cable to the garage or shed, if run underground, is subject to certain requirements; and cables concealed in floors and walls in certain circumstances are required to have an earthed metal covering, be enclosed in steel conduit or have additional mechanical protection.

e. Principles of cable routing. BS 7671 contains criteria for the routing and positioning of cables, so as to give protection against electric shock and fire as a result of mechanical damage to a cable. For example, such criteria are given for cables concealed in walls or buried in the ground.

f. Current ratings of circuits to fixed current-using equipment such as a shower or cooker.

### In the above context, diagrams are given as Follows:

**Diagram 1(a)** indicates the many electrical appliances that can be found in the home and how they might be supplied.

**Diagram 1(b)** indicates earthing and bonding arrangements that can be necessary.

**Diagram 2(a)** indicates earthing arrangements as might be provided by electricity distributors.

**Diagram 2(b)** indicates the earthing arrangement as might need to be provided by the consumer.

## Key to diagrams

| | | |
|---|---|---|
| Single pole switch | 13A socket-outlet | Zone around bath or shower (up to 3m above floor and 3m from edge of bath or shower, as defined in BS 7671:2001). This is a 'special location' where supplementary protection is required against the additional risks of injury. |
| Double pole switch (DPS) | Shaver socket-outlet | Live and neutral conductors |
| Pull cord | Light fitting | Circuit protective conductors |
| Fused connection unit | Protected light fitting | Main equipotential bonding |
| Fused connection unit with DPS | | Supplementary equipotential bonding conductors |
| Not always fitted | | Earthing conductor |

## Diagram 1(a) Illustration of fixed electrical installation that might be commonly encountered in a new or upgraded existing dwellings

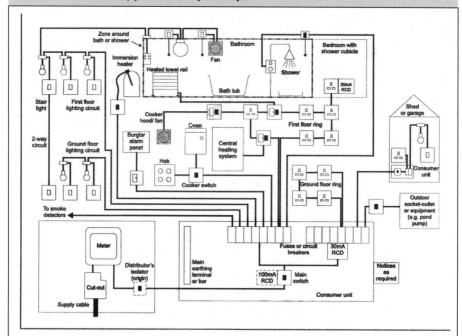

**Notes:**

1.  See the general rules in BS 7671:2001.

2.  The RCD component in the main switch is required for TT systems (see Diagram 2(b)). Individual circuit 30mA RCDs may be required to avoid unnecessary tripping.

3.  The notices include advice on periodic testing and regular test operation of the RCDs.

4.  The zone shown around the bath or shower corresponds to zone 3 in Section 601 of BS 7671:2001.

    The socket-outlet shown in the bedroom with the shower cubicle must be outside zone 3.

## Diagram 1(b) Illustration of earthing and bonding conductors that might be part of the electrical installationa shown in Diagram 1(a)

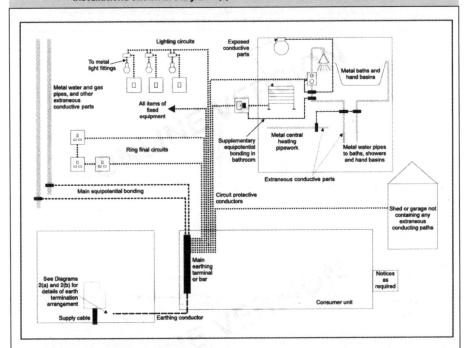

**Notes:**

1.  See the general rules in BS 7671:2001.

2.  Circuit protective conductors are taken to all items of fixed electrical equipment and local isolation and switching devices which appear in Diagram 1(a).

3.  In the case of a protective multiple earthing (PME) supply (see Diagram 2(a)), consult the electricity distributor.

4.  Supplementary bonding is required in bathrooms to an extent dependent upon the presence of metallic fixtures, fittings and pipework: see Section 601 of BS 7671:2001.

**Diagram 2(a) Example earthing arrangement where the electricity distributor provides the earth connection (referred to as TN-C-S where the connection is made to A, or TN-S where the connection is made to B- the most common systems in urban areas)**

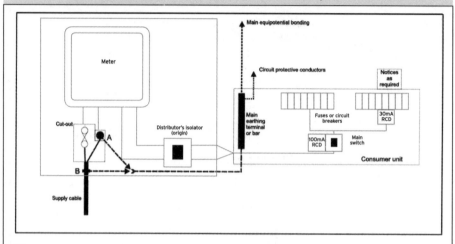

**Notes:**

1.  Connection A shows the arrangement where an electricity distributor provides a combined protective earthing and neutral conductor as part of a protective multiple earthing system (referred to as TN-C-S).

    Connection B shows the arrangement where an electricity distributor provides a protective earthing conductor (usually the metallic covering of the supply cable) that is separate from the neutral conductor (as part of a system referred to as TN-S).

2.  Connection A or B can only be made by the electricity distributor or its appointed agent.

**Diagram 2(b) Example earthing arrangement where consumers provide their own earthing connection (referred to as a TT system)**

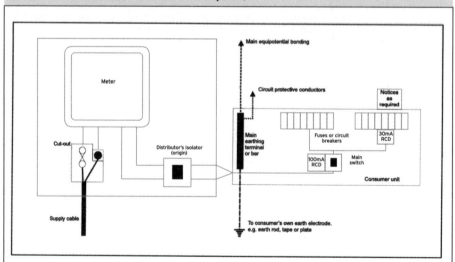

**Notes:**

1.  BS 7671:2001 requires that the part of the installation between the origin and the first RCD shall comply with the requirements for protection by Class II equipment or equivalent insulation. For the arrangement shown, this applies to the consumer unit and the wiring connecting it to the supplier's equipment.

2.  The 100mA RCD component of the main switch should be of the time delayed type.

# APPENDIX B: COPIES OF BS 7671 AND MODEL FORMS

The BS 7671 and IEE forms and notes on the following pages are taken from IEE Guidance Note 3, 2002 edition, and are available for downloading from the IEE website at www.iee. org/Publish/WireRegs/forms.cfm.

**They appear in the order:**

## Introduction
1.    Introduction to Appendix 6 of BS 7671:2001 (Model forms for certification and reporting).

**Initial inspection and testing**

2.    Notes for short form and full versions of Electrical Installation Certificate.

3.    Form 1 - Short form of Electrical Installation Certificate (for use when one person is responsible for the design, construction, inspection and testing of an installation), including guidance for recipients.

4.    Form 2 - Full Electrical Installation Certificate, including guidance for recipients (standard form from Appendix 6 of BS 7671).

5.    Form 3 - Schedule of Inspections (from Appendix 6 of BS 7671) with notes.

6.    Form 4 - Schedule of Test Results (from Appendix 6 of BS 7671) with notes.

## Minor works
7.    Notes on completion of Minor Electrical Installation Works Certificate.

8.    Form 5 - Minor Electrical Installation Works Certificate, including guidance for recipients (from Appendix 6 of BS 7671).

## COPIES OF BS 7671 AND IEE MODEL FORMS P
# CERTIFICATION AND REPORTING

## Introduction
i.    The Electrical Installation Certificate required by Part 7 of BS 7671 shall be made out and signed or otherwise authenticated by a competent person or persons in respect of the design, construction, inspection and testing of the work. ii.   The Minor Works Certificate required by Part 7 of BS 7671 shall be made out and signed or otherwise authenticated by a competent person in respect of the inspection and testing of an installation.

iii.   The Periodic Inspection Report required by Part 7 of BS 7671 shall be made out and signed or otherwise authenticated by a competent person in respect of the inspection and testing of an installation.

iv.   Competent persons will, as appropriate to their function under (i) (ii) and (iii) above, have a sound knowledge and experience relevant to the nature of the work undertaken and to the technical standards set down in this British Standard, be fully versed in the inspection and testing procedures contained in this Standard and employ adequate testing equipment.

v.    Electrical Installation Certificates will indicate the responsibility for design, construction, inspection and testing, whether in relation to new work or further work on an existing installation.

Where design, construction and inspection and testing are the responsibility of one person, a Certificate with a single signature declaration in the form shown below may replace the multiple signatures section of the model form.

**FOR DESIGN, CONSTRUCTION, INSPECTION & TESTING.**

I being the person responsible for the Design, Construction, Inspection & Testing of the electrical installation (as indicated by my signature below), particulars of which are described above, having exercised reasonable skill and care when carrying out the Design, Construction, Inspection & Testing, hereby CERTIFY that the said work for which I have been responsible is to the best of my knowledge and belief in accordance with BS 7671:...............
amended to ................ (date) except for the departures, if any,

detailed as follows.

vi.   A Minor Works Certificate will indicate the responsibility for design, construction, inspection and testing of the work described in Part 4 of the certificate.

vii.   A Periodic Inspection Report will indicate the responsibility for the inspection and testing of an installation within the extent and limitations specified on the report.

viii. A schedule of inspections and a schedule of test results as required by Part 7 (of BS 7671) shall be issued with the associated Electrical Installation Certificate or Periodic Inspection Report.

ix.   When making out and signing a form on behalf of a company or other business entity, individuals shall state for whom they are acting.

x.   Additional forms may be required as clarification, if needed by non-technical persons, or in expansion, for larger or more complex installations.

xi.   The IEE Guidance Note 3 provides further information on inspection and testing on completion and for periodic inspections.

## Electrical installation certificates Notes for Forms 1 and 2

1.    The Electrical Installation Certificate is to be used only for the initial certification of a new installation or for an alteration or addition to an existing installation where new circuits have been introduced.

      It is not to be used for a Periodic Inspection for which a Periodic Inspection Report form should be used. For an alteration or addition which does not extend to the introduction of new circuits, a Minor Electrical Installation Works Certificate may be used.

      The original Certificate is to be given to the person ordering the work (Regulation 742-01-03). A duplicate should be retained by the contractor.

2.    The Certificate is only valid if accompanied by the Schedule of Inspections and the Schedule(s) of Test Results.

3.    The signatures appended are those of the persons authorised by the companies executing the work of design, construction and inspection and testing respectively. A signatory authorised to certify more than one category of work should sign in each of the appropriate places.

4.    The time interval recommended before the first periodic inspection must be inserted (see IEE Guidance Note 3 for guidance).

5.    The page numbers for each of the Schedules of Test Results should be indicated, together with the total number of sheets involved.

6.    The maximum prospective fault current recorded should be the greater of either the short-circuit current or the earth fault current.

7.    The proposed date for the next inspection should take into consideration the frequency and quality of maintenance that the installation can reasonably be expected to receive during its intended life, and the period should be agreed between the designer, installer and other relevant parties.

# COPIES OF BS 7671 AND IEE MODEL FORMS                    P

Form 1                                                    Form No.    /1

## ELECTRICAL INSTALLATION CERTIFICATE (notes 1 and 2)

(REQUIREMENTS FOR ELECTRICAL INSTALLATIONS – BS 7671 (IEE WIRING REGULATIONS))

| DETAILS OF THE CLIENT (note 1) |
| --- |
| ............................................................................ |

**INSTALLATION ADDRESS**

............................................................................

...................................................Postcode ...............

| DESCRIPTION AND EXTENT OF THE INSTALLATION Tick boxes as appropriate | |
| --- | --- |
| Description of installation: ................................................... | New installation ☐ |
| Extent of installation covered by this Certificate: ...................... | |
| ............................................................................ | Addition to an existing installation ☐ |
| ............................................................................ | Alteration to an existing installation ☐ |

**FOR DESIGN, CONSTRUCTION, INSPECTION & TESTING**

I being the person responsible for the Design, Construction, Inspection & Testing of the electrical installation (as indicated by my signature below), particulars of which are described above, having exercised reasonable skill and care when carrying out the Design, Construction, Inspection & Testing, hereby CERTIFY that the said work for which I have been responsible is to the best of my knowledge and belief in accordance with BS 7671 : ......., amended to .......... (date) except for the departures, if any, detailed as follows:

> Details of departures from BS 7671 (Regulations 120-01-03, 120-02):

The extent of liability of the signatory is limited to the work described above as the subject of this Certificate.

Name (IN BLOCK LETTERS):...........................................    Position: ................................................

Signature (note 3): .....................................................    Date:......................................................

For and on behalf of: ..................................................

Address: ..................................................................

............................................................................

...............................................Postcode .................    Tel No: ...................................................

**NEXT INSPECTION**

I recommend that this installation is further inspected and tested after an interval of not more than ........... years/months (notes 4 and 7)

**SUPPLY CHARACTERISTICS AND EARTHING ARRANGEMENTS** Tick boxes and enter details, as appropriate

| Earthing arrangements | Number and Type of Live Conductors | | Nature of Supply Parameters | Supply Protective Device Characteristics |
| --- | --- | --- | --- | --- |
| TN-C ☐ | a.c. ☐ | d.c. ☐ | Nominal voltage, U/Uo[1] .............................V | |
| TN-S ☐ | 1-phase, 2-wire ☐ | 2-pole ☐ | Nominal frequency, f [1] .............................Hz | Type: ........................ |
| TN-C-S ☐ | 1-phase, 3-wire ☐ | 3-pole ☐ | Prospective fault current, Ipf [2] (note 6) ........kA | ................................ |
| TT ☐ | 2-phase, 3-wire ☐ | other ☐ | External loop impedance, Ze [2] ...................Ω | |
| IT ☐ | 3-phase, 3-wire ☐ | | (Note: (1) by enquiry, (2) by enquiry or by measurement) | Nominal current rating |
| | 3-phase, 4-wire ☐ | | | ................................A |
| Alternative source ☐ of supply (to be detailed on attached schedules) | | | | |

## P COPIES OF BS 7671 AND IEE MODEL FORMS

---

**PARTICULARS OF INSTALLATION REFERRED TO IN THE CERTIFICATE** Tick boxes and enter details, as appropriate

| Means of Earthing | Maximum Demand |
|---|---|
| Distributor's facility ☐ | Maximum demand (load)........................................................Amps per phase |

**Details of Installation Earth Electrode** (where applicable)

| Installation earth electrode ☐ | Type (e.g. rod(s), tape, etc.) ............................... | Location | Electrode resistance to earth |
|---|---|---|---|
| | | ...................................... | ...................................Ω |

**Main Protective Conductors**

| Earthing conductor: | material ........................... csa ...........................mm² | connection verified ☐ |
|---|---|---|
| Main equipotential bonding conductors | material ........................... csa ...........................mm² | connection verified ☐ |

To incoming water and/or gas service ☐    To other elements ..........................................................

**Main Switch or Circuit-breaker**

BS, Type ......................... No. of poles ................. Current rating .................A    Voltage rating ...........................V

Location ..................................................................................................    Fuse rating or setting ..............A

Rated residual operating current I ₘ =...................... mA, and operating time of............ms (at I ₘ)

(applicable only where an RCD is suitable and is used as a main circuit-breaker)

---

**COMMENTS ON EXISTING INSTALLATION:** (In the case of an alteration or additions see Section 743)

..........................................................................................................................................................

..........................................................................................................................................................

..........................................................................................................................................................

..........................................................................................................................................................

..........................................................................................................................................................

..........................................................................................................................................................

..........................................................................................................................................................

..........................................................................................................................................................

---

**SCHEDULES** (note 2)

The attached Schedules are part of this document and this Certificate is valid only when they are attached to it.

............ Schedules of Inspections and ............ Schedules of Test Results are attached.

(Enter quantities of schedules attached)

---

## GUIDANCE FOR RECIPIENTS

This safety Certificate has been issued to confirm that the electrical installation work to which it relates has been designed, constructed and inspected and tested in accordance with British Standard 7671 (The IEE Wiring Regulations).

You should have received an original Certificate and the contractor should have retained a duplicate Certificate. If you were the person ordering the work, but not the user of the installation, you should pass this Certificate, or a full copy of it including the schedules, immediately to the user.

The 'original' Certificate should be retained in a safe place and be shown to any person inspecting or undertaking further work on the electrical installation in the future. If you later vacate the property, this Certificate will demonstrate to the new owner that the electrical installation complied with the requirements of British Standard 7671 at the time the Certificate was issued. The Construction (Design and Management) Regulations require that for a project covered by those Regulations, a copy of this Certificate, together with schedules, is included in the project health and safety documentation.

For safety reasons, the electrical installation will need to be inspected at appropriate intervals by a competent person. The maximum time interval recommended before the next inspection is stated on Page 1 under 'Next Inspection'.

This Certificate is intended to be issued only for a new electrical installation or for new work associated with an alteration or addition to an existing installation. It should not have been issued for the inspection of an existing electrical installation. A 'Periodic Inspection Report' should be issued for such a periodic inspection.

# COPIES OF BS 7671 AND IEE MODEL FORMS                    P

Form 2                                                    Form No.      /2

## ELECTRICAL INSTALLATION CERTIFICATE (notes 1 and 2)
### (REQUIREMENTS FOR ELECTRICAL INSTALLATIONS – BS 7671 (IEE WIRING REGULATIONS))

**DETAILS OF THE CLIENT** (note 1) ................................................................................................................

................................................................................................................

................................................................................................................

---

**INSTALLATION ADDRESS**

................................................................................................................

................................................................................................................

................................................Postcode ........................................

---

**DESCRIPTION AND EXTENT OF THE INSTALLATION** Tick boxes as appropriate

(note 1)

Description of installation: ........................................

Extent of installation covered by this Certificate: ........................................

................................................................................................................

................................................................................................................

................................................................................................................

| | |
|---|---|
| New installation | ☐ |
| Addition to an existing installation | ☐ |
| Alteration to an existing installation | ☐ |

---

**FOR DESIGN**

I/We being the person(s) responsible for the design of the electrical installation (as indicated by my/our signatures below), particulars of which are described above, having exercised reasonable skill and care when carrying out the design, hereby CERTIFY that the design work for which I/we have been responsible is to the best of my/our knowledge and belief in accordance with BS 7671 : ......., amended to ..........
(date) except for the departures, if any, detailed as follows:

> Details of departures from BS 7671 (Regulations 120-01-03, 120-02):

The extent of liability of the signatory or the signatories is limited to the work described above as the subject of this Certificate.

For the DESIGN of the installation:                    **(Where there is mutual responsibility for the design)

Signature: ........................ Date ............. Name (BLOCK LETTERS): .......................................Designer No.1

Signature: ........................ Date ............. Name (BLOCK LETTERS): .......................................Designer No.2**

---

**FOR CONSTRUCTION**

I/We being the person(s) responsible for the construction of the electrical installation (as indicated by my/our signatures below), particulars of which are described above, having exercised reasonable skill and care when carrying out the construction, hereby CERTIFY that the construction work for which I/we have been responsible is to the best of my/our knowledge and belief in accordance with BS 7671 : ......., amended to .......... (date) except for the departures, if any, detailed as follows:

> Details of departures from BS 7671 (Regulations 120-01-03, 120-02):

The extent of liability of the signatory is limited to the work described above as the subject of this Certificate.

For CONSTRUCTION of the installation:

Signature: ........................................................... Date ..................

Name (BLOCK LETTERS): ........................................................... Constructor

---

**FOR INSPECTION & TESTING**

I/We being the person(s) responsible for the inspection & testing of the electrical installation (as indicated by my/our signatures below), particulars of which are described above, having exercised reasonable skill and care when carrying out the inspection & testing, hereby CERTIFY that the work for which I/we have been responsible is to the best of my knowledge and belief in accordance with BS 7671 : ......., amended to ....... (date) except for the departures, if any, detailed as follows:

> Details of departures from BS 7671 (Regulations 120-01-03, 120-02):

The extent of liability of the signatory is limited to the work described above as the subject of this Certificate.

For INSPECTION & TEST of the installation:

Signature: ........................................................... Date ..................

Name (BLOCK LETTERS): ........................................................... Inspector

---

**NEXT INSPECTION (notes 4 and 7)**

I/We the designer(s) recommend that this installation is further inspected and tested after an interval of not more than ............ years/months

## P   COPIES OF BS 7671 AND IEE MODEL FORMS

---

### PARTICULARS OF THE SIGNATORIES TO THE ELECTRICAL INSTALLATION CERTIFICATE (note 3)

**Designer (No 1)**
Name: ..................................   Company: ..................................
Address: ..................................
..................................   Postcode: ..................................   Tel No: ..................................

**Designer (No 2)**
**(if applicable)**   Name: ..................................   Company: ..................................
Address: ..................................
..................................   Postcode: ..................................   Tel No: ..................................

**Constructor**
Name: ..................................   Company: ..................................
Address: ..................................
..................................   Postcode: ..................................   Tel No: ..................................

**Inspector**
Name: ..................................   Company: ..................................
Address: ..................................
..................................   Postcode: ..................................   Tel No: ..................................

---

### SUPPLY CHARACTERISTICS AND EARTHING ARRANGEMENTS Tick boxes and enter details, as appropriate

| Earthing arrangements | Number and Type of Live Conductors | | Nature of Supply Parameters | Supply Protective Device Characteristics |
|---|---|---|---|---|
| TN-C ☐ | a.c. ☐ | d.c. ☐ | Nominal voltage, U/Uo[1] ...........................V | |
| TN-S ☐ | 1-phase, 2-wire ☐ | 2-pole ☐ | Nominal frequency, f [3] ..........................Hz | Type:...................... |
| TN-C-S ☐ | 1-phase, 3-wire ☐ | 3-pole ☐ | Prospective fault current, Ipf [2] (note 6) ........kA | ...................... |
| TT ☐ | 2-phase, 3-wire ☐ | other ☐ | External loop impedance, Ze [2] .................Ω | |
| IT ☐ | 3-phase, 3-wire ☐ | | (Note: (1) by enquiry, (2) by enquiry or by measurement) | Nominal current rating ...................A |
| | 3-phase, 4-wire ☐ | | | |
| Alternative source of supply (to be detailed on attached schedules) ☐ | | | | |

---

### PARTICULARS OF INSTALLATION REFERRED TO IN THE CERTIFICATE Tick boxes and enter details, as appropriate

**Means of Earthing**

Distributor's facility ☐

**Maximum Demand**

Maximum demand (load) .....................................................Amps per phase

**Details of Installation Earth Electrode (where applicable)**

| | Type (e.g. rod(s), tape, etc.) | Location | Electrode resistance to earth |
|---|---|---|---|
| Installation earth electrode ☐ | .................. | .................. | ..................Ω |

**Main Protective Conductors**

Earthing conductor:   material ..................   csa ..................mm²   connection verified ☐

Main equipotential bonding conductors   material ..................   csa ..................mm²   connection verified ☐

To incoming water and/or gas service ☐   To other elements ..................

**Main Switch or Circuit-breaker**

BS, Type..................   No. of poles ..................   Current rating ..................A   Voltage rating ..................V

Location ..................   Fuse rating or setting ..................A

Rated residual operating current I Δn = ...... mA, and operating time of ..................ms (at I Δn)

(applicable only where an RCD is suitable and is used as a main circuit-breaker)

---

### COMMENTS ON EXISTING INSTALLATION: (In the case of an alteration or additions see Section 743)

..................................................................................................
..................................................................................................
..................................................................................................
..................................................................................................

---

### SCHEDULES (note 2)

The attached Schedules are part of this document and this Certificate is valid only when they are attached to it.

.......... Schedules of Inspections and .......... Schedules of Test Results are attached. (Enter quantities of schedules attached)

## COPIES OF BS 7671 AND IEE MODEL FORMS
P

### ELECTRICAL INSTALLATION CERTIFICATE
### GUIDANCE FOR RECIPIENTS (to be appended to the Certificate)

This safety Certificate has been issued to confirm that the electrical installation work to which it relates has been designed, constructed and inspected and tested in accordance with British Standard 7671 (The IEE Wiring Regulations).

You should have received an original Certificate and the contractor should have retained a duplicate Certificate. If you were the person ordering the work, but not the user of the installation, you should pass this Certificate, or a full copy of it including the schedules, immediately to the user.

The 'original' Certificate should be retained in a safe place and be shown to any person inspecting or undertaking further work on the electrical installation in the future. If you later vacate the property, this Certificate will demonstrate to the new owner that the electrical installation complied with the requirements of British Standard 7671 at the time the Certificate was issued. The Construction (Design and Management) Regulations require that for a project covered by those Regulations, a copy of this Certificate, together with schedules, is included in the project health and safety documentation.

For safety reasons, the electrical installation will need to be inspected at appropriate intervals by a competent person. The maximum time interval recommended before the next inspection is stated on Page 1 under 'Next Inspection'.

This Certificate is intended to be issued only for a new electrical installation or for new work associated with an alteration or addition to an existing installation. It should not have been issued for the inspection of an existing electrical installation. A 'Periodic Inspection Report' should be issued for such a periodic inspection.

The Certificate is only valid if a Schedule of Inspections and Schedule of Test Result are appended.

# P   COPIES OF BS 7671 AND IEE MODEL FORMS

Form 3                                                                      Form No.     /3

## SCHEDULE OF INSPECTIONS

### Methods of protection against electric shock

(a)   **Protection against both direct and indirect contact:**

☐ (i)   SELV (note 1)

☐ (ii)  Limitation of discharge of energy

(b)   **Protection against direct contact:  (note 2)**

☐ (i)    Insulation of live parts

☐ (ii)   Barriers or enclosures

☐ (iii)  Obstacles  (note 3)

☐ (iv)   Placing out of reach  (note 4)

☐ (v)    PELV

☐ (vi)   Presence of RCD for supplementary protection

(c)   **Protection against indirect contact:**

(i)   EEBADS including:

☐      Presence of earthing conductor

☐      Presence of circuit protective conductors

☐      Presence of main equipotential bonding conductors

☐      Presence of supplementary equipotential bonding conductors

☐      Presence of earthing arrangements for combined protective and functional purposes

☐      Presence of adequate arrangements for alternative source(s), where applicable

☐      Presence of residual current device(s)

☐ (ii)   Use of Class II equipment or equivalent insulation  (note 5)

☐ (iii)  Non-conducting location: (note 6) Absence of protective conductors

☐ (iv)   Earth-free equipotential bonding: (note 7) Presence of earth-free equipotential bonding conductors

☐ (v)    Electrical separation  (note 8)

### Prevention of mutual detrimental influence

☐ (a)   Proximity of non-electrical services and other influences

☐ (b)   Segregation of band I and band II circuits or band II insulation used

☐ (c)   Segregation of safety circuits

### Identification

☐ (a)   Presence of diagrams, instructions, circuit charts and similar information

☐ (b)   Presence of danger notices and other warning notices

☐ (c)   Labelling of protective devices, switches and terminals

☐ (d)   Identification of conductors

### Cables and conductors

☐ (a)   Routing of cables in prescribed zones or within mechanical protection

☐ (b)   Connection of conductors

☐ (c)   Erection methods

☐ (d)   Selection of conductors for current-carrying capacity and voltage drop

☐ (e)   Presence of fire barriers, suitable seals and protection against thermal effects

### General

☐ (a)   Presence and correct location of appropriate devices for isolation and switching

☐ (b)   Adequacy of access to switchgear and other equipment

☐ (c)   Particular protective measures for special installations and locations

☐ (d)   Connection of single-pole devices for protection or switching in phase conductors only

☐ (e)   Correct connection of accessories and equipment

☐ (f)   Presence of undervoltage protective devices

☐ (g)   Choice and setting of protective and monitoring devices for protection against indirect contact and/or overcurrent

☐ (h)   Selection of equipment and protective measures appropriate to external influences

☐ (i)   Selection of appropriate functional switching devices

Inspected by ...............................................        Date     ................................................

**Notes:**

T     to indicate an inspection has been carried out and the result is satisfactory
C     to indicate an inspection has been carried out and the result was unsatisfactory
N/A   to indicate the inspection is not applicable
LIM   to indicate that, exceptionally, a limitation agreed with the person ordering the work prevented the inspection or test being carried out

1.   SELV – an extra-low voltage system which is electrically separated from earth and from other systems. The particular requirements of the Regulations must be checked (see Regulations 411-02 and 471-02)

2.   Method of protection against direct contact – will include measurement of distances where appropriate

3.   Obstacles – only adopted in special circumstances (see Regulations 412-04 and 471-06)

4.   Placing out of reach – only adopted in special circumstances (see Regulations 412-05 and 471-07)

5.   Use of Class II equipment – infrequently adopted and only when the installation is to be supervised (see Regulations 413-03 and 471-09)

6.   Non-conducting locations – not applicable in domestic premises and requiring special precautions (see Regulations 413-04 and 471-10)

7.   Earth-free local equipotential bonding – not applicable in domestic premises, only used in special circumstances (see Regulations 413-05 and 471-11)

8.   Electrical separation (see Regulations 413-06 and 471-12)

COPIES OF BS 7671 AND IEE MODEL FORMS                                    P

## Form 4

## SCHEDULE OF TEST RESULTS

Contractor: ......................................

Test Date: ......................................

Signature ......................................

Method of protection against indirect contact: ......................................

Equipment vulnerable to testing: ......................................

Address/Location of distribution board: ......................................

* Type of Supply: TN-S/TN-C-S/TT
* Ze at origin: ........ohms
* PFC: ........kA

Instruments
loop impedance: ......................................
continuity: ......................................
insulation: ......................................
RCD tester: ......................................

Form No        /4

**Description of Work:**

| Circuit Description | Overcurrent Device | | *Short-circuit capacity: .......kA | Wiring Conductors | | Continuity | | | Insulation Resistance | | Polarity | Earth Loop Impedance | Functional Testing | | Remarks |
|---|---|---|---|---|---|---|---|---|---|---|---|---|---|---|---|
| | type | Rating I$_n$ | | live | cpc | (R$_1$ + R$_n$)* | R$_2$* | Ring | Live/Live | Live/Earth | | Zs | RCD time | Other | |
| | | A | | mm² | mm² | Ω | Ω | | MΩ | MΩ | | Ω | ms | | |
| 1 | 2 | 3 | | 4 | 5 | *6 | *7 | *8 | *9 | *10 | *11 | *12 | *13 | *14 | 15 |
| | | | | | | | | | | | | | | | |
| | | | | | | | | | | | | | | | |
| | | | | | | | | | | | | | | | |
| | | | | | | | | | | | | | | | |
| | | | | | | | | | | | | | | | |
| | | | | | | | | | | | | | | | |

**Test Results**

**Deviations from Wiring Regulations and special notes:**

* See notes on schedule of test results

## P    COPIES OF BS 7671 AND IEE MODEL FORMS

## Notes on schedule of test results

\*        **Type of supply** is ascertained from the supply company or by inspection.

\*        **Ze at origin.** When the maximum value declared by the electricity supplier is used, the effectiveness of the earth must be confirmed by a test. If measured the main bonding will need to be disconnected for the duration of the test.

\*        **Short-circuit capacity** of the device is noted, see Table 7.2A of the On-Site Guide or 2.7.15 of GN3.

\*        **Prospective fault current (PFC).** The value recorded is the greater of either the short-circuit current or the earth fault current. Preferably determined by enquiry of the supplier.

**The following tests, where relevant, shall be carried out in the following sequence:**

**Continuity of protective conductors, including main and supplementary bonding**

Every protective conductor, including main and supplementary bonding conductors, should be tested to verify that it is continuous and correctly connected.

\*6       **Continuity**

Where Test Method 1 is used, enter the measured resistance of the phase conductor plus the circuit protective conductor (R1+ R2).

See 10.3.1 of the On-Site Guide or 2.7.5 of GN3.

During the continuity testing (Test Method 1) the following polarity checks are to be carried out:

a. every fuse and single-pole control and protective device is connected in the phase conductor only;

b. centre-contact bayonet and Edison screw lampholders have outer contact connected to the neutral conductor;

c. wiring is correctly connected to socket-outlets and similar accessories.

Compliance is to be indicated by a tick in polarity column 11.

(R1 + R2) need not be recorded if R2 is recorded in column 7.

\*7       Where Test Method 2 is used, the maximum value of R2 is recorded in column 7.

Where the alternative method of Regulation 413-02-12 is used for shock protection, the resistance of the circuit protective conductor R2 is measured and recorded in column 7.

See 10.3.1 of the On-Site Guide or 2.7.5 of GN3.

\*8       **Continuity of ring final circuit conductors**

A test shall be made to verify the continuity of each conductor including the protective conductor of every ring final circuit.

See 10.3.2 of the On-Site Guide or 2.7.6 of GN3.

\*9,\*10   **Insulation resistance**

All voltage sensitive devices to be disconnected or test between live conductors (phase and neutral) connected together and earth.

The insulation resistance between live conductors is to be inserted in column 9.

The minimum insulation resistance values are given in Table 10.1 of the On-Site Guide or Table 2.2 of GN3.

See 10.3.3(iv) of the On-Site Guide or 2.7.7 of GN3.

**All the preceding tests should be carried out before the installation is energised.**

\*11      **Polarity**

A satisfactory polarity test may be indicated by a tick in column 11.

Only in a Schedule of Test Results associated with a Periodic Inspection Report is it acceptable to record incorrect polarity.

## COPIES OF BS 7671 AND IEE MODEL FORMS                          P

*12    **Earth fault loop impedance Zs**

This may be determined either by direct measurement at the furthest point of a live circuit or by adding (R1 + R2) of column 6 to Ze. Ze is determined by measurement at the origin of the installation or preferably the value declared by the supply company used.

Zs = Ze + (R1 + R2). Zs should be less than the values given in Appendix 2 of the On-Site Guide or Appendix 2 of GN3.

*13    **Functional testing**

The operation of RCDs (including RCBOs) shall be tested by simulating a fault condition, independent of any test facility in the device.

Record operating time in column 13. Effectiveness of the test button must be confirmed.

See Section 11 of the On-Site Guide or 2.7.16 of GN3.

*14    All switchgear and controlgear assemblies, drives, control and interlocks, etc. must be operated to ensure that they are properly mounted, adjusted and installed.

Satisfactory operation is indicated by a tick in column 14.

**Earth electrode resistance**

The earth electrode resistance of TT installations must be measured, and normally an RCD is required.

For reliability in service the resistance of any earth electrode should be below 200Ω. Record the value on Form 1, 2 or 6, as appropriate.

See 10.3.5 of the On-Site Guide or 2.7.13 of GN3.

# P   COPIES OF BS 7671 AND IEE MODEL FORMS

Form 5

## MINOR ELECTRICAL INSTALLATION WORKS CERTIFICATE
(REQUIREMENTS FOR ELECTRICAL INSTALLATIONS – BS 7671 (IEE WIRING REGULATIONS))

To be used only for minor electrical work which does not include the provision of a new circuit

---

**PART 1 : Description of minor works**

1.   Description of the minor works: ..................................................................................................

2.   Location/Address: ........................................................................................................................

3.   Date minor works completed: .......................................................................................................

4.   Details of departures, if any, from BS 7671

......................................................................................................................................................

......................................................................................................................................................

......................................................................................................................................................

---

**PART 2 : Installation details**

1.   System earthing arrangement:                TN-C-S ☐    TN-S ☐    TT ☐

2.   Method of protection against indirect contact: ............................................................................

3.   Protective device for the modified circuit:        Type BS ........................... Rating ......................A

4.   Comments on existing installation, including adequacy of earthing and bonding arrangements:
(see Regulation 130-07) ...............................................................................................................

......................................................................................................................................................

......................................................................................................................................................

......................................................................................................................................................

---

**PART 3 : Essential Tests**

1.   Earth continuity: satisfactory   ☐

2.   Insulation resistance:

Phase/neutral .................................................MΩ

Phase/earth ...................................................MΩ

Neutral/earth .................................................MΩ

3.   Earth fault loop impedance   ...............................................................Ω

4.   Polarity: satisfactory   ☐

5.   RCD operation (if applicable): Rated residual operating current I∆n ..........mA and operating time of ..........ms (at I∆n)

**PART 4 : Declaration**

1.   I/We CERTIFY that the said works do not impair the safety of the existing installation, that the said works have been designed, constructed, inspected and tested in accordance with BS 7671 : .......... (IEE Wiring Regulations), amended to ............................... and that the said works, to the best of my/our knowledge and belief, at the time of my/our inspection, complied with BS 7671 except as detailed in Part 1.

2.   Name: ..............................................          3.  Signature: .......................................................

For and on behalf of: .......................................          Position: ...........................................................

Address: ........................................................

......................................................................          Date: ...............................................................

......................................................................

.................................................Postcode ................

## COPIES OF BS 7671 AND IEE MODEL FORMS                                    P

### MINOR ELECTRICAL INSTALLATION WORKS CERTIFICATE
### GUIDANCE FOR RECIPIENTS (to be appended to the Certificate)

This Certificate has been issued to confirm that the electrical installation work to which it relates has been designed, constructed and inspected and tested in accordance with British Standard 7671 (The IEE Wiring Regulations).

You should have received an original Certificate and the contractor should have retained a duplicate. If you were the person ordering the work, but not the owner of the installation, you should pass this Certificate, or a copy of it, to the owner.

A separate Certificate should have been received for each existing circuit on which minor works have been carried out. This Certificate is not appropriate if you requested the contractor to undertake more extensive installation work, for which you should have received an Electrical Installation Certificate.

The Certificate should be retained in a safe place and be shown to any person inspecting or undertaking further work on the electrical installation in the future. If you later vacate the property, this Certificate will demonstrate to the new owner that the minor electrical installation work carried out complied with the requirements of British Standard 7671 at the time the Certificate was issued.

## Notes on completion of minor electrical installation works certificate

### Scope

The Minor Works Certificate is intended to be used for additions and alterations to an installation that do not extend to the provision of a new circuit. Examples include the addition of a socket-outlet or a lighting point to an existing circuit, the relocation of a light switch, etc. This Certificate may also be used for the replacement of equipment such as accessories or luminaires, but not for the replacement of distribution boards or similar items. Appropriate inspection and testing, however, should always be carried out irrespective of the extent of the work undertaken.

### Part 1 Description of minor works

1,2     The minor works must be so described that the work that is the subject of the certification can be readily identified.

4     See Regulations 120-01-03 and 120-02. No departures are to be expected except in most unusual circumstances. See also Regulation 743-01-01.

### Part 2 Installation details

2     The method of protection against indirect contact shock must be clearly identified, e.g. earthed equipotential bonding and automatic disconnection of supply using fuse/circuit-breaker/RCD.

4     If the existing installation lacks either an effective means of earthing or adequate main equipotential bonding conductors, this must be clearly stated. See Regulation 743-01-02.

Recorded departures from BS 7671 may constitute non-compliance with the Electricity Supply Regulations 1988 as amended or the Electricity at Work Regulations 1989. It is important that the client is advised immediately in writing.

### Part 3 Essential tests

The relevant provisions of Part 7 (Inspection and Testing) of BS 7671 must be applied in full to all minor works. For example, where a socket-outlet is added to an existing circuit it is necessary to:

1     establish that the earthing contact of the socket-outlet is connected to the main earthing terminal;

2     measure the insulation resistance of the circuit that has been added to, and establish that it complies with Table 71 A of BS 7671;

3     measure the earth fault loop impedance to establish that the maximum permitted disconnection time is not exceeded;

4     check that the polarity of the socket-outlet is correct;

5     if the work Is protected by an ROD) verify the effectiveness of the ROD.

### Part 4 Declaration

1, 3     The Certificate shall be made out and signed by a competent person in respect of the design, construction, inspection and testing of the work.

1, 3     The competent person will have a sound knowledge and experience relevant to the nature of the work undertaken and to the technical standards set down in BS 7671, be fully versed in the inspection and testing procedures contained in the Regulations and employ adequate testing equipment.

2     When making out and signing a form on behalf of a company or other business entity, individuals shall state for whom they are acting.

# APPENDIX C: OLDER PRACTICE THAT CAN BE ENCOUNTERED IN ALTERATION WORK

When carrying out work on existing, older installations, some features will be encountered which differ from those found in modern installations.

Electrical installations began to be commonplace in domestic dwellings as early as the 1920s, and over the years there have been considerable changes to the types of wiring materials and other equipment being installed, and in the ways that electrical installations are structured. From the electrical safety point of view, these changes have had two main causes: advances in technology and amendments to the Wiring Regulations published by the Institution of Electrical Engineers (issued as British Standard BS 7671 since 1992).

This appendix presents examples of the types of features just mentioned, which may be unfamiliar to those who find them and may be a safety hazard. Also included, where applicable, are comments about changes in the Wiring Regulations relevant to the equipment concerned.

## Use of a gas, water or other service pipe as an earth
(No proper means of earthing for the electrical installation)

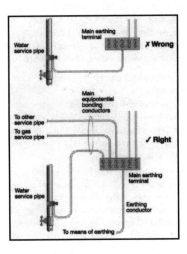

It is not permitted to use a gas, water or other metal service pipe as a means of earthing for an electrical installation. (This does not preclude equipotent bonding connections to these pipes.) It never has been permitted for gas pipes, and has not been permitted for other service pipes since 1966.

Every electrical installation requires a proper means of earthing. The most usual type is an electricity distributor's earthing terminal, provided for this purpose near the electricity meter

### Absence of, or inadequately sized, main equipotential bonding conductors

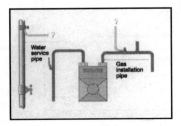

Prior to 1966 the Wiring Regulations contained no requirements for main equipotential bonding.
Since then, the installation of main equipotential bonding conductors has been required to water service pipes, gas installation pipes, oil supply pipes and certain other 'earthy' metalwork that may be present on the premises.
During the 1980s new Regulations were introduced, requiring the minimum size of main equipotential bonding conductors to be larger than previously called for, particularly where there is a PME (protective multiple earthing) electricity supply. For most dwellings the minimum size now permitted to be installed is 10mm².

## Absence of, or inadequately sized, supplementary equipotential bonding

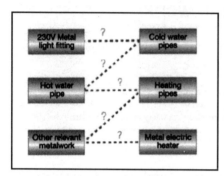

Prior to 1981 there were virtually no requirements in the Wiring Regulations for supplementary equipotential bonding conductors.

Since then, the installation of supplementary equipotential bonding conductors has been required in installations and locations of increased electric shock risk, such as bathrooms and shower rooms.

During the 1980s and 1990s the requirements for the sizing of supplementary equipotential bonding conductors were amended. For most dwellings the minimum size now permitted to be installed without mechanical protection is 4mm$^2$.

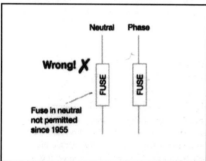

### Double-pole fusing

In many installations put in up to the 1950s, the circuits have a fuse in the neutral conductor as well as in the phase conductor. This is a potentially dangerous practice for ac installations, and ceased to be permitted by the Wiring Regulations in about 1955.

In the event of a short circuit, there is a 50% chance that the fuse in the neutral conductor will operate. When this happens, the phase conductor is not automatically disconnected from the faulty circuit as would now normally be expected, thereby leaving a danger for the unwary.

### Voltage-operated earth-leakage circuit-breakers

Two basic types of earth-leakage circuit-breaker used to be recognised by the Wiring Regulations: the current-operated type and the voltage- operated type. Today, only the current-operated type is recognised (now called residual current devices or RCDs).

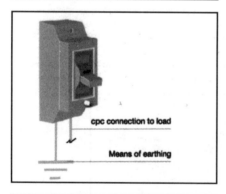

The voltage-operated type ceased to be recognised in 1981. It can be distinguished by its two separate earthing terminals – one for an earthing connection to the load and one for an earthing connection to a means of earthing (often a driven rod). The main drawback with this type of device is that a parallel earth path can render it disabled.

### No circuit protective conductors in lighting circuits

Lighting circuits installed before 1966, and not including metalwork needing to be earthed, often do not include a circuit protective conductor Consequently, any new or replacement light fittings, switches or other components must be of a type not requiring earthing, e.g. non-metallic varieties, unless new circuit protective (earthing) conductors are provided. Otherwise, there will be a potential danger of indirect contact (electric shock).

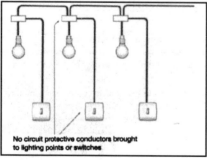

No circuit protective conductors brought to lighting points or switches

All lighting circuits installed since 1966 (with the exception of certain extra-low voltage circuits) have been required to include a circuit protective conductor.

## Non-13A socket-outlets

The installation of socket-outlets other than the current standard 13A square-pinnel type was common prior to the early 1950s.These outlets accept non-fused plugs (some with an earth pin and some without), generally having round pins.

These older types of socket-outlet designed for non-fused plugs must not be connected to a ring circuit. Such an arrangement can be dangerous.

In addition, socket-outlets that will accept unearthed (2-pin) plugs must not be used to supply equipment needing to be earthed. It is strongly recommended that such outlets be taken out of service.

## No RCD protection for socket- outlets likely to supply portable equipment outdoors (or insufficient number of such socket-outlets so protected)

A person receiving an electric shock when using portable electrical equipment outdoors can be at great risk of death or serious injury. The risk is significantly reduced if the socket-outlet supplying the equipment is provided with sensitive RCD protection (fitted either at the socket-outlet itself or at the consumer unit). However; prior to 1981 the Wiring Regulations did not require such protection.

Nowadays, sensitive RCD protection[6] is required for all socket-outlets which having a rating of 32A or less, and which may reasonably be expected to supply portable equipment for use outdoors. The initial requirement, in 1981, was for this protection to be provided to at least one such socket-outlet. However, this was found to be inadequate.

## Green coloured protective conductors or sleeving instead of green-yellow

The Wiring Regulations used to accept the single colour green for the identification of protective conductors.

However, since 1977 a green-yellow coding has been required for all protective conductors installed.

The older green sleeving or tape should be replaced with the new green-yellow striped variety whenever connections are re-made.

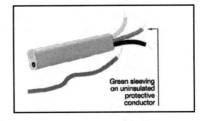

Green sleeving on uninsulated protective conductor

## Concealed cables outside of Permitted zones in walls

Until the latter part of the 1980s the Wiring Regulations did not contain any specific requirements for the positioning of cables concealed in walls and partitions.

Today's requirements are given in Regulation 522-06-06 in BS 7671, and are illustrated here.

To avoid striking a cable, extreme care should always be taken in any activity that involves penetrating a wall or partition, even when it is known that any concealed cables were installed in recent years. Where the cables were installed prior to 1980 they are particularly likely

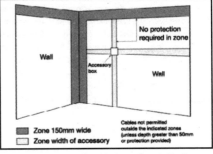

No protection required in zone

Wall

Accessory box

Wall

■ Zone 150mm wide
□ Zone width of accessory

Cables not permitted outside the indicated zones (unless depth greater than 50mm or protection provided)

to be found outside of the zones illustrated opposite. A cable and stud detector should always be used before attempting to drill into walls, floors or ceilings.

---

6  The RGD should have a rated residual operating current of not more than 30mA.

## 2.5mm² twin-and-earth cables incorporating circuit protective conductor or only 1 .0mm²

For some years, 2.5mm² twin-and-earth PVC/PVC cables to BS 6004 were manufactured with a circuit protective conductor (cpc) of only 1mm², rather than 1.5mm² as is incorporated today.

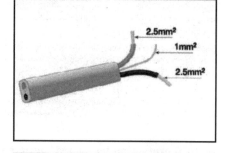

The size of the cpc was increased to 1.5mm² in BS 6004 because in certain circumstances the 1mm² cpc may not always be properly protected against thermal effects in the event of an earth fault. This is where the cable is used in a ring final circuit protected by a 30A semi-enclosed (rewirable) fuse. If this is the case, a competent electrician should be consulted about upgrading the cables and/or the consumer unit.

## Accessories on wooden mounting blocks

It was commonplace up to the mid-1960s for accessories such as socket-outlets, lighting switches and ceiling roses to be fixed to wooden mounting blocks.

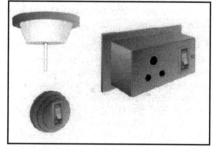

The design of the accessories is often such that the wooden block is used to form part of the enclosure for the unsheathed cores and terminations of cables connecting to the accessory. However, depending on the particular characteristics of the material from which the block is made, it may not satisfy the ignitability requirements of the current Wiring Regulations (BS 7671) for such use.

## Cables of imperial (non-metric) sizes

Up until the beginning of the 1970s, cables could still be purchased having imperial, rather than metric, sized conductors. Many such cables are still to be found in older installations.

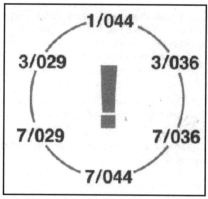

Their conductors may be single-stranded (as in 1/.044) or may have three, seven or more strands (as in 3/.029, 7/.029 and 19/.044). To the inexperienced eye these cables may be difficult to recognise, other than perhaps by comparison of their conductors with those of metric cables. The important thing to appreciate, however, is that their current-carrying capacity and voltage drop characteristics are likely to be different from those which may at first be expected. It would therefore be prudent to engage a competent electrician to establish whether the performance limits are being exceeded, or would be if a new appliance with a higher rating (e.g. washing machine, dishwasher, towel rail, appliances rated at more than 2kW) were to be connected.

Finally, it should be noted that copper conductors of imperial cables may be of the tinned type, giving them an unfamiliar colour.

## Tough rubber-sheathed (TRS), vulvanised rubber insulation (VRI) cables

Prior to the use of PVC insulated cables becoming common in the 1960s, most cables installed in domestic dwellings were of the rubber insulated, tough rubber-sheathed (TRS) type. These are easily recognisable by their black exterior.

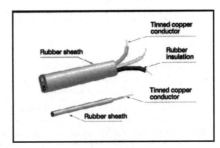

The extent to which the insulation and sheath deteriorate in service depends very much on whether the cable has been subjected to overloading and / or excessive temperature, or the rubber has been exposed to direct sunlight. Deterioration results in a loss of insulating properties, with the rubber becoming dry and inflexible - perhaps with a tendency to crumble.

Such wiring installations should be tested by a competent person at the earliest opportunity, but otherwise left undisturbed until replacement, as they are beyond their normally expected safe working life

## Lead-sheathed cables

Lead-sheathed cables may be found in some installations dating from before about 1948. These have rubber-insulated, tinned copper conductors and an outer sheath of lead.

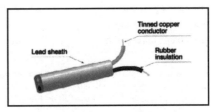

For reasons of protection against indirect contact (electric shock) it is essential that the lead sheath of every such cable is, and will remain, properly earthed.

The conductor insulation, being made of rubber, is prone to deterioration as described above for TRS cables.

Again, such wiring installations should be tested by a competent person at the earliest opportunity as they are beyond their normally expected safe working life.

# APPENDIX D: NEW HARMONISED CABLE IDENTIFICATION COLOURS

Amendment No 2 to BS 7671:2001 published on 31 March 2004 specifies new (harmonised) cable core colours for all new fixed wiring in electrical installations in the UK. It includes guidance for alterations and additions to installations wired in the old cable colours.

Table D1 gives the new cable core colours for ac power circuits.

| Table D1 Identification of conductors in ac power and lighting circuits | |
| --- | --- |
| Conductor | Colour |
| Protective conductor | Green-and-yellow |
| Neutral | Blue |
| Phase of single phase circuit | Brown |
| Phase 1 of 3-phase circuit | Brown |
| Phase 2 of 3-phase circuit | Black |
| Phase 3 of 3-phase circuit | Grey |

The new (harmonised) colour cables may be used on site from 31 March 2004. New installations or alterations to existing installations may use either new or old colours, but not both, from 31 March 2004 until 31 March 2006. Only the new colours may be used after 31 March 2006.

For single phase installations in domestic premises, the new colours are the same as those for flexible cables to appliances, namely green- and-yellow, blue and brown for the protective, neutral and phase conductors respectively.

Further information, including cable identification colours for extra-low voltage and dc power circuits, is available from the following sources:

*New wiring colours.* Leaflet published by the IEE, 2004. Available for downloading from the IEE website at www.iee.org/cablecolours.

*ECA comprehensive guide to harmonised cable colours, BS 7671: 2001* Amendment No 2, Electrical Contractors' Association, March 2004.

*New fixed wiring colours - A practical guide.* National Inspection Council for Electrical

# APPENDIX E: AUTHORISED COMPETENT PERSON SELF-CERTIFICATION SCHEMES FOR ELECTRICAL INSTALLATION WORK

## Full scope schemes

The following organisations are authorised run competent person self-certification schemes for registered electrical installers who can do all types electrical installation work in dwellings:

**BRE Certification Ltd**

Bucknalls Lane, Garston, Watford, Herts WD25 9XX

Tel: 0870 609 6093

Website: www.partp.co.uk

**British Standards Institution**

BSI Product Services, Maylands Avenue, Hemel Hempstead, Herts HP2 4SQ

Tel: 01442 230442

Website: www.bsi-global.com/kitemark

**ELECSA Limited**

44-48 Borough High Street, London SE1 1XB

Tel: 0870 749 0080 Website: www.elecsa.org.uk

**NAPIT Certification Limited**

Floor 4, Mill 3, Pleasley Vale Business Park, Outgang Lane, Pleasley Vale, Mansfield, Notts NG198RL Tel: 0870 444 1392 Website: www.napit.org.uk

**NICEIC Group Limited**

Warwick House, Houghton Hall Park, Houghton Regis, Dunstable, Bedfordshire LU5 6ZX

Tel: 0800 013 0900 Website: www.niceic.org.uk

## Defined scope schemes

The following organisations are authorised run competent person self-certification schemes for registered installers who can do electrical work as an adjunct to or arising out of other work:

**CORGI Services Limited**

1 Elmwood, Chineham Park, Crockford Lane, Basingstoke, Hants RG24 8WG

Tel: 01256 372200 Website: www.corgi-gas-safety.com

**ELECSA Limited** Address and contact details as above

**NAPIT Certification Limited** Address and contact details as above

**NICEIC Group Limited** Address and contact details as above

**OFTEC (Oil Firing Technical Association Limited)**

Foxwood House, Dobbs Lane, Kesgrave, Ipswich IPS 2QQ

Tel: 0845 658 5080 Website: www.oftec.co.uk

# STANDARDS REFERRED TO

### BS 7671:2001

Requirements for Electrical Installations (IEE Wiring Regulations 16th Edition). The Institution of Electrical Engineers, 2004, ISBN 0 86341 373 0, (incorporating Amendments No 1:2002 and No 2:2004).

### BS EN 60439-3:1991

Specification for low-voltage switchgear and controlgear assemblies. Particular requirements for low-voltage switchgear and controlgear assemblies intended to be installed in places where unskilled persons have access to their use.

## Other publications referred to

### Institution of Electrical Engineers (IEE)

*Electrician's guide to the Building Regulations*, 2005. ISBN 0 86341 463 X. Available from www.iee.org.

*IEE Guidance Note 1: Selection and erection of equipment 4th edition*, 2002. ISBN 0 85296 989 9.

*IEE Guidance Note 2: Isolation and switching, 4th edition*, 2002. ISBN 0 85296 990 2.

*IEE Guidance Note 3: Inspection and testing, 4th edition*, 2002. ISBN 0 85296 991 0.

*IEE Guidance Note 4: Protection against fire, 4th edition*, 2003. ISBN 0 85296 992 9.

*IEE Guidance Note 5: Protection against electric shock, 4th edition*, 2003. ISBN 0 85296 993 7.

*IEE Guidance Note 6: Protection against overcurrent, 4th edition*, 2003. ISBN 0 85296 994 5.

*IEE Guidance Note 7: Special locations, 2nd edition (incorporating the 1st and 2nd amendments)*, 2003. ISBN 0 85296 995 3.

*IEE On-Site Guide* (BS 7671 IEE Wiring Regulations. 16th edition), 2002. ISBN 0 85296 987 2.

*New wiring colours*, 2004. Leaflet available to download at www.iee.org/cablecolours.

### Electrical Contractors' Association (EGA) and National Inspection Council for Electrical Installation Contracting (NICEIC)

*ECA comprehensive guide to harmonised cable colours, BS 7671:2001 Amendment No 2*, ECA, March 2004.

*Electrical Installers' Guide to the Building Regulations*, NICEIC and ECA, August 2004. Available from www.niceic.org.uk and www.eca.co.uk.

*New fixed wiring colours - A practical guide*, NICEIC, Spring 2004.

# APPROVED DOCUMENTS

The following documents have been approved and issued by the First Secretary of State for the purpose of providing practical guidance with respect to the requirements of the Building Regulations 2000 (as amended).

**Approved Document A: Structure**

2004 edition incorporating 2004 amendments

**Approved Document B: Fire safety**

2000 edition incorporating 2000 and 2002 amendments

**Approved Document C: Site preparation and resistance to contaminants and moisture**

2004 edition

**Approved Document Di Toxic substances**

1992 edition incorporating 2002 amendments

**Approved Document E: Resistance to the passage of sound**

2003 edition incorporating 2004 amendments

**Approved Document F: Ventilation**

2006 edition

**Approved Document G: Hygiene**

1992 edition incorporating 1992 and 2000 amendments

**Approved Document H: Drainage and waste disposal**

2002 edition

**Approved Document J: Combustion appliances and fuel storage systems**

2002 edition

**Approved Document J: 2002 Editiontt Guidance and Supplementary Information on the UK Implementation of European Standards for Chimneys and Flues**

**Approved Document K: Protection from falling collision and impact**

1998 edition incorporating 2000 amendments

**Approved Document L1A: Conservation of fuel and power**

New dwellings 2006 edition

**Approved Document L1B: Conservation of fuel and power**

Existing dwellings 2006 edition

**Approved Document L2A: Conservation of fuel and power**

New buildings other than dwellings 2006 edition

**Approved Document L2B: Conservation of fuel and power**

Existing buildings other than dwellings 2006 edition

**Approved Document M: Access to and use of buildings**

2004 edition

**Approved Document N: Glazing - safety in relation to impact, opening and cleaning**

1998 edition incorporating 2000 amendments

**Approved Document P: Electrical safety**

2006 edition

**Approved Document to support regulation 7: Materials and workmanship**

1992 edition incorporating 2000 amendments

HOUSEBUILDER'S YEAR BOOK 2008

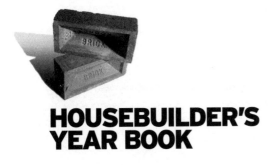

# HOUSEBUILDER'S YEAR BOOK

# CONTACTS

**Professional Organisations**

**Standards Organisations**

**Building Control Organisations**

**Research Organisations**

**Information Organisations**

**Industry Organisations**

**Product Organisations**

**Government and Related Organisations**

**Training and Good Practice Organisations**

# Professional Organisations

**Association of Building Engineers (ABE):**
Lutyens House
Billing Brook Road
Weston Favell
Northampton
Northamptonshire
NN3 8NW
Tel: +44 (0) 845 126 1058
Fax +44 (0) 1604 784220
Email: building.engineers@abe.org.uk
www.abe.org.uk

**Association of Consulting Engineers (ACE):**
Alliance House
12 Caxton Street
London
SW1H 0QL
Tel: 020 7222 6557
Fax: 020 7222 0750
Email: consult@acenet.co.uk
www.acenet.co.uk

**Civil Engineering Contracts Association (CECA):**
55 Tufton Street
London SW1P 3QL
Tel: 020 7227 4620
Fax: 020 7227 4621
www.ceca.co.uk

**The Chartered Institute of Building Services Engineers (CIBSE):**
222 Balham High Road
London
SW12 9BS
Tel +44 (0)20 8675 5211
Fax +44 (0)20 8675 5449
www.cibse.org

**The Chartered Institute of Building (CIOB):**
Englemere
Kings Ride
Ascot
Berkshire
SL5 7TB
Tel: (0)1344 630700
Fax: (0)1344 630777
Email: reception@ciob.org.uk
www.ciob.org.uk

**Institute of Maintenance & Building Management (IMBM):**
Keets House
30 East Street
Farnham
Surrey
GU9 7SW
Tel: 01252 710994
Fax: 01252 737741
Email: info@imbm.org.uk
www.imbm.org.uk

**Institution of Civil Engineers (ICE):**
One Great George Street
Westminster
London
SW1P 3AA
Tel: 020 7222 7722
Email: ukregions@ice.org.uk
www.ice.org.uk

**Institution of Structural Engineers (IStructE):**
11 Upper Belgrave Street
London
SW1X 8BH
United Kingdom
Tel: 020 7235 4535
Fax: 020 7235 4294
www.istructe.org.uk

**Property Consultants Society**
Basement Office,
1 Surrey Street,
Arundel,
West Sussex,
BN18 9DT
Tel:01903 883787
Fax:01903 889590
Email:pcs@p-c-s.org.uk
www.p-c-s.org.uk

**Royal Institute of British Architects (RIBA):**
66, Portland Place
London
W1B 1AD
Tel: 0207 580 5533.
Fax: 0207 251 1541.
Email: info@inst.riba.org
www.riba.org

**Royal Institution of Chartered Surveyors (RICS):**
RICS Contact Centre
Surveyor Court
Westwood Way
Coventry CV4 8JE
Tel: 0870 333 1600
Fax: 0207 334 3811
Email: contactrics@rics.org
www.rics.org.uk

# Standards Organisations

**British Board of Agreement (BBA):**
Bucknalls Lane
Garston
Watford WD25 9BA
Tel: 01923 665300
Fax: 01923 665301
Email: contact@bba.star.co.uk
www.bbacerts.co.uk

**British Standards Institute (BSI):**
389 Chiswick High Road
London
W4 4AL
Tel: 020 8996 9001
Fax: 020 8996 7001
Email: cservices@bsi-global.com
www.bsi-global.com

# Building Control Organisations

**Association of Consultant Approved Inspectors (ACAI):**
c/o 14 Berkeley Street
London
W1J 8DX
Email: hon.sec@acai.org.uk
www.acai.org.uk

**LABC:**
(National organisation representing local authority building control departments in England, Wales and Northern Ireland)
137 Lupus Street
London
SW1V 3HE
Tel: 020 7641 8737
Fax: 020 7641 8739
Email: info@labc.uk.com
www.labc.uk.com

# Research Organisations

**Building Services Research and Innovation Association (BSRIA):**
BSRIA Ltd
Old Bracknell Lane West
Bracknell
Berkshire
RG12 7AH
Tel: 01344 465600
Fax: 01344 465626
Email: bsria@bsria.co.uk
www.bsria.co.uk

**Building Research Establishment (BRE):**

**BRE**

Bucknalls Lane

Watford

WD25 9XX

Tel: 01923 664000

Email: enquiries@bre.co.uk

www.bre.co.uk

**Construction Industry Research and Information Association (CIRIA):**

London office

Classic House

174 - 180 Old Street

London EC1V 9BP

Tel: 020 7549 3300

Fax: 020 7253 0523

Email: enquiries@ciria.org

www.ciria.org.uk

**Construction Innovation and Research Strategy Panel (CRISP):**

www.crisp-uk.org.uk

**National Physical Laboratory (NPL):**

Hampton Road

Teddington

Middlesex

TW11 0LW

Tel: 020 8977 3222

Fax: 020 8943 6458

Email: enquiry@npl.co.uk

www.npl.co.uk

**Timber Research and Development Association (TRADA):**

Stocking Lane

Hughenden Valley

High Wycombe

HP14 4ND

Tel: 01494 569600

Fax:01494 565487

Email: information@trada.co.uk

www.trada.co.uk

# Information Organisations

**Abacus Construction Index**

(Professionally edited directory of recommended websites relevant to construction in the USA and UK.

www.construction-index.com

**The Building Centre**

26 Store Street

London

WC1E 7BT

Tel: 020 7692 4000

www.buildingcentre.co.uk

**National Calculation Methodology : SBEM:**

www.ncm.bre.co.uk

# Industry Organisations

**Association of Plumbing and Heating Contractors (APHC):**

14 Ensign House

Ensign Business Centre

Westwood Way

Coventry

CV4 8JA

Tel: 024 7647 0626

Fax: 024 7647 0942

www.licensedplumber.co.uk

**British Wood Preserving and Damp-proofing Association (BWPDA):**

www.bwpda.co.uk

**Structural Waterproofing Group (basement waterproofing)**

**The Property Care Association (damp or timber decay)**

Lakeview Court

Ermine Business Park

Huntingdon

Cambridgeshire

PE29 6XR

Tel: 0870 121 6737

Email: eleana@property-care.org

www.structuralwaterproofing.org

www.property-care.org

## The Wood Protection Association (pre-treatment services):

1 Gleneagles House

Vernongate

Derby DE1 1UP

Email: info@wood-protection.org

www.wood-protection.org

## British Woodworking Federation (BWF):

55 Tufton Street

London

SW1P 3QL

Tel: 0870 458 6939

Fax: 0870 458 6949

Email: bwf@bwf.org.uk

www.bwf.org.uk

## Builders Merchant Federation (BMF):

15 Soho Square

London

W1D 3HL

Tel: 020 7439 1753

Fax: 020 7734 2766

Email: info@bmf.org.uk

www.bmf.org.uk

## Construction Industry Computer Association (CICA):

National Computing Centre

Oxford House

Oxford Road

Manchester

M1 7ED

Tel: 0161 242 2262

Fax: 0161 242 2499

www.cica.org.uk

## Construction Industry Council (CIC):

26 Store Street

London

WC1E 7BT

Tel: 020 7399 7400

Fax: 020 7399 7425

Email: info@cic.org.uk

www.cic.org.uk

## Construction Industry Board (CIB):

www.ciboard.org.uk

## Electrical Contractors Association (ECA):

ESCA House

34 Palace Court

London

W2 4HY

Tel: 020 7313 4800

Fax: 020 7221 7344

Email:  ECAinfo@eca.co.uk

www.eca.co.uk

## Federation of Master Builders (FMB):

Federation of Master Builders (FMB)

Gordon Fisher House

14-15 Great James Street

London

WC1N 3DP

Tel: 020 7242 7583

Fax: 020 7404 0296

www.fmb.org.uk

## Heating and Ventilating Contractors Association (HVCA):

Esca House

34 Palace Court

London

W2 4JG

Tel: 020 7313 4900

Fax: 020 7727 9268

Email: contact@hvca.org.uk

www.hvca.org.uk

**National Federation of Builders (NFB):**

55 Tufton Street

London

SW1P 3QL

Tel: 0870 8989 091

Fax: 0870 8989 096

Email: national@builders.org.uk

www.builders.org.uk

**National Federation of Roofing Contractors (NFRC):**

Roofing House

31 Worship Street

London

EC2A 2DX

Tel: 020 7638 7663

www.nfrc.co.uk

**National Inspection Council for Electrical Installation Contracting (NICEIC):**

www.niceic.org.uk

**National Security Inspectorate (NSI):**

NICEIC

Warwick House

Houghton Hall Park

Houghton Regis

Dunstable

Bedfordshire

LU5 5ZX

Tel: 0870 013 0382

Fax: 01582 539090

Email: enquiries@niceic.com

www.nsi.org.uk

**Communications & Information Technology Association (CTIA):**

Suite 1C, Oak House,

Woodlands Business Park

Breckland,

Linford Wood West

Milton Keynes

MK14 6EY

Tel: 01908 220220

www.cita.org.uk

# Product Organisations

**Automatic Entrance Systems Installers Federation (AESIF):**

The Hayloft

High Street

Holme, Newark

Nottinghamshire NG23 7RZ

Tel: 08700 347058

Fax: 08700 347059

Email: info@aesif.org.uk

www.aesif.org.uk

**British Aggregates Association (BAA):**

Email: enquiries@british-aggregates.com

The British Aggregates Association

PO Box 99, Lanark ML11 8WA

Tel: 01206 274057.

www.british-aggregates.com

**Brick Development Association (BDA):**

Woodside House

Winkfield, Windsor

Berkshire

SL4 2DX

Telephone: 01344 885 651

Fax: 01344 890 129

Email: brick@brick.org.uk

www.brick.org.uk

**British Cement Association (BCA):**

Riverside House

4 Meadows Business Park

Station Approach

Blackwater

Camberley, Surrey

GU17 9AB

Tel: 01276 608700

Fax: 01276 608701

Email: info@bca.org.uk

www.bca.org.uk

**British Constructional Steelwork Association (BCSA):**

4 Whitehall Court

Westminster
London
SW1A 2ES
Tel: 020 7839 8566
Fax: 020 7976 1634
Email: gillian.mitchell@steelconstruction.org
www.steelconstruction.org

**The Concrete Society:**
Riverside House
4 Meadows Business Park
Station Approach
Blackwater
Camberley
Surrey GU17 9AB
Tel: 01276 607140
Fax: 01276 607141
www.concrete.org.uk

**Construction Products Association (CPA):**
The Building Centre
26 Store Street
London
Tel: 020 7323 3770
Fax: 020 7323 0307
Email: enquiries@constructionproducts.org.uk
www.constructionproducts.org.uk

**Council for Aluminium in Building:**
Bank House
Bond's Mill
Stonehouse
Gloucestershire
GL10 3RF
Tel: 01453 828851
Fax: 01453 828861
Email: enquiries@c-a-b.org.uk
www.c-a-b.org.uk

**Glass and Glazing Federation (GGF):**
44-48 Borough High Street
London
SE1 1XB

Tel: 0870 042 4255
Fax: 0870 042 4266
Email: info@ggf.org.uk
www.ggf.org.uk

**Lead Sheet Association:**
www.leadroof.com

Steelbiz:
www.steelbiz.org

**Quarry Products Association (QPA):**
Gillingham House
38-44 Gillingham Street
London,
SW1V 1HU
Tel: 020 7963 8000
Fax: 020 7963 8001
Email: info@qpa.org
www.qpa.org

**Timber Trade Federation (TTF):**
The Building Centre
26 Store Street
LONDON
WC1E 7BT
Tel: 020 3205 0067
Email: ttf@ttf.co.uk
www.ttf.co.uk

**UK Steel (trade association):**
Broadway House
Tothill Street
London
SW1H 9NQ
Tel: 020 7222 7777
Fax: 020 7222 2782
Email: enquiries@uksteel.org.uk
www.uksteel.org.uk

## Government and Related Organisations

**The Central Government Task Force (CGTF):**
www.rethinkingconstruction.org/about/cgtf.html

**Crown copyright (HMSO):**
www.hmso.gov.uk

**The Government Construction Clients Panel (GCCP):**
www.property.gov.uk/services/construction/gccp/gccppub.html

**Health and Safety Executive (HSE):**
Infoline 0845 345 0055
www.hse.gov.uk

**The Housing Forum/The Local Government Task Force (part of Constructing Excellence):**
Constructing Excellence
25 Buckingham Palace Road
Victoria,London
SW1W 0PP
Tel: 020 7592 1100
Fax: 020 7592 1101
Helpdesk: 0845 605 55 56
Email: helpdesk@constructingexcellence.org.uk
www.constructingexcellence.org.uk

**The Local Government Task Force (part of Constructing Excellence):**
www.constructingexcellence.org.uk

**Sustainable Development (DTLR):**
**Sustainable Development Unit**
Defra
1C Nobel House
17 Smith Square
London
SW1P 3JR
Tel: 020 7238 5811
Email: sdudiv@defra.gsi.gov.uk
www.sustainable-development.gov.uk

**The Stationery Office:**
St Crispins
Duke Street
Norwich
NR3 1PD
Tel: 01603 622211
www.tso.org.uk

**Trade Partners UK (DTI sponsored):**
UK Trade & Investment Enquiry Service
Tay House
300 Bath Street
Glasgow
G2 4DX
Tel: 020 7215 8000
www.tradepartners.gov.uk

## Training and Good Practice Organisations

**Construction Industry Training Board (CITB):**
ConstructionSkills
Bircham Newton
Kings Lynn
Norfolk
PE31 6RH
Phone: 01485 577577
Email: information.centre@cskills.org
www.citb.org.uk

**Construction Benchmarking Gateway (KPI Website):**
www.kpizone.com

**Construction Best Practice Programme (part of Constructing Excellence):**
www.constructingexcellence.org.uk

**Key Performance Indicators (KPI):**
BRE
Bucknalls Lane
Watford
WD25 9XX

Tel: 01923 664000

Email: enquiries@bre.co.uk

www.cbpp.org.uk

**Key Performance Indicators Website (Construction Benchmarking Gateway):**

www.kpizone.com

**Movement for Innovation (M41 part of Constructing Excellence):**

www.constructingexcellence.org.uk

**Rethinking Construction (part of Constructing Excellence)**

www.constructingexcellence.org.uk

# OTHER GREAT BOOKS
# FROM OVOLO PUBLISHING

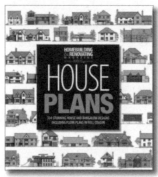

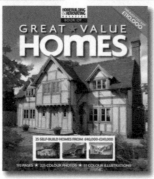

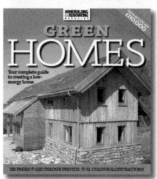
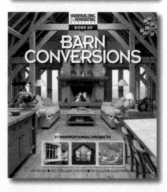

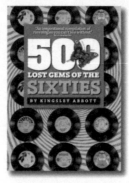

# www.ovolobooks.co.uk